45⁰

SMITHSONIAN SCIENTIFIC SERIES

Editor-in-chief
CHARLES GREELEY ABBOT, D.Sc.
Secretary of the
Smithsonian Institution

Published by
SMITHSONIAN INSTITUTION SERIES, Inc.
NEW YORK

GREAT INVENTIONS

By
CHARLES GREELEY ABBOT, D.Sc.

*Secretary of the
Smithsonian Institution*

VOLUME TWELVE
OF THE
SMITHSONIAN SCIENTIFIC SERIES

FOREWORD

WITH THIS VOLUME the Smithsonian Scientific Series is completed. It has cost more of effort on the part of the Smithsonian Institution than was anticipated. An exacting standard of accuracy and interest in text and illustrations has required more time than was expected for the preparation of the books. It is my hope that the quality of the finished product may be found to justify the long delay in completion.

As Secretary of the Smithsonian Institution, I wish to thank the subscribers for the interest which they have evinced in its work and welfare. As a direct result of this interest, a large sum has already been added through royalties from sales of the Series, to the resources of the Institution, for the furtherance of its scientific investigations.

As Editor-in-Chief, I wish to thank the authors, editors, and collaborators for their painstaking efforts to maintain the high quality of the Series. I wish also to compliment the publishers, the Smithsonian Institution Series, Inc., for steadily clinging to a high ideal of excellence in the make-up and printing of the books. They may justly have pride in the beautiful examples of bookmaking which have resulted.

C. G. ABBOT,
Secretary

PREFACE

Primitive inventions such as the means of producing fire, the awl, the wheel, water craft, and others, which enabled man to outdistance the beasts, have already been covered in Volume 7 of this Series. Many authors of popular books, moreover, have dealt with great inventions historically, tracing in general terms the gradual perfecting of devices from inventor to inventor, but with little attempt to explain in detail the methods of operation.

Several considerations have given a different scope to this volume. With the realization that there would be no room to explain their operations if all the inventions that might claim to be great were even mentioned, the number chosen here had to be sharply limited. Generally, too, to save space, neither have the first rudiments been traced nor the latest refinements fully explained. My purpose was rather to select and explain the operation in their simpler forms of a few inventions, conceived mainly in the nineteenth and twentieth centuries, which have had the very greatest influence on our present lives. Most of the machines considered may be examined as actual specimens or models in the United States National Museum. Many illustrations given are from that source, but in addition I am deeply indebted to several of the great manufacturing organizations for illustrative photographs, as will appear in the acknowledgments of the individual plates.

In the New Hampshire farmhouse of my boyhood, our rooms were all freezing cold in winter except the kitchen and at times the sitting-room, when the great fireplace had a roaring open fire in it. Upstairs there was a library of books left by my great-uncle, who was an inventor. It was my delight on a Saturday holiday from school to steal away into the arctic upstairs room and pore over a drab-covered book now in my library called "Elements of Technology," being a course of lectures by Jacob Bigelow, M.D., Rumford Professor in Harvard University, Boston, 1829. On the opening page it was shown how the great pyramid of Gizeh overtopped not only St. Paul's in London and the tower of Strassburg Cathedral, but even St. Peter's at Rome. The things in that book which fascinated my young mind were the descriptions of the watch and the clock, including an account of how the clock strikes, and particularly the description of the double-acting condensing steam engine of Watt and the mysteries of its valve mechanisms. To trace out the operation of such things I was willing to shiver with cold for hours.

It is with the belief that boys' natures have not changed since I was a boy that this book is prepared. They have not reached the antiquarian stage where they care particularly about the man responsible for an invention, but they do want to know how a thing works. Heroes, though very imposing to them, are few and far between, and it takes a Lindbergh of action rather than a Watt of invention to be a hero in their sight. Therefore, I have dwelt little on the history of invention, but have tried to explain without forbidding technicality the operating principles of simpler types of the most important electrical and mechanical devices, showing by lettered diagrams and descriptions how they work. In some instances I have quoted classical original sources such as the writings of Faraday and Henry to give a vivid sense of being at the fountain head. The book is not, however, for experts. Every invention described here has many whole volumes written about it that the expert may consult. This sketch is only for those who would like to get just a little better understanding of how such things as radio differ from out-and-out miracles.

CONTENTS

ILLUSTRATIONS

LIST OF PLATES

LIST OF TEXT FIGURES

CHAPTER I

PIONEERING IN ELECTRICITY

Over a century ago, in the year 1831, Michael Faraday at the Royal Institution in London, and Joseph Henry in Albany, N. Y., independently discovered that electricity can be generated from magnetism. Ten years before that a Frenchman, Arago, and an Englishman, Sir Humphrey Davy, had discovered independently that an electric current circulating around a bar of iron converts the bar into a magnet. A year before that, in 1819, Oersted in Denmark had discovered that a bar magnet, free to turn, tends to set itself at right angles to a nearby wire carrying electric current. From these discoveries come directly the dynamo and motor, the telegraph and telephone, and indirectly the electric light, radio, and almost all the appliances for the household, the office, the workshop, the moving vehicle, or the hospital, wherein electricity nowadays serves us. Oersted, Arago, Davy, Faraday, and Henry were all interesting personalities, apart from their pioneering discoveries.

Hans Christian Oersted (1777–1851) was the son of an apothecary at Rudjöbing on the island of Langeland. School facilities were of the scantiest. The barber taught a little German to Hans and his brother Anders, and the barber's wife helped them to learn to read and write. As the barber knew no more of arithmetic than how to add and subtract, a school-boy friend of somewhat more advantages added multiplication and division. The baker helped the boys to learn to draw, and the burgomaster gave them a bit of French. Finally the local surveyor added a little more mathematics. At 12 years of age Hans began to assist his father, the apothecary, and so learned a little of chemistry.

Yet the boys made the most of this patchwork of education, and in 1794 both entered the University of Copenhagen. Anders became a jurist. At that time the bent of Hans was toward literature and philosophy, and in 1797 he won the University gold medal with his essay, "On the Limits of Poetry and Prose." His doctor's thesis was entitled "The Architectonics of Natural Metaphysics," a subject which would require to be "chewed and digested" even in the title. But the invention of the electric pile by Volta in 1800, and opportunities that came to him for foreign travel and the meeting with philosophers of Germany, Italy, and France, turned Oersted's attention more and more to physics.

For many years he sought to discover the intimate connection, which many philosophers felt must exist, between electricity and magnetism. But in spite of this general expectation, Oersted's paper, "*Experimenta circum Effectum Conflictus electrici in Acum magneticum,*" published in 1820, in which he announced that the electric current "exercises determined and similar impressions on the direction of a magnetic needle" near it, was so absolutely the first hint of certainty that, says Forbes, "There was not even, so far as I am aware, a suspicion that he had been, however remotely or dimly, anticipated." So great was the enthusiasm over this discovery that Oersted was awarded the prize of the French Institute and the Copley medal of the Royal Society of London, and he was elected a knight of the order of Danebrog. He wrote much to popularize science. A selection of his writings entitled "The Spirit in Nature" ("*Der Geist in der Natur*") was published in 1850.

PIONEERING IN ELECTRICITY

Dominique François Jean Arago (1786–1853) came of an able family, and received good educational training. After attending the École Polytechnique, instead of entering the army, as intended, he became secretary of the Paris Observatory, where he enjoyed association with the great Laplace. He was sent in 1806 with Biot to make geodetic observations in Spain and remained to complete the work after Biot returned to Paris. Napoleon Bonaparte's invasion of Spain at this time threw Arago into great danger. Making his escape toward Algiers from the Balearic Islands, he was captured by a Spanish privateer and imprisoned in Spain for three months. Being released by Spain at the demand of the Dey of Algiers, he spent six months in Africa before returning to Marseilles.

Succeeding Lalande at the age of 23 as professor of analytical geometry at the École Polytechnique, Arago became an astronomer at the Paris Observatory, and in 1830 its director, and in the same year perpetual secretary of the Academy of Sciences. Besides his greatness as a scientist, he served with distinction in the French Chamber of Deputies, and in 1848 became Minister of War and Marine in the Provisional Government. In this capacity he abolished flogging in the French navy and slavery in the French colonies. The counter-revolution succeeding, he resigned his post as astronomer in 1852, but Prince Louis Napoleon refused to accept his resignation.

The other three great electrical discoverers were self-made, self-educated men. Sir Humphrey Davy (1778–1829) was the son of a wood carver at Penzance in Cornwall. After a grammar-school education and reading with a clergyman, he was apprenticed to a surgeon. At 20 years of age he received an appointment as a laboratory assistant in Doctor Beddoes' "Pneumatic Institution." In 1800 his first scientific papers attracted so much favorable notice that in 1801 he was chosen to lecture at the Royal Institution. He became professor of chemistry there in 1802 and director in 1805. In 1807 came his great discovery of the nature of the fixed alkalies, which he succeeded in decomposing by aid of the electric current. This gave him great scientific distinction. He was knighted in 1812, and made a baronet in 1818. For seven successive years, 1820 to 1827, he was elected president of the Royal Society of London, but resigned in 1827 on account of failing health. It is difficult to say whether Sir Humphrey Davy made a greater discovery in the nature of the fixed alkalies, or when, in 1812, by the brilliance of his lectures, he attracted the attention of the young genius, Michael Faraday, and later took him under his patronage.

Michael Faraday (1791–1867) was the son of a blacksmith, and at the age of 13 years he was apprenticed to a bookbinder and stationer. So in 1804 he began to carry around a daily news sheet to the subscribers, just about as newsboys do now, except that, having only the one copy, he had to wait at each place until it was read. Later he learned to bind books, and the handling of books gave him his opportunity for a self-made education. He acknowledged particular delight in Mrs. Marcet's "Conversations in Chemistry." His attention was directed toward electricity by the article in an encyclopaedia which he was employed to bind.

Thus he prepared himself for his great opportunity which came at the age of 21. A friend who knew his interests invited him to hear a course of lectures by Sir Humphrey Davy at the Royal Institution. Faraday took notes of a set of four lectures on chemistry, carefully wrote and bound them, and sending them to Sir Humphrey, so greatly interested him that when the laboratory servant was dismissed for cause a little later, he engaged Faraday as assistant at 25 shillings a week with lodgings at the Institution. Thus Faraday began his career of experimenting under the inspiring guidance of one of the greatest chemists of the age. Indeed, an experimental physicist should always begin as a chemist. The care which he learns in making quantitative analyses with fragile ap-

PLATE 1

Hans Christian Oersted. From the Rosenwald Museum of Science and Industry, Chicago, Ill.

PLATE 2

Sir Humphrey Davy.   From a print published by Agnen and Zanetti

PLATE 3

Michael Faraday. Discoverer of magneto-electricity

PLATE 4

Joseph Henry. Discoverer of electric self-induction. First Secretary, Smithsonian Institution

paratus gives his mind and hand a training ever useful in physical observations.

In 1813 Sir Humphrey and Lady Davy began a grand tour of Europe, and Faraday was taken in the combined functions of assistant, secretary, and valet to Sir Humphrey. They traveled, of course, by carriage, loaded with apparatus and papers. Sir Humphrey was well known and highly honored by the Continental scientists. Thus it came about that Faraday saw the latest discoveries and met the great men of France, Switzerland, and Italy, of whom he afterwards became a valued scientific peer.

On his return to the Royal Institution, Faraday's gifts as an experimenter and lecturer became more and more apparent; so much so, indeed, that even the great Sir Humphrey Davy may have felt at times some jealousy of his brilliant colleague. In 1829 Faraday succeeded to the directorship of the Royal Institution on the death of Davy.

In 1831 he made his epoch-making discovery that electricity can be generated from magnetism. From that time until his death in 1867 he conducted many thousands of keen and fertile experiments on all sorts of subjects in physics and chemistry. His fame as a lecturer was so extraordinary that his lecture courses were thronged, the audiences including even royalty itself. It is conceded by the most eminent of scientific men that next to Sir Isaac Newton, Faraday was the greatest exponent of physical science that England ever produced.

Joseph Henry (1799–1878) was born of Scotch ancestry in Albany, N. Y. His father died when the boy was but 9 years old, and his schooling was interrupted at 13 to apprentice him to a watchmaker. Although always of an ingenious, mechanical turn, Joseph Henry did not remain long at watchmaking and for a time was rather an idle boy. He had a considerable leaning toward the theater. At 16, however, he read Rev. George Gregory's "Lectures on Experimental Philosophy, Astronomy, and Chemistry, intended chiefly for the use of Young Persons." Henry wrote, many years after, on one of its blank leaves:

This book, although by no means a profound work, has, under Providence, exerted a remarkable influence on my life. It accidentally fell into my hands when I was about sixteen years old, and was the first book I ever read with attention. It opened to me a new world of thought and enjoyment; invested things before almost unnoticed with the highest interest; fixed my mind on the study of nature, and caused me to resolve at the time of reading it that I would immediately commence to devote my life to the acquisition of knowledge.

The remarkable influence which single scientific books written for young persons exercised in the lives of Faraday and Henry may well encourage scientific men to attempt popular exposition.

Awakened to greater interests, Henry resumed his education at Albany Academy with a view to practicing medicine, but in 1826 he accepted the post of teacher of mathematics and philosophy there. Pioneering electrical and magnetic experiments which he made at Albany led to his appointment in 1832 to the chair of natural philosophy at Princeton University. Becoming a recognized national and international figure in science, he was elected in 1846 first Secretary of the Smithsonian Institution. The following resolution of the Board of Regents indicates the standing which Henry had in the minds of leading men of that time.

Resolved, that it is essential, for the advancement of the proper interests of the trust, that the Secretary of the Smithsonian Institution be a man possessing weight of character, and a high grade of talent; and that it is further desirable that he possess eminent scientific and general acquirements; that he be a man capable of advancing science and promoting letters by original research and effort, well qualified to act as a respected channel of communication between the institution and scientific and literary individuals and societies in this and foreign countries; and, in a word, a man worthy to represent before the world of science and of letters the institution over which this Board presides.

Joseph Henry deserves a place in the front rank of eminent Americans. His work in electricity, though notable, was not his greatest service to his country or the world.

PIONEERING IN ELECTRICITY

As the first Secretary of the Smithsonian Institution he framed the policies which have made of it, next to the Republic itself, perhaps the greatest contribution made by America to world culture during the nineteenth century. Henry's liberal free distribution of Smithsonian information and publications; his establishment of the

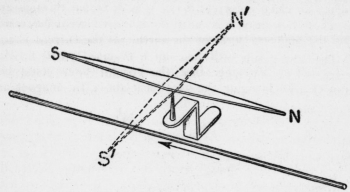

FIG. 1. How electric current deflects a magnet. Effect first used by Zweigger for the galvanometer, a measurer of the strength of the electric current

International Exchange Service, for the exchange of scientific literature, now made perpetual by treaties between approximately 20 nations; his collection and preservation in the United States National Museum of American fauna, flora, and ethnological data; his establishment of a national weather service; his outstanding part in the organization and promotion of scientific societies—these, and other measures which he took, so greatly stimulated American science, and so closely cemented the friendly relations between the cultures of the new world and the old, that it would be difficult to give him too high a place among great Americans.

Oersted's discovery enabled all investigators of electric currents to measure, and measurement is the soul of all scientific and technical progress. Figures 1 and 2 show

how Zweigger used Oersted's wire and magnet to make the galvanometer, or electric current measurer.[1] In Figure 1 we have the simplest type, where a straight wire lies north and south under the axis of a magnetic needle suspended by a pivot. The magnet, of course, naturally points in the direction S N toward the magnetic pole of the earth. But when an electric current flows, it is deflected through an angle to a position S'N' until the current force is balanced by the magnetic force of the earth. If the current is reversed the needle will take up a reversed position. It occurred to Zweigger that the current force could be doubled by bringing the wire back above the magnet as

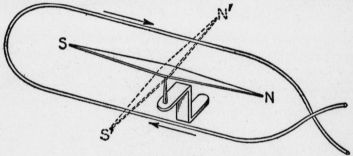

FIG. 2. Zweigger's improved galvanometer

in Figure 2, for the current in the upper branch would tend to deflect the magnet in the same sense as that in the lower branch. From this it was easy to see that the current force could be still further increased by completing several loops enclosing the magnetic needle. Still greater sensitiveness of the galvanometer came about by reducing the directing force of the earth's magnetism. This was accomplished by attaching a second magnetic needle, with its poles reversed to those of the first, a little lower and parallel to the first. It thus became the "astatic" galvanometer used by scientists for many years. Let Faraday

[1] Named after Galvani, the Italian of the eighteenth century who studied the physiological actions of electric currents.

tell in his own words[2] how he constructed his galvanometer as illustrated in Figure 3. Possibly some of my young readers will wish to try Faraday's experiments with the simple apparatus he describes.

The galvanometer was roughly made, yet sufficiently delicate in its indications. The wire was of copper covered with silk, and made sixteen or eighteen convolutions. Two sewing-needles were magnetized and fixed on to a stem of dried grass parallel to each other, but in opposite directions, and about half an inch apart; this system was sus-

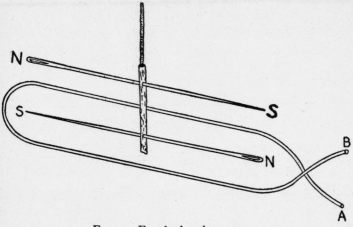

FIG. 3. Faraday's galvanometer

pended by a fibre of unspun silk, so that the lower needle should be between the convolutions of the multiplier, and the upper above them. The latter was by much the most powerful magnet, and gave terrestrial direction to the whole; [Fig. 3] represents the direction of the wire and of the needles when the instrument was placed in the magnetic meridian: the ends of the wires are marked A and B for convenient reference hereafter. The letters S and N designate the south and north ends of the needle when affected merely by terrestrial magnetism; the end N is therefore the marked pole. The whole instrument was protected by a glass jar.

The experiments of Arago and of Davy amount to this, that whenever a magnetic metal such as iron, steel, nickel,

[2] The quotations below are from Faraday's "Experimental Researches in Electricity," vol. 1, Bernard Quaritch, publisher, London, 1839.

or cobalt finds itself in the proximity of an electric current, magnetism is produced in the metal, either temporarily, during the continuance of the inducing current, or permanently if the metal is capable of permanent magnetization. Beyond this result, moreover, they proved that a coil of nonmagnetic wire, while carrying an electric current, acquires the properties of a magnet even though containing

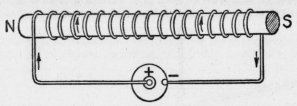

FIG. 4. Magnetism produced by electricity and the enhancement of the effect by means of soft iron

no magnetic metal. But the strength of such a magnetic coil is enormously enhanced by inserting therein a bar of soft iron (Fig. 4).

If electric currents can produce magnetism, may not magnetism produce electric currents? This was the question which many scientists asked from 1820 to 1830, and Faraday tried several experiments unsuccessfully during that decade for the purpose of demonstrating that magnetism can produce electricity.

The experiments of Henry by which he demonstrated that electricity could be produced through magnetism, though perhaps a little earlier than Faraday's in the making, were not published until later, and were by no means so extensive as Faraday's. The latter conducted a brilliant and thorough campaign to establish the relation beyond doubt, and to clear up every puzzling detail. His first inkling of the truth seems to have come from an experiment described in paragraph 10 of his work. He is led to suspect a temporary electrical effect, positive so long as the magnetic force is increasing, negative while it is decreasing, and zero when it is constant. He therefore conducts the following train of experiments leading up to the famous experiment of the ring, performed August 29, 1831.

The results which I had by this time obtained with magnets led me to believe that the battery current through one wire, did, in reality, induce a similiar current through the other wire, but that it continued for an instant only, and partook more of the nature of the electrical wave passed through from the shock of a common Leyden jar than of the current from a voltaic battery, and therefore might magnetise a steel needle, although it scarcely affected the galvanometer.

This expectation was confirmed; for on substituting a small hollow helix, formed round a glass tube, for the galvanometer, introducing a steel needle, making contact as before between the battery and the inducing wire, and then removing the needle before the battery contact was broken, it was found magnetised.

When the battery contact was first made, then an unmagnetised needle introduced into the small indicating helix, and lastly the battery contact broken, the needle was found magnetised to an equal degree apparently as before; but the poles were of the contrary kind.

.　.　.　.　.　.

In the preceding experiments the wires were placed near to each other, and the contact of the inducing one with the battery made when the inductive effect was required; but as the particular action might be supposed to be exerted only at the moments of making and breaking contact, the induction was produced in another way. Several feet of copper wire were stretched in wide zigzag forms, representing the letter W, on one surface of a broad board; a second wire was stretched in precisely similar forms on a second board, so that when brought near the first, the wires should everywhere touch, except that a sheet of thick paper was interposed. One of these wires was connected with the galvanometer, and the other with a voltaic battery. The first wire was then moved towards the second, and as it approached, the needle was deflected. Being then removed, the needle was deflected in the opposite direction. By first making the wires approach and then recede, simultaneously with the vibrations of the needle, the latter soon became very extensive; but when the wires ceased to move from or towards each other, the galvanometer-needle soon came to its usual position.

As the wires approximated, the induced current was in the *contrary* direction to the inducing current. As the wires receded, the induced current was in the *same* direction as the inducing current. When the wires remained stationary, there was no induced current.

.　.　.　.　.　.

A welded ring was made of soft round bar-iron, the metal being seven eighths of an inch in thickness, and the ring six inches in external diameter. Three helices were put round one part of this ring, each containing about twenty-four feet of copper wire one twentieth of an inch thick; they were insulated from the iron and each other, and superposed in the manner before described, occupying about nine inches in length upon the ring. They could be used separately or

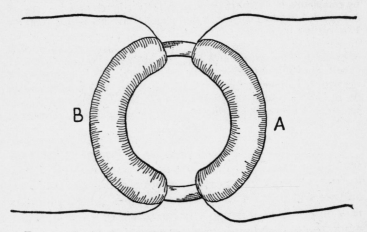

FIG. 5. Faraday's iron ring experiment, whereby he first produced electricity by magnetism

conjointly; the group may be distinguished by the letter A [Fig. 5]. On the other part of the ring about sixty feet of similar copper wire in two pieces were applied in the same manner, forming a helix B, which had the same common direction with the helices of A, but being separated from it at each extremity by about half an inch of the uncovered iron.

The helix B was connected by copper wires with a galvanometer three feet from the ring. The helices of A were connected end to end so as to form one common helix, the extremities of which were connected with a battery of ten pairs of plates four inches square. The galvanometer was immediately affected, and to a degree far beyond what has been described when with a battery of tenfold power helices *without iron* were used; but though the contact was continued, the effect was not permanent, for the needle soon came to rest in its natural position, as if quite indifferent to the attached electro-magnetic arrangement. Upon breaking the contact with the battery, the needle was again powerfully deflected, but in the contrary direction to that induced in the first instance.

. . . . .

When the battery contact was made in one direction, the galvanometer-needle was deflected on the one side; if made in the other direction, the deflection was on the other side. The deflection on breaking the battery contact was always the reverse of that produced by completing it. The deflection on making a battery contact always indicated an induced current in the opposite direction to that from the battery; but on breaking the contact the deflection indicated an induced current in the same direction as that of the battery. No making or breaking of the contact at B side, or in any part of the galvanometer circuit, produced any effect at the galvanometer. No continuance of the battery current caused any deflection of the galvanometer-needle. As the above results are common to all these experiments, and to similar ones with ordinary magnets to be hereafter detailed, they need not be again particularly described.

We must pass over the numerous confirmatory, though searching, tests by which Faraday, like a master experimenter, set aside every other hypothesis than the true one, and we will pass on to his explanation of a highly important observation of Arago's, in the course of which Faraday made the first dynamo ever invented.

If a plate of copper be revolved close to a magnetic needle, or magnet, suspended in such a way that the latter may rotate in a plane parallel to that of the former, the magnet tends to follow the motion of the plate; or if the magnet be revolved, the plate tends to follow its motion; and the effect is so powerful, that magnets or plates of many pounds weight may be thus carried round. If the magnet and plate be at rest relative to each other, not the slightest effect, attractive or repulsive, or of any kind, can be observed between them. This is the phenomenon discovered by M. Arago; and he states that the effect takes place not only with all metals, but with solids, liquids, and even gases, *i.e.* with all substances.

. . . . .

Upon obtaining electricity from magnets by the means already described, I hoped to make the experiment of M. Arago a new source of electricity; and did not despair, by reference to terrestrial magneto-electric induction, of being able to construct a new electrical machine. . . . . .

The magnet has been already described. To concentrate the poles, and bring them nearer to each other, two iron or steel bars, each about six or seven inches long, one inch wide, and half an inch thick, were put across the poles as in [Fig. 6] and being supported by twine from slipping, could be placed as near to or far from each other as was required. . . . . .

A disc of copper, twelve inches in diameter, and about one fifth of an inch in thickness, fixed upon a brass axis, was mounted in frames so as to allow of revolution . . , its edge being at the same time introduced more or less between the magnetic poles [Fig. 6]. The edge of the plate was well amalgamated for the purpose of obtaining a good but moveable contact, and a part round the axis was also prepared in a similar manner.

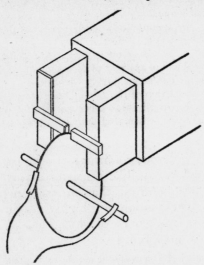

FIG. 6. Faraday's dynamo. The first continuous-current machine for producing electricity from magnetism and motion

Conductors or electric collectors of copper and lead were constructed so as to come in contact with the edge of the copper disc. . . . Copper wires, one sixteenth of an inch in thickness, attached, in the ordinary manner, by convolutions to the other ends of these conductors, passed away to the galvanometer.

. . . . .

All these arrangements being made, the copper disc was adjusted as in [Fig. 6], the small magnetic poles being about half an inch apart, and the edge of the plate inserted about half their width between them. One of the galvanometer wires was passed twice or thrice loosely round the brass axis of the plate, and the other attached to a conductor, which itself was retained by the hand in contact with the amalgamated edge of the disc at the part immediately between the magnetic poles. Under these circumstances all was quiescent, and the galvanometer exhibited no effect. But the instant the plate moved, the galvanometer was influenced, and by revolving the plate quickly the needle could be deflected 90° or more.

. . . . . Afterwards, when the experiments were made more carefully, a permanent deflection of the needle of nearly 45° could be sustained.

Here, therefore, was demonstrated the production of a permanent current of electricity by ordinary magnets.

When the motion of the disc was reversed, every other circumstance remaining the same, the galvanometer needle was deflected with equal power as before; but the deflection was on the opposite side, and the current of electricity evolved, therefore, the reverse of the former.

. . . . . .

The *relation of the current* of electricity produced, to the magnetic pole, to the direction of rotation of the plate, &c. &c., may be expressed by saying, that when the unmarked pole is beneath the edge of the plate, and the latter revolves horizontally, screw-fashion, the electricity which can be collected at the edge of the plate nearest to the pole is positive. As the pole of the earth may mentally be considered the unmarked pole, this relation of the rotation, the pole, and the electricity evolved, is not difficult to remember. Or if, in [Fig. 7] the circle represent the copper disc revolving in the direction of the arrows, and *a* the outline of the unmarked pole placed beneath the plate, then the electricity collected at *b* and the neighbouring parts is positive,

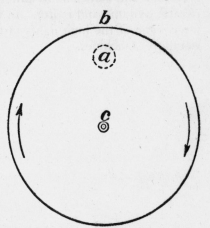

FIG. 7. Electric current and magnetic polarity and direction of motion

whilst that collected at the centre *c* and other parts is negative.

The substance of these experiments of Faraday's is to prove that whenever a conductor of electricity is subjected to an increase or decrease of magnetic force, whether by generating a magnet where none had been before; by destroying a magnet which had previously existed; by moving a magnet to or from a conductor; or finally by moving a conductor to or from a magnet—in all these cases electricity is produced in the conductor. The current lasts only so long as a change of magnetic force is going on, and reverses when the change of force of magnetism alters from waxing to waning.

Faraday went on to prove what everybody now knows, that the effects produced by friction of fur on glass, by heating a junction of two metals, by dropping copper and zinc plates into acid, or by bringing up a magnet toward a conductor, are due to the same agency—ELECTRICITY.

We have now rehearsed the fundamental investigations necessary and sufficient to anticipate the invention of the electric dynamo and motor. In the next chapter we shall trace some of the high lights in the development of these wonderful machines.

CHAPTER II

DYNAMOS AND MOTORS

THE discovery of Faraday proved to be the most fruitful of modern times. It opened possibilities as wonderful as Aladdin's lamp. Previously the sources of electricity—frictional, thermal, and chemical—had been so puny that such a thing as the continuous electric generation of a single horsepower for the industries would have been a fantastic dream. But now emerged the germs of a method whereby any amount of mechanical power might be transformed into electricity, and in that state could be transported by wires for long distances and then retransformed into whatever form of energy might be desired. In our own time even wires may sometimes be eliminated, and distant effects are produced by wireless and unseen agencies. Nothing but the efficacy attributed to prayer by men in all countries and all ages can compare in wonderfulness with this great discovery.

It is startling to reflect how many of our most ordinary appliances depend on the magnetic production of electricity. Without it not only would the street car again be horse-drawn, but the automobile and the airplane would stop. For without electromagnetic sparking devices, how could gasoline engines function? The electric light would, of course, disappear, and with it the greatest guarantee of safety after twilight in the great cities. The telephone and telegraph would be idle, and the daily newspaper would therefore become of merely local interest. Wars might continue long after peace had been declared, as indeed happened in America, where the bloody battle of

New Orleans occurred January 8, 1815, two weeks after the treaty of peace with Great Britain was signed at Ghent. Radiotelegraphy, telephony, and broadcasting would all disappear. Power plants would have to be associated with every separate factory, because long-distance transmission of power would cease. The rivers could furnish power only to factories situated on their banks. Such metals as aluminum, and all chemicals that require electrical separations, would become rarities, and their prices would soar accordingly. Hospital practice would again be without X-ray appliances, and households would be without electric work-lightening devices. Ships in distress at sea, no longer able to signal their S O S calls and no longer provided with gyrocompass, radio direction finders, or fire-signaling apparatus, would often sink, as formerly, with none to rescue or help.

THE DYNAMO

Although no one in 1831 could have foreseen the enormous development of electromagnetism attained in our time, inventors were keenly alive to the opportunity afforded by Faraday's discovery. Electromagnetic inventions quickly multiplied. Pixii, in 1831, by rotating a permanent horseshoe magnet beneath a pair of fixed coils, wound upon bobbins, produced alternating electric currents. At the suggestion of Ampère, the great French physicist, for whom the unit of electric current was afterwards named, Pixii introduced what we now call the commutator. He thus constructed his direct-current magnetic machine of 1832. Except for Faraday's direct-current disk, shown in Figure 6, Pixii's is believed to be the earliest continuously acting electromagnetic current generator.

Without detailing the gradual improvements in the art, let us pass to the next great step, which was the substitution of an electrically excited field magnet of soft iron in place of the permanent magnets of Pixii and Faraday. Such an electromagnet, separately excited, was introduced by Page in 1838, but in 1848 Jacob Brett passed the direct current developed by his machine itself around his soft-iron field magnet. As yet, however, it was considered necessary to temporarily excite the field electromagnet from an independent source before the current of the machine itself should be formed. The coil system that we now call the armature had by this time advanced from a device of only two coils to one of many coils, an increase which, like the many cylinders of a fine automobile, tends to steady the output and diminish its fluctuations.

It had been known for many years that more powerful permanent magnets could be produced from a given weight of metal if the metal were divided into many laminae, rather than concentrated into a single bar. But it was for quite another reason that Pulvermacher, in 1847, introduced the practice of laminating the iron frame on which the coils of the armature were by that date customarily being wound. For he perceived that the alternate waxing and waning of the electric current in each coil of the armature tends to set up induced currents in every piece of metal nearby and especially in the metal of the armature frame itself. This not only wastes energy by producing heat, but these induced waste or eddy currents, by their secondary induction effects, hinder the full production of the coil currents themselves. Hence Pulvermacher's improvement, which checked the circulation of eddy currents, marked a great step forward in raising the efficiency of the dynamo-electric machine.

It was not until 1867 that Wilde, Siemens, and Wheatstone discovered independently that it is unnecessary to use auxiliary current to preliminarily excite the field magnet of a direct-current dynamo. The slight residual magnetism remaining, even in the softest iron, added to that induced by the earth's field, is sufficient to start a feeble current as soon as the armature rotates, which rapidly augments the magnetization of the field.

Several types of windings of the armature had by this

time been devised. Possibly one of the easiest to understand is the ring armature type of Pacinotti (1860), used also in the Gramme and other dynamos but now generally abandoned. In the diagram, Figure 8, we shall for the sake of simplicity consider the field to be produced by a permanent horseshoe magnet. Between the poles N and S

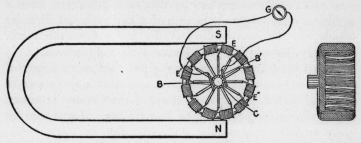

Fig. 8.   Diagram of the Pacinotti-Gramme dynamo

rotates the armature E′, E, E″. The ring is made of a bundle of soft-iron wires, wound with many groups of turns of insulated copper wire. All the turns are connected in series so as to make a continuous coil around the whole circumference of the ring. From each junction of two coils there passes radially a bar of copper to the commutator, C, which comprises a split tube of copper bars, separated from each other by nonconducting material, such as hard rubber. The outer surface of this compounded commutator tube is turned true, so that the two brushes B B′ may press steadily upon it as it rotates and draw off from it the direct current.

Faraday conceived of magnets and electrically conducting wires as possessing fields made up of "lines of force" spreading into the surrounding medium. These were very real to him. The conception was given mathematical and quantitative standing by Clerk Maxwell, the great mathematical physicist who invented that electromagnetic theory of light from which sprang our radio. The hundredth anniversary of Clerk Maxwell's birth was cele-

PLATE 5

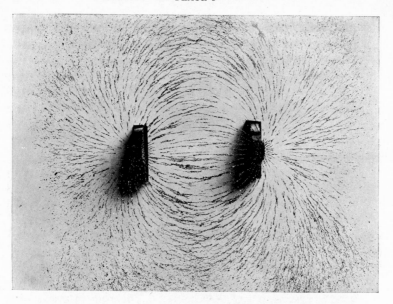

Iron filings and lines of force. Upper: Iron filings above a horseshoe magnet. Lower: Iron filings above a short-circuited horseshoe magnet

PLATE 6

Field structure of direct-current mill motor, 14 pole, 2,500 h.p.   Courtesy of the General Electric Company

brated in October, 1931, at the University of Cambridge, immediately after the Faraday Centenary celebration at London, and was attended by many of the world's greatest scientific men.

We shall understand more clearly the action of the dynamo by adopting in our thinking the Faraday-Maxwell lines of force. Plate 5, upper, shows a photograph of fine iron filings strewed to cover thinly a plate of glass above the poles of a horseshoe magnet. This illustration shows the course of the lines of equal force as they pass from pole to pole of the magnet. It may also be shown, though less strikingly, by means of iron filings strewed on a glass plate lying at right angles to an electrically conducting wire which pierces the plate, that the lines of force form rings around the electric current. Plate 5, lower, similarly prepared with iron filings on glass, shows how the magnetic lines of force are altered and practically all gathered up by a soft-iron ring like the armature of Pacinotti between the poles of a horseshoe magnet. Iron, soft steel, nickel, and cobalt all possess in different degrees this property of concentrating magnetic lines of force and stealing them away from the air, known as high magnetic permeability. The degree of concentration of a magnetic field, or in other words, its intensity, is customarily indicated as "the number of lines of force per unit area."

Whenever a closed loop of electrical conductor cuts through lines of force, electric current is set up in the loop. The intensity of the current is proportional to the number of lines of force cut per second. In order to take properly into account the direction as well as the intensity of such a current, both plus and minus signs are used in electromagnetic induction formulae. If in a coil moving at a certain rate in a certain magnetic field there is induced a current C, then the coil will carry the current $-C$ if turned to present its opposite face and again moved through the magnetic field in exactly the same manner as at first.

Consider the loop shown in Figure 9 mounted so as to

rotate on the axis XY in a uniform magnetic field indicated by the parallel arrows. Suppose this magnetic field
to extend indefinitely above and below the plane of the
paper, where the axis at the loop is shown lying. Let us
now follow the current strength developed in the loop as
it rotates through a complete turn of 360° starting from

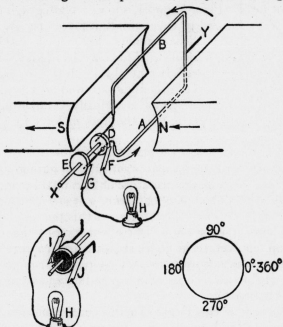

FIG. 9. Upper: Alternating-current dynamo diagram. Lower: Direct-current dynamo diagram

the point N as 0°. It is clear that the ends of the loop cut
no magnetic lines, and merely serve to complete the circuit. The two sides cut lines equally, but in opposite
senses so that the current in the two sides tends to flow
oppositely, as it must do to flow at all around a loop.

Let the uniform angular velocity per second be represented by θ;
let the uniform magnetic field be represented by f lines per unit area
of cross section, and let the radius of the loop be represented by r.

It is clear that the side A is cutting lines at the rate $+rf\,\theta$ as it passes the position 0°, and the side B is cutting at the rate $-r\,f\,\theta$ at the same instant. The rate of cutting lines becomes zero for both sides at 90°, and $-rf\,\theta$ and $+rf\,\theta$ at 180°. To readers with a slight knowledge of trigonometry it will be plain that in any instant the side A is cutting

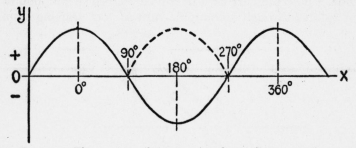

FIG. 10. Fluctuation of current in alternating- and direct-current dynamo windings

magnetic lines of force at the rate $rf\,\theta\,cos\,\varphi$, and the side B at the rate $-rf\,\theta\,cos\,\varphi$, where φ is the angle reached from 0° at the instant in question. Hence the total current in the loop is proportional to $2\,rf\,\theta\,cos\,\varphi$ at any instant whatever.

In Figure 10 we see how the current waxes and wanes as the loop revolves. The curve shown there is a pure cosine curve, or, as it is more commonly called, a pure sine curve. From 270° to 90° the current is positive, and from 90° to 270° it is negative.

Suppose now two rings, D and E, are connected to the two ends of the loop shown in Figure 9 and that conducting brushes, F and G, are provided to connect to an external circuit, $F\,H\,G$. The current at H will then alternate in direction and strength as represented in Figure 10.

Next, instead of using the two continuous rings, F and G, let there be substituted the two separated half-rings, I and J, Figure 9. Then while the current is positive, as shown in Figure 10, from 270° to 90°, the brushes, I and J, will act exactly as did the brushes F and G, before. But in the other half of the rotation, where the current in the loop is reversed, brush I takes the place of brush G, and

[23]

brush *J* takes the place of brush *F*. Thus the current is reversed in the outer circuit, also. Just as two negatives make one affirmative, the negative half of the cycle becomes positive in the outside circuit, as shown by the dotted line in Figure 10. In this way the alternating current becomes always direct, though violently fluctuating in its strength. This defect is reduced by multiplying coils in the armature to make up a complete cylinder and correspondingly multiplying the commutator segments.

Multiple poles in the magnetic field are also usual in large modern direct-current dynamos. It would lead to wasteful diffusion of the lines of force to allow them to stream quite across a dynamo several feet in diameter. Several or many poles are located around just outside the circumference of the armature, and arranged with alternately north and south polarity. The lines of force pursue a scalloped course from pole to pole through the armature, and each pole piece includes two sets of lines of force. Wire and electrical resistance are saved in multipolar dynamos by forming the armature coils tangentially between north and south field poles near together, instead of radially across the dynamo, as shown in Figure 9. Various special forms of winding permit this arrangement. There must be a pair of commutator brushes for every pair of principal poles in a "lap-wound" multipolar direct-current dynamo. Sometimes small extra pole pieces are used between the main poles to promote more efficient commutation of the current. This device for preventing sparking at the brushes was invented by Richard H. Mather of Windsor, Conn., and protected by United States Patent No. 321,990, issued July 14, 1885. Plate 6, showing a General Electric direct-current motor field, indicates these supplementary pole pieces clearly. The pole pieces about which the field coils are wound are sometimes of cast steel, but often, like the armature frames, are built up of thin sheets of mild steel, punched to form and laid beside each other to make up a considerable thickness. Plate 7, upper, shows this con-

PLATE 7

Upper: Laminated field pole for use with compensated direct-current machines. Lower: Armature and shaft for direct-current mill motor. Type as indicated in Plate 6. Courtesy of the General Electric Company

PLATE 8

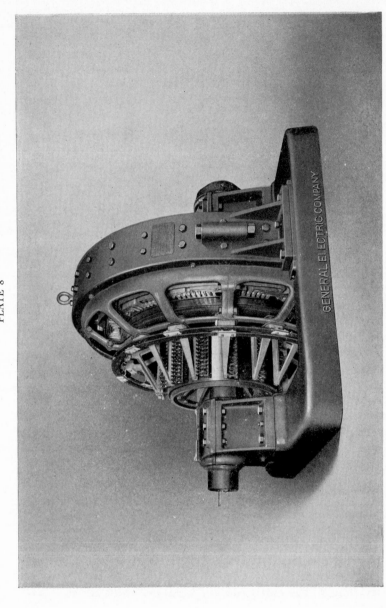

Direct-current motor, 14 pole, 2,600 h.p.   Courtesy of the General Electric Company

struction. In the armature frames, the thin steel punchings are separated by thin insulators in order to cut down the eddy currents. Several different types of coil windings for armatures are in use, some of considerable complexity. Readers particularly interested in the technical details of the modern direct-current dynamo should consult some of the excellent treatises available. Here we must confine ourselves to the inspection of Plates 6, 7, lower, and 8, which show some of the details as they have been worked out by the ablest manufacturers.

Let us now mention some of the great names in American electrical invention. Dr. Elihu Thomson of Lynn, Mass., won world-wide fame. Born at Manchester, England, in 1853, he came with his parents to Philadelphia as a boy of 5. He taught in the Philadelphia High School as a young man and conducted there some of his most interesting experiments. After his discovery of electric welding, he devoted himself to commercial scientific work, but remained always a public-spirited citizen. As a member of the corporation of the Massachusetts Institute of Technology, his influence was of great value. He held more than 700 patents, including some of the most fundamental in the electrical art. Among his many honors were the Rumford, John Fitz, Kelvin, and Faraday medals. He was a member of the National Academy of Sciences. Dr. K. T. Compton, president of the Massachusetts Institute of Technology, said of him:

More than any man now living, or in fact, more than any man in history, it seems to me that Professor Thomson has combined in a most remarkable way the constructive powers of the inventor, the thoroughness and soundness of the man of science, and the kindly balance of the ideal philosopher, teacher, and friend. Because of these qualities he is held in equally high esteem by engineers and in the most highbrow academic circles.

Dr. E. W. Rice, honorary chairman of the board of the General Electric Company, tells the following little story, not less creditable to Doctor Thomson's versatile ingenuity than to the extraordinary kindness of his heart.

I regard it as the most fortunate event in my life that I met Elihu Thomson when I was young. I was but a boy in my teens when we met in the Philadelphia High School in 1876. He was still a young man of but 23, although already recognized as a brilliant teacher with a growing reputation as a lecturer and scientist. . . . I was fortunate enough to interest him in my efforts to make a telescope. Being too poor to buy one, I had resolved to build one and had read all I could find on the subject. . . . As Professor Thomson was a chemist, I thought he might be willing to tell me how to make the proper alloy, and so, rather hesitantly, I presented my problem.

I shall never forget his cordial response. He acted as if the problem were of the utmost importance and of great personal interest. To my delight, he said that he too had made a telescope and had also decided upon the reflecting type, but that speculum metal was no longer used, as a mirror of glass was much better.

He then told me that he had devised a new and simple way of making a glass mirror without machinery and without moulds. . . . He demonstrated the theoretical correctness of the process, and stated that the only geometrical form that could result from such a process was a section of a perfect sphere. The process was so ridiculously simple as to be incredible, but I went ahead, and by following his instructions, eventually succeeded in making a satisfactory glass mirror for a small telescope.

To Doctor Thomson we owe, among his hundreds of inventions, the three-phase armature winding of dynamos patented January 13, 1880. The original specification contained a statement that this winding was connected to a commutator to produce direct current for arc lights, or to collector rings for use with alternating currents. The first machine of this type, and, in fact, the first dynamo with three-phase winding, is a machine wound by Doctor Thomson himself in 1879 at Philadelphia and now preserved in the United States National Museum and shown in Plate 10. The great power generators of today are three-phase machines of the same principle, and the transmission lines are lines fed from such three-phase dynamos. The machine, as a generator for arc lights, came into very extensive use, and after the introduction of alternating current systems about 1886, it also soon became the standard form of alternating current dynamo.

One of his most important inventions was that of the magnetic blow-out, shown in the Thomson patent No. 283,167 of August 14, 1883, which applies to the use of a magnetic field to blow out any arc or disturb any arc formed on the opening of a circuit. This magnetic blow-out, practically without modification, has been very widely used. The electric street car controllers of the present time employ the magnetic blow-out, as do many other kinds of control apparatus for high-powered electric circuits. Another important application, somewhat different from mere switching, is the lightning arrester, which employs the magnetic blow-out, covered by patent No. 321,464 of July 7, 1885, which was filed November 8, 1884. Not only does this arrester employ the magnetic blow-out principle, but it also shows for the first time a "horn" arrester, whereby an arc or connection formed by lightning is gradually opened or broken by the rise of the arc between wider and wider gaps between the discharge pieces.

Doctor Thomson demonstrated as early as 1879 the step-down transformer for reducing the voltage of alternating current to the requirements of practice. The transformer system of electrical distribution did not come into commercial application until 1887, and there were interferences in the Patent Office between the claims of different inventors. Doctor Thomson received broad claims on his invention in this field in his patent No. 698,156 of April 22, 1902.

One of his most important inventions was that of electric welding, now called the resistance method. He disclosed for the first time the art of joining metals by placing pieces in contact and passing through the contact a current of electricity sufficient to fuse and unite the pieces. The basic patent for this was No. 347,140 of August 10, 1886. The applications of this method have increased amazingly and are still rapidly growing in number. A more detailed statement of this invention may be found in the Research

Narratives of The Engineering Foundation. A whole group of inventions followed the original patent referred to above—many of them of importance in the electric welding art. They formed the basis of the organization known as the Thomson Electric Welding Company.

Before the practical development of the incandescent lamp by Edison, the electric arc had come into rather wide use. A number of practical arc lamps were designed by different inventors. Many thousands of arc lamps were once in operation under the patents of the Thomson-Houston system, and only in recent years has the use of these arc lamps decreased because of the introduction of large, high-power incandescent lamps made on the tungsten gas-filled principle.

The Association of Electrical Inspectors has given Doctor Thomson the name of "father of electric safety grounding" because the grounded secondary in the transformer was introduced by him as a means for saving life. High-tension primary lines may become connected with low-voltage secondary lines, and it would then be very dangerous if anyone touched the apparatus while standing on a grounded surface, such as a damp floor. After the complete remedy was found in the grounding of the secondary, there was then no objection to the introduction on a large scale of the transformer system. It required more than 20 years, however, before the use of such safety arrangements as the grounded secondary became mandatory.

One of the most fruitful of Doctor Thomson's investigations was the discovery of the repulsion principle with alternating current—an important principle lying at the base of much of the alternating-current development of the years following. The induction motor for single-phase work and the repulsion motor and combinations of these are based on the discovery of electromagnetic repulsion by alternating currents. In 1889 there was an exhibit at the Paris Exposition of such apparatus. It is now housed in

PLATE 9

Dr. Elihu Thomson

PLATE 10

Original Thomson three-phase dynamo. Wound by Dr. Elihu Thomson in 1879. In the National Museum

the Royal Institution in London, as supplementary to the Faraday apparatus, and it was used by Dr. J. A. Fleming in a famous lecture before the Society of Arts (London), May 14, 1890, republished in the United States in the Electrical World, of June 14 and 21, 1890. In connection with these repulsion experiments may be mentioned what is known as the shaded pole, which was extensively in-

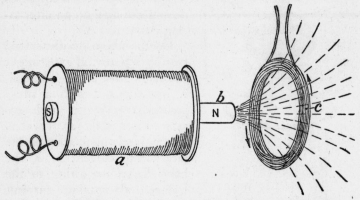

Fig. 11. The electric repulsion principle. Diagram to illustrate Dr. Elihu Thomson's invention of the electric repulsion motor

troduced into apparatus such as meters and in fan motors run by alternating currents; a repulsion motor based on the same principles was the first alternating-current motor.

The repulsion-motor principle is most striking. Referring to Figure 11, suppose a current to be started in a coil, *a*, which of course immediately produces a magnetic field whose lines of force emanate as indicated from the soft iron core, *b*. According to the principles of induction a momentary current is induced in the coil, *c*, which in its turn sets up a magnetic field oppositely directed to that emanating from *b*. Hence, there is a momentary repulsion of the coil. If now the current in *a* is broken, the repulsion changes to momentary attraction. If the current is again

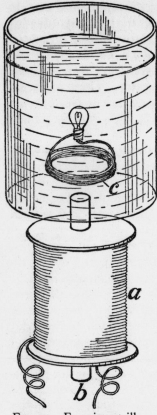

FIG. 12. Experiment illustrating electric repulsion

started in reverse sense there is a momentary repulsion. By suitably modifying the self induction of the coil, c, the phases of the currents in a and c can be so adjusted that the repulsion impulses far outweigh the attraction impulses during the flow of an alternating current in a.

Doctor Thomson illustrated this by a beautiful experiment shown in Figure 12. The coil, c, is connected with a small incandescent lamp and immersed in a glass jar of water. Immediately upon starting the alternating current in a, the lamp lights up owing to the induced alternating current, and with its coil it rises toward the surface of the water until reaching such a point that gravity balances repulsion. By altering the strength of the electric current, the lamp may be made to vary in brightness and to bob up and down in a mysterious manner. The principle of repulsion was applied by Doctor Thomson in measuring instruments, electric arc lamps, and alternating-current motors.

Another of his important inventions that has come into extensive use is the Thomson integrating wattmeter. The first practical device of this kind was the one which was produced in Lynn in 1889 and submitted in Paris in a meter competition, with the result that the Paris prize of 10,000 francs was divided between the Thomson and Aron meters. This Thomson recording wattmeter was used by the electrical jury at the World's Fair at Chicago in 1893, as a standard of comparison for all other meters presented.

Other pioneer inventions of Doctor Thomson, patents Nos. 428,648 and 508,654 of 1890 and 1893, relate to cooling of transformers by oil and by water. These principles are very widely used. The Thomson patent No. 617,546, January 10, 1899, filed February 28, 1898, was the pioneer patent for the so-called contactor system of control, which became of the greatest value in railway work and is today the practically universally adopted method of control.

Besides these important inventions in the field of electrical production and distribution, Doctor Thomson was among the first in the study of radio waves and wireless transmission, and in high-frequency alternating-current work generally, such as the singing arcs. He also took a prominent part in X-ray development. Quite out of the electrical line was his continuous centrifugal separator for separating cream from milk, patented with his colleague, Professor Houston, in 1877. These partners founded the celebrated electrical firm of Thomson and Houston at Lynn, Mass., now a branch of the General Electric Company.

Alternating-current electrical engineering owes much to Nikola Tesla, born 1857 in Smiljan, Lika, a border land of what was then Austria-Hungary. He was of Serbian stock. His father and uncle were clergymen of the Greek church. It was intended to educate Nikola also for the church, but his genius for mechanism and science was too strong, and he was allowed to attend the Polytechnic School at Gratz. It is said that while studying there the Gramme direct-current ring-armature dynamo, he felt instinctively that the commutator and brushes were unnecessary to the successful production and use of electricity. Studying languages to aid him in the engineering profession, Tesla gravitated to Paris, and at length to New York. A warm admirer of Thomas A. Edison, he obtained a place immediately in the Edison works and afterwards in the Westinghouse Company. But not for long. Tesla's inventive genius demanded free expression.

At that time, about 1885, alternating current had little general application. Few electrical engineers either used it or understood it, and the efficiency of such alternators as had been constructed was low. Tesla was a pioneer in the art. He perfected his valuable invention of the application of the polyphase rotating field to the induction motor. Of basic importance were his patents Nos. 382,279 and 382,280, granted May 1, 1888, in which he set forth the principles of this valuable type of alternating-current machine, surpassing all others in mechanical simplicity.

Tesla experimented at great length with high-frequency alternating currents, and with the properties of induction, capacity, and insulation associated with them. So astonishing and novel were his demonstrations, that after an extraordinary lecture before the American Institute of Electrical Engineers, delivered at Columbia College on May 20, 1891, he was urgently invited to visit Europe to repeat his experiments before audiences there. In 1892 he gave a lecture in London before the Institution of Electrical Engineers, and by special request repeated it the next day at the Royal Institution. After that he addressed the Société Internationale des Electricians and the Société française de Physique in Paris. When he returned to America, so great was the fame of these lectures that when in February, 1893, after addressing the Franklin Institute in Philadelphia, Tesla repeated his lecture a week later in Saint Louis before the National Electric Light Association, 5,000 people crowded the hall. All of these lectures were illustrated with experimental effects so novel, astonishing, and even terrifying in the behavior of currents at frequencies of 100,000 to 1,000,000 alternations per second, wherein all the resources of induction and capacity, the arc, the spark, and the glow discharge were reinforced by sound theory and surpassing ingenuity, that the audiences were spellbound.

One of the most colorful personalities among great American inventors of electrical devices was George Westinghouse (1846–1914). Even his birth was surrounded with the atmosphere of successful invention. On that day his father, after an all-night inventive vigil which absorbed him so entirely that he totally forgot even his approaching parenthood, solved the last difficulty of a successful invention. Returning to his home from the shop he learned for the first time of the birth of his famous son. The last words of his wife to him in the morning had been "Well, good luck to the new invention," and her first words to him at night were "How does the machine come on?"

A railroad accident started young Westinghouse on his career. Two cars ran off the track, and his inventive mind conceived a great saving of time if a car replacer were at hand on which cars could be drawn back upon the rails by the traction of an engine. A small company was formed to make and sell his invention, and other railroad appliances were soon added to its output. It was while traveling for this company that he took the last vacant seat in the train beside a young lady so engaging that he fell in love on the spot and soon made her his wife. The marriage was wholly congenial. Mrs. Westinghouse had much executive ability and relieved him of many cares in later life. She survived him only a few weeks, and they are buried together in Arlington National Cemetery.

A second railway accident, a head-on collision between two trains that could not be stopped in time with the hand brakes then in use, incited Westinghouse to his greatest invention, celebrated and used the world over— the automatic air brake. But that story must be reserved to a later chapter. Here we will mention his electrical interests and inventions, which, however, grew out of his development of the air brake. Yet we must not omit the extraordinary adventure of the gas well.

It was after his success with the air brake, in 1884, that his son, George Westinghouse, Jr., was born in New York. As soon as prudent, Mr. and Mrs. Westinghouse were returning to Pittsburgh, then in the midst of the excitement over the discovery of natural gas at Murrysville. This interested Westinghouse greatly. His wife chaffed him a little on the probability of his thereafter spending all his time at Murrysville. "Not," said he, "if I can use your garden." Sure enough, he drilled close to the stable, and at 1,575 feet the workmen struck a gas well that blew the machinery and mud over the entire lawn with a roar that brought a crowd to the scene. The force of the gas current was so great that stones and planks brought to confine it were hurled aside like straws. But after a week of effort, Westinghouse contrived an invention that stopped the flow. Then he bought an old franchise broad enough to conduct any kind of business under, piped the city, invented and patented improved devices for distributing gas of high pressure and selling it at low pressure, bought other properties on which to prospect for new wells, added other public service enterprises, and at length his "Philadelphia Company" became expanded to control nearly all the public services of Pittsburgh and its suburbs.

It was his varied railroad work that led Westinghouse into the line of electrical inventions. As early as 1875 he became interested in railway signaling and safety devices, and later he combined a Massachusetts company which manufactured signal apparatus with the Interlocking Switch and Signal Company to form the Union Switch and Signal Company. Between 1881 and 1891 he obtained 15 patents on inventions in this field, mainly relating to combinations of electrical and compressed air elements, especially in block signaling.

Among the engineers of the Union Switch and Signal Company was William Stanley, whose invention of an automatically regulating dynamo had caught Westinghouse's attention. Another gifted young engineer who was made a member of the Westinghouse staff about this time was Nikola Tesla, whose basic inventions relating to the polyphase alternating-current and induction motors we have already mentioned. Little by little the company entered the incandescent lighting field in competition with the Edison interests. But Westinghouse, with his quick mind, perceived the advantage of the alternating-current system over the direct current, because of its cheaper transmission and the simpler mechanism required.

English patents had been issued in 1883 to Gaulard and Gibbs for a system of alternating-current distribution through transformers. Westinghouse purchased several Gaulard-Gibbs transformers and set Stanley to experimenting with them. Stanley made improvements adaptable to alternating-current transmission for power and lighting. Westinghouse thereupon purchased the Gaulard-Gibbs rights for $50,000, and organized the Westinghouse Electric Company early in the year 1886. By the following autumn a test installation was prepared with a new constant-voltage alternating-current dynamo by Stanley, a battery of transformers, and 400 lamps operated from a 2,000-volt supply over a 4-mile transmission line. It was a revolutionary move, inaugurating an era of cheap power for lighting and other purposes, so that the small towns as well as the great cities could enjoy the comfort of the electric light.

Great opposition was encountered from the established direct-current industry of Edison. Books, pamphlets, and news articles painted in vivid colors the terrible dangers of high-voltage transmission. In New York City, especially, the opposition to alternating-current power circuits was most bitter. Edison himself published an article entitled "The Dangers of Electric Lighting" in the North American Review; Westinghouse countered with "A Reply to Mr. Edison" in the following number. About that time, too, electrocution was introduced as the death penalty in New York, which tended to prejudice the public against high-voltage alternating-current transmission. But little by little the Westinghouse system prospered, until finally its great coup was achieved in obtaining the contract for lighting the Chicago World's Fair of 1893. There was used at the Fair a battery of 12 great alternators furnishing the Tesla multiphase current, operating 250,000 lamps of 16 candlepower, so made as to avoid infringing on the Edison patents.

Shortly afterwards the Westinghouse company contracted to furnish for the Niagara Falls project three great generators. The first 5,000-horsepower turbo-alternator was installed within 18 months and exceeded specifications, yielding 5,135 horsepower. Within a few years 10 such Westinghouse units were installed at Niagara, aggregating 55,000-horsepower capacity.

George Westinghouse was one of the most prolific of American inventors, entering a very wide range of fields. Among his electrical patents may be cited as of basic importance United States Patents Nos. 342,553 and 366,544 covering improvements in the alternating-current transformer, and the protection of transformer insulation from humidity.

He was not only an inventor himself, but the inspirer of a brilliant corps of engineers and of a loyal corps of workmen. He was also president, not only in name but in fact, of the Westinghouse group of industries, and as such managed the funds and activities with a free hand to promote the great projects which his pioneering brain conceived. The country will seldom see the equal, in inventive genius or in wide-ranging, far-seeing pioneering instinct, of the founder of the Westinghouse industries.

We shall reserve the story of his great competitor, Thomas A. Edison, until we come to speak of electric lighting, and shall now continue with our account of alternating-current machines.

George Westinghouse. Inventor of the air brake and many electrical devices

PLATE 12

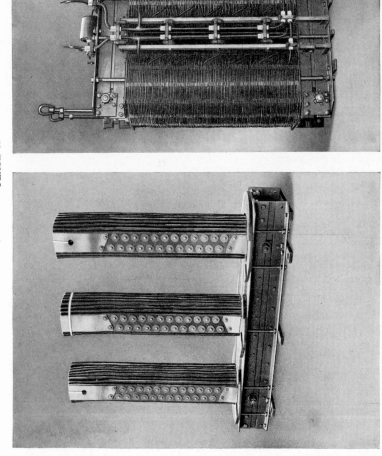

Left: Core for three-phase transformer. Right: Core and coils for three-phase transformer, type H. Design with interleaved disk windings. Courtesy of the General Electric Company

DYNAMOS AND MOTORS

THE ALTERNATING-CURRENT DYNAMO

More and more in recent years the large power-generating plants employ the alternating-current instead of the direct-current dynamo. On the one hand this avoids the use of the split commutator, which, though fairly efficient, is less so than the simple slip rings sufficient for the alternator. But a far more important consideration relates to long-distance electrical transmission. To understand this point we must recall that the loss of energy in transmitting electric current is due to its dissipation in the form of heat. It has been shown that the heat produced in a wire is proportional to the square of the current strength multiplied by the electrical resistance, that is, to C^2R. The energy, or wattage, of the current is proportional to the current multiplied by the voltage, that is, to CV. It is clear that the energy transmitted, equaling the product CV, is the same if $C = 1$ and $V = 10,000$ as when $C = 100$ and $V = 100$. But in the former case the heat loss is proportional to $1 \times 10,000R = 10,000R$, while in the latter case it is proportional to $100 \times 100 \times 100R = 1,000,000R$. Hence it is clear that for very long lines, where the electrical resistance is unavoidably great, the only recourse to diminish the dissipation of the electric energy in useless heat is to carry a small current at high voltage.

This may be accomplished easily by employing a device called the transformer, of which there are several types. The transformer comes directly from the experiments of Faraday, which were cited in Chapter I, and indeed may be said to be his invention. If two coils of wire be wound on the same iron or soft-steel magnetic circuit, of which one of the possible arrangements is shown in Figure 13, and an alternating current be passed through the primary coil, *a*, it will induce an alternating current in the secondary coil, *b*. If we neglect the small losses of energy due to eddy currents and other causes, the voltages of the

secondary and primary current may be regarded as in
the same ratio as the number of turns of wire in the two
coils, and the current strength in the two coils as in this
same ratio inverted. Hence, if it is desired to raise the
voltage and diminish the current from an alternating-
current dynamo by 100-fold to save heat losses in long-

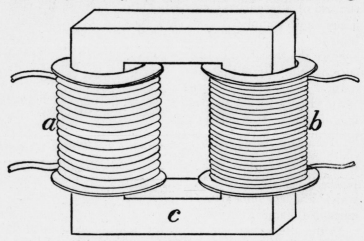

FIG. 13. A step-up transformer, to convert alternating current
of moderate voltage to alternating current of higher voltage

distance transmission, it is only necessary to introduce a
step-up transformer whose secondary has about 100 times
as many turns of wire as its primary. At the place where
it is to be used, the high voltage may be reduced again to
a voltage suitable for lamps and other ordinary purposes
by employing a device that is the reverse of the step-
up transformer.

Naturally much thought by many inventors has gone
to the improvement of the details of this fundamentally
simple device. The magnetic core circuit is, of course,
laminated to reduce eddy currents. The insulation of
the secondary coils from each other and from the primary
coils must be high. The mechanical stresses and the

heating effects during use require careful attention. Differences of phase relations of alternation of the currents form an important branch of transformer theory. Various types of connections have been evolved to suit different problems. All of these technical details may be studied by the interested reader in many excellent treatises on the use of alternating currents. Plate 12 shows the core design and completed core and coils of a transformer built for three-phase alternating-current work.

Since the transformer deals exclusively with alternating current, the alternating-current dynamo is obviously its natural companion. Alternators have therefore grown in favor rapidly within the last 30 years, during which time long-distance transmission of electricity has greatly multiplied. Another factor favorable to the alternator is the increasing use of the steam turbine as a prime mover because of its great efficiency in converting heat into power. The steam turbine runs naturally at high speeds, which are less obnoxious to alternators than to direct-current dynamos.

In the alternating generator, the field magnets must be actuated by direct currents. Hence a small direct-current dynamo is usually provided as a part of an alternating machine. But for many reasons, the places of the field magnets and the armature are frequently interchanged from the usual positions in direct-current dynamos, so that the armature is outside and stationary, while it is the field within that rotates. The convenient words "stator" and "rotor" have been added to the technical language used in connection with the alternator and other similar machines, the stator being the outer, stationary part, and the rotor the inner, revolving part.

Thus, with the alternating-current dynamo we may picture the prime mover, which may be a water wheel or a steam turbine, as possibly on the same shaft with the field rotor. The auxiliary direct-current dynamo sends its current into the field-rotor coils through a pair of brushes resting on a pair of slip rings upon the shaft. The rapid rotation of the field magnets induces in the armature coils alternating currents which flow into the primary coils of a step-up transformer. High voltage currents induced thereby in the transformer's secondary coils may be carried hundreds of miles over the gracefully looping transmission lines which we have become accustomed to seeing crossing the country in long stretches from one steel tower to another. At the distant city, where current is needed for light and power, the step-down transformer reduces the voltage again to a safe figure.

Thus the alternating generator has the advantage of mechanical simplicity, owing to the absence of the commutator. Electrically, however, there is a complexity so great that it is impossible to explain it in a book of this character; we can only give some slight indications of its nature. Plates 13 and 14 give a good idea of the alternating-current generator.

Alternating-current, like direct-current dynamos are usually multipolar, and their armatures are multicoil. The conductors are shaped rods of copper inserted within slots formed by many insulated steel punchings pressed side by side. Designers give close attention to the magnetic leakage and interference, which, owing to the interaction of the moving field poles and induction of the armature currents, are very complicated problems. The number of field poles required in alternator depends mainly on the speed at which it is to be driven, and the number of cycles of alternation per second desired of the current. In America experience has led to the selection of the two rates of alternation, 60 cycles and 25 cycles per second, as most suitable. The former is better for incandescent electric lighting because the fluctuations of current are then so rapid that the eye does not perceive flickering. Formerly 25 cycles were preferred for driving large motors and for some other uses, but the present tendency is toward 60 cycles for most purposes. If the prime mover drives at moderate speed it is

PLATE 13

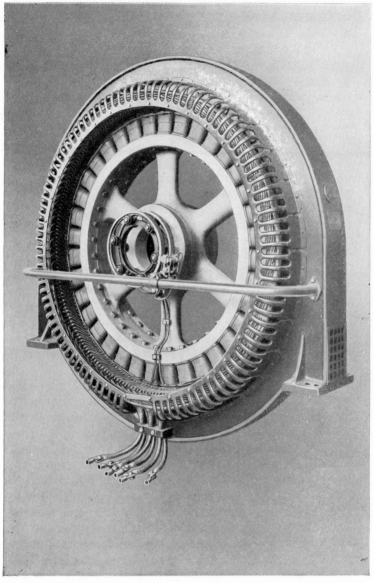

Alternating-current generator. Approximate diameter, 6 feet.
Courtesy of the General Electric Company

PLATE 14

Rotating field of alternator. Approximate diameter 4½ feet. Courtesy of the General Electric Company

necessary to have rather numerous field poles, sometimes 30 or even 50, to produce a 60-cycle current. On the other hand, to operate with rapidly rotating steam turbines, alternators are usually built with 2, 4, or 6 poles. Radio alternators, to produce enormous numbers of cycles, drive at great speeds, and have many poles.

Another feature of the alternating-current circuit is its phase number. If all the coils of the armature are connected in a single circuit with only two terminals, the machine is single-phase. If the coils are arranged in two separated groups with four terminals it is two-phase. But the most common arrangement of all is the three-phase system, in which the armature is wound in three independent coils 120° apart. Plate 10 shows a machine wound by Dr. Elihu Thomson with his own hands in this manner in the year 1879. It is on exhibition in the United States National Museum, where it was deposited by the General Electric Company. This machine has a rotating armature with fixed coils, and was designed to give direct current if desired, but the same general principle applies to the machines with rotating field coils.

In the three-phase system, three independent equal voltages are generated during each cycle at 120° phase angle apart, as indicated by Figure 14. The three sets of armature coils will have, of course, six terminals. But it is usual to connect three similar terminals together either within or outside the armature. If a wire were connected to this common junction it would carry no current, provided the loads on other wires were well balanced. Hence the neutral wire is often omitted, leaving but three wires for the line. A load, composed for instance of electric lights, may be thrown in between any two wires of a three-wire system, or the three wires may all be used at once in the appropriate manner to operate an alternating-current motor. It is clear that the reversal of the current, however many times per second it occurs, does not prevent the current from causing the glowing of incandescent lamps, for the wires in the lamps become hot merely because they offer a high resistance to the passage of the current in either direction. It is not the same with arc lamps, for arcs are not readily reversible. As we shall see in Chapter VI, there is usually a marked difference between the positive and negative poles of the arc, which hinders their interchange. Preferably they should be used on direct

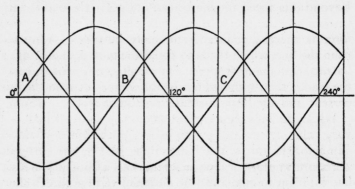

FIG. 14. Three-phase alternating current diagram

current. But direct current can be derived from an alternating-current system by the use, for example, of the mercury rectifier, described in Chapter III.

THE DIRECT-CURRENT MOTOR

Direct-current dynamos can be used as motors, and often are, though a machine originally constructed as a motor differs somewhat from a dynamo. If a line current passes through the field coils of a dynamo and actuates them, its passage through the armature requires the rotation of the armature relative to the field in order that the armature coils may tend to enclose a maximum number of lines of force. The same arrangements of the commutator which produce direct current in the dynamo are suitable to guide the current for the purposes of a motor. Plate 15, upper, gives a disassembled view of a direct-current motor.

[42]

DYNAMOS AND MOTORS

When a machine is operating as a motor, the coils of the revolving armature cut the lines of force of the field just as they would if the machine were operating as a dynamo. This produces an electromotive force opposed to that of the line. With no load, the speed of the motor increases until the back electromotive force of the motor approximately equals the driving electromotive force of the line. Beyond this speed the motor can not go. If a load is then thrown on, the motor slows, but the back electromotive force is thereby reduced, and more current is admitted from the line, which tends to speed the motor, and brings a balance at some new speed. The energy required to carry the load is then supplied by the difference between the line current and the back current from the motor.

While the self-regulatory tendency just described is a very valuable one, it is not to be forgotten that it would be damaging to throw the full voltage of the line into the armature at starting before any back electromotive force had built up to moderate the current. To avoid this danger, direct-current motors are equipped with a starting box in which the connections are so disposed that while the full voltage of the line enters the field coils at the first contact, there is a resistance interposed in the armature circuit, which is gradually withdrawn to zero when full speed is attained. A magnetic clutch holds the handle in the full-speed position. If the current fails, the handle is released and flies back to the "off" position, thus avoiding a possible neglect of precaution in restarting the motor.

In direct-current motors two methods of winding are in use for different purposes. In one type, called a shunt-wound motor, the armature and the field coils are in separate circuits between the two wires of the line. In the other type, called a series motor, the field coils and the armature coils are connected together to make one circuit across the line. In a shunt-wound motor the field coils are many and of small wire, in order to produce a strong field with the weak current diverted from the armature. In a series motor the field coils are few and of heavy wire, so that while producing strong magnets they will interpose but little resistance to the full current of the line which passes through them and thence to the armature. Shunt-wound motors are more uniform in their speeds under different loads but have a weak pick-up at starting. Series motors are more variable with changing loads but are strong at starting. For the latter reason they are often preferred for street cars and other electric and motor vehicles. For some purposes a combination of the two types, called the compound motor, is preferred.

THE ALTERNATING-CURRENT MOTOR

Alternating-current motors are more difficult to understand and less simple in operation than direct-current motors. These difficulties postponed for a time their general employment in the industry. Yet they offer certain very remarkable compensating advantages. These motors are of several types. First, we may consider the squirrel-cage type of induction motor, well suited to the three-phase 60-cycle alternating current.

As with alternating-current dynamos, it is preferable to construct the alternating-current motor armature as a stator outside the field rotor. Referring to Figure 14, the three-phase current coming in over the line energizes consecutively the armature coils which are arranged in three groups, spaced 120° apart around the circumference of the armature. That is to say, when the current in group number one reaches its maximum positive value, in group number two, 120° distant, the current is still negative but approaching zero, and in group number three, 120° farther around, the current is negative and approaching its negative maximum. The condition is often described as a revolving field. This means, not that the lines of force from the stator revolve, but that as they wax and wane

PLATE 15

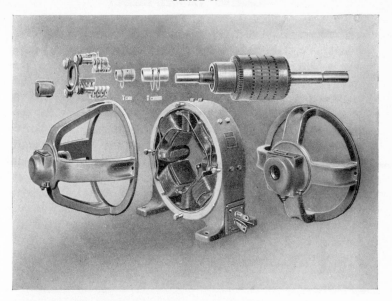

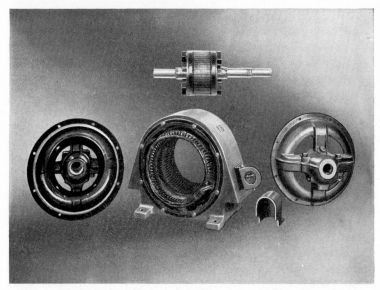

Upper: Disassembled direct-current motor. Lower: Disassembled alternating-current induction motor. Courtesy of the General Electric Company

in their regular progression the effect is similar to that which would be produced if the fixed armature were replaced by a horseshoe magnet which should actually revolve, carrying its lines of force around with it with its axis in the axis of the rotor. If this were actually the case, it is clear that such a magnet would drag with it a drum-wound rotor free to turn on the same axis. For only by turning could such a rotor avoid continually cutting the lines of force.

This leads us to the squirrel-cage rotor construction. It is merely a slotted cylinder of iron with insulated copper bars in the longitudinal slots all connected to a copper ring at each end (Plate 15, lower, top figure.) There is no connection of the rotor to the line currents. All that goes on in the squirrel cage is by induction. Hence this type of motor is often called the induction motor. It is not essential to use a three-phase current with an induction motor, for a single-phase current, although it will not start the rotor, will carry the rotor around after it has once acquired speed by other means. A two-phase current, however, will start such a motor.

Induction motors on no load run at a speed synchronous with the alternations of the driving current. If there are two phases in the armature, the 60-cycle current requires of the rotor 3,600 revolutions per minute. If there are eight phases, the rotor speed will be reduced to 900 revolutions. With load the rotor speed slows down, but ordinarily the slip of squirrel-cage rotors behind synchronous speed at full load does not exceed 4 per cent. The squirrel-cage motor is weak at starting and best at full load, but has no capacity for speed regulation. It is sometimes spoken of as the constant-speed motor. Other more complex types of induction motor exist. Plate 15, lower, shows a disassembled induction motor.

Other types of alternating-current motors require fuller consideration than befits this volume. The interested reader is advised to consult some of the excellent textbooks on the subject. We shall content ourselves here with a few more observations on special features of the induction motor. If such a motor is driven above synchronous speed by an outside power, it becomes a generator, and will supply power to the line. Full load as a generator will be delivered to the line with about the same amount of slip above synchronous speed as the machine displays when dragging behind synchronous speed with the slip accompanying full-load conditions as a motor. This property is useful in certain electrified railroad installations to return power to the line and act as a brake on down-grade stretches.

The "synchronous motor" is essentially the same as an alternating-current dynamo. It requires direct current to actuate its rotor field. It is not self-starting, but must be brought into synchronism with the alternations of the current of the line. Once in operation it remains in step with the line at all loads within its range. Its synchronous action depends on the fact that its field is separately excited by direct current, so that the field poles are continuing. They can therefore be in harmony with the revolving field of the fixed armature only when the rotations of the field are at an equal rate with the changes in direction of the armature current. As the synchronous motor will not start by itself, a short squirrel-cage winding is sometimes built into the rotor, by means of which it is brought nearly to synchronous speed with no load before the direct current is applied to the rotor. Its perfect speed regulation and its capacity to operate under a wide range of so-called "power factors" give the synchronous motor a special value in certain kinds of installations.

For the uses of wireless communication, alternating currents of enormous frequency are required, ranging from 100,000 to 30,000,000 cycles per second. It is possible to attain some of these frequencies by spark gaps placed in parallel with condensers. Also alternating-current generators of enormous frequency are in use,

PLATE 16

Alexanderson high-frequency dynamo for radio transmission. Top removed to show details. Courtesy of the General Electric Company

PLATE 17

Washington electric pumping plant

although these are now yielding to large electron-tube generators. Dr. E. F. W. Alexanderson, chief engineer of the General Electric Company, devised in 1913 an alternating generator of 100,000 cycles for long-distance wireless transmission. It comprises a large, strong, steel wheel with narrow rim in which are milled slots on the opposite faces, thus resembling a gear wheel whose teeth are not cut through to the rim of the wheel. The slots are filled with nonmagnetic material in order to present a smooth surface and thus reduce air friction. The wheel runs at high speed between two water-cooled laminated armatures, wire-wound in many open slots. As each wheel-slot in succession passes by an armature conductor it changes the induction. The field magnetic flux is carried by pole pieces through the armature laminations and the rotating wheel. The air spaces are very narrow— only 0.015 inch in width—so that great accuracy and stiffness are required in the wheel, as it revolves at some 20,000 revolutions per minute. (See Gen. Elec. Rev., vol. 23, p. 815, 1920.) In Plate 16 the device is shown with top half removed, exposing details.

It is related that after one of Faraday's lectures, in the course of which he demonstrated electrical devices, a member of the English government rather patronizingly said to him in substance: "Very interesting, Mr. Faraday, but of what practical use is it?" "Some day, My Lord, you will tax it!" was Faraday's reply. That day came long ago. The total generation of electric power in the United States in the year 1930 is reported by the American Institute of Electrical Engineers as 96 billion kilowatt-hours, equal to over 120 billion horsepower-hours. From 1921 to 1928 the average rate of increase per year was 11.5 per cent. Over 60 per cent of the electric power is being produced by steam-driven dynamos. The tendency in recent years is toward the combination of the steam turbine with the alternating-current dynamo. Most recently the Emmet mercury-vapor turbine, which operates at a higher temperature and with greater efficiency, is beginning to be associated with the steam turbine as a prime mover. In the usual engineering practice of 1920 it took, on an average, 30,000 British thermal units of heat to produce one kilowatt-hour. The average had declined in 1930 to 18,500 B.t.u.

In 1930 a plant using the new Emmet mercury-vapor turbine combined with a steam turbine required but 10,180 B.t.u. per kilowatt-hour. This is an efficiency of 33.4 per cent, as computed from the total energy of the fuel. Taking account of the temperatures of the gases, 56 per cent is the maximum limit of possible conversion of the heat into mechanical energy, according to the principles of thermodynamics. These figures show the high efficiency now reached in the combined processes of combustion, heating of liquids, conversion of heat into mechanical energy, and finally into electric energy. The electric dynamo units are growing larger. For example, the United Electric Light and Power Company recently installed two 160,000-kilowatt generators in the same space that was previously occupied by two 35,000-kilowatt units, and the Brooklyn Edison Company installed two 160,000-kilowatt generators in place of two of 50,000. In this country the great alternating generators are often constructed to deliver current at 15,000 to 20,000 volts potential, while in Europe there are several plants where voltages of 25,000 to 35,000 are generated.

The beauty of electric power installations is well shown in Plate 17, which depicts the high-level pumping plant of the Washington Water Works. In each transverse row there are three Westinghouse motors driving Worthington centrifugal pumps. All are 60-cycle alternating-current machines, of 2,200 volts pressure, and from 500 to 770 horsepower. The twin pumps have each 10,000,000 gallons capacity, and the single ones on the left 20,000,000 gallons.

CHAPTER III

ELECTRONS AND X RAYS

As our story approaches the subjects of electric lighting, X rays, and wireless, we come into the field of the play of molecules, atoms, and electrons. These structures are invisible even with the most powerful microscopes. Nevertheless, Sir J. J. Thomson, Lord Rutherford of Nelson, and their colleagues of the Cavendish Laboratory at Cambridge, England, by their ingenious experiments, have prepared a way into this enticing domain, into which many other physicists in Europe and America have pressed onward during the last 30 years.

We all know of matter in three states, gaseous, liquid, and solid, as, for instance, air, water, and copper. Long ago it was found that many solids could be melted into liquids, and liquids changed into gases, if only they are heated to suitable temperatures. In the case of water, summer temperatures suffice to melt winter's ice into liquid water, and the cook-stove turns water plentifully into steam. What we see and call steam, to be sure, is but a cloud of liquid water drops, similar to the fleecy clouds in the atmosphere. Real steam is invisible, like air itself. It occurs in the little, apparently vacant space just in front of the end of the spout of a boiling teakettle.

Gases, such as air, hydrogen, oxygen, nitrogen, and the rest, behave very differently at atmospheric pressure and in vacua. For instance, at atmospheric pressure they strongly resist the flow of electricity, unless their resistance is broken down by high voltages, as in lightning flashes, the spark, and the arc. But when the pressure is reduced to 1/1,000 part of atmospheric pressure or less, an electric current at moderate voltage easily sets up a continuing discharge.

The coloring displayed in the discharge of electricity through vacuum tubes is very striking. Recently, in Europe as well as in America advertising signs have been increasingly intricate, ingenious, and often beautiful, as displayed by red, yellow, and greenish-blue electric discharges through evacuated glass tubing. At the Colonial Exposition at Paris in 1931 a long avenue was entirely lighted at night by many 25-foot columns of such lights.

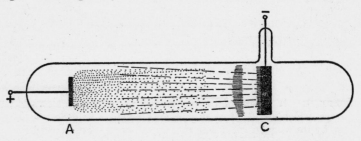

Fig. 15. Electric discharge in a high vacuum (diagrammatic)

Each column had six vertical glass tubes, each about an inch in diameter, with three greenish-blue and three red tubes arranged alternately. To obtain these colors the alternate tubes probably contained the gases of mercury and neon.

The electric discharge through high vacuum is indicated by the diagram, Figure 15. The current flows from the positive pole or "anode," *A*, to the negative pole or "cathode," *C*, and produces a glow which has several interesting features. For a considerable distance from the anode there is seen the beautifully colored "positive glow." Then comes a dark space called the "Faraday dark space," then a new region of "negative glow," and after it the "Crookes dark space." Finally comes the velvety, feebly glowing region close to the cathode.

ELECTRONS AND X RAYS

At fairly low pressures bluish rays of light are plainly seen moving from the cathode in straight lines across the Crookes dark space. As they fall on the glass walls of the discharge tube, they excite thereon a greenish phosphorescence. These are the so-called "cathode rays." At still higher vacua the cathode discharge continues, but is invisible.

THE ELECTRON

Sir J. J. Thomson, Cavendish professor of physics and Master of Trinity College, Cambridge, performed the

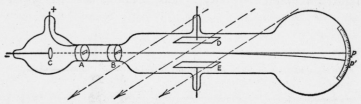

FIG. 16. J. J. Thomson's discovery of the electron. Cathode rays, which are electrons in motion, tending to be deflected to p' by the magnetic field indicated by the arrows, are restored to p by the electric field, DE. From the electric and magnetic quantities involved, Thomson determined the charge and mass of the electron

epoch-making experiment illustrated by Figure 16 and described in the following abstract of the account of Doctor Thomson himself in a paper entitled, "On Bodies Smaller than Atoms," which was published in the Smithsonian Report for the year 1901. He showed, in fact, that objects more than a thousand times lighter than a hydrogen atom exist.

These [cathode] rays are now known to consist of negatively electrified particles moving with great rapidity. We can determine the electric charge carried by a given mass of these particles by measuring the effect of electric and magnetic forces to deflect them. It was some time, however, before a deflection by an electric force was observed, and many attempts to obtain this deflection were unsuccessful. By reducing the pressure of the gas inside the tube to such an extent that there was very little gas left to conduct, I was able to obtain the deflection of the rays by an electrostatic field. The cathode rays are also deflected by a magnet. Let us adjust these forces so that the effect of the electric force just balances that of the magnetic force. From the magnitudes of the electric and magnetic forces required for such a balance it was found that to carry unit charge of electricity by the particles forming the cathode rays only requires a mass of these particles amounting to one ten-thousandth of a milligram, while to carry the same charge by hydrogen atoms would require a mass of one-tenth of a milligram.

In Figure 16, the anode, A, is perforated by a slit to allow free course to certain rays from the cathode, C. A metal diaphragm, B, containing a narrow slit, is inserted so that only a single fine pencil of rays is permitted to pass to the end of the tube. A powder of zinc blende is deposited there to reveal by its phosphorescence the exact spot hit by the rays. D and E are two plates electrically charged to any desired difference. Outside of the discharge tube is a uniform magnetic field indicated by the arrows. It is at right angles to the path of the cathode rays and also at right angles to the electric field between D and E. Without turning on the electric field, the rays are deflected by the magnet into a curved path leading to p' as shown. But with a suitable electric field, D, E, the magnetic deflection can be balanced so as to bring the rays back to the straight course ending at p.

Doctor Thomson continues:

The exceedingly small mass of these particles for a given charge compared with that of the hydrogen atoms might be due either to the mass of each of these particles being very small compared with that of a hydrogen atom, or else to the charge carried by each particle being large compared with that carried by the atom of hydrogen. It is therefore essential that we should determine the electric charge carried by one of these particles. The problem is as follows: Suppose in an inclosed space we have a number of electrified particles each carrying the same charge, it is required to find the charge on each particle. It is easy by electrical methods to determine the total quantity of electricity on the collection of particles, and knowing this we can find the charge on each particle if we can count the number of particles. To count these particles the first step is to make them visible. We can do this by availing ourselves of a discovery made by C. T. R. Wilson, working in the Cavendish Laboratory. Wilson has shown that when positively and negatively electrified particles are present in moist dust-free air a cloud is produced when the air is cooled by a sudden expansion, though this amount of expansion would be quite insufficient to produce condensation when no electrified particles are present: the water condenses round the electrified particles, and, if these are not too numerous, each particle becomes the nucleus of a little drop of water. Now Sir George Stokes has shown how we can calculate the rate at which a drop of water falls through air if we know the size of the drop, and conversely we can determine the size of the drop by measuring the rate at which it falls through the air. Hence by measuring the speed with which the cloud falls we can determine the volume of each little drop. The whole volume of water deposited by cooling the air can easily be calculated, and dividing the whole volume of water by the volume of one of the drops we get the number of drops, and hence the number of the electrified particles. We saw, however, that if we knew the number of particles we could get the electric charge on each particle; proceeding in this way I found that the charge carried by each particle was about . . . 2.17×10^{-20} electro-magnetic units. . . . In the electrolysis of solutions . . . the atom of hydrogen will carry a charge equal to 2.27×10^{-20} electro-magnetic units. . . . These numbers are so nearly equal that, considering the difficulties of the experiments, we may feel sure that the charge on one of these gaseous particles is the same as that on an atom of hydrogen in electrolysis. This result has been verified in a different way by Professor Townsend, who used a method by which he found, not the absolute value of the electric charge on a particle, but the ratio of this charge to the charge on an atom of hydrogen, and he found that the two charges were equal.

As the charges on the particle and the hydrogen atom are the same, the fact that the mass of these particles required to carry a given charge of electricity is only one-thousandth part of the mass of the hydrogen atoms shows that the mass of each of these particles is only about one one-thousandth of that of a hydrogen atom. . . . We have obtained from the matter [occurring in the cathode rays] particles having a much smaller mass than that of the atom of hydrogen, the smallest mass hitherto recognized. These negatively electrified particles, which I have called corpuscles, have the same electric charge and the same mass whatever be the nature of the gas inside the tube or whatever the nature of the electrodes; the charge and mass are invariable. They therefore form an invariable constituent of the atoms or molecules of all gases and presumably of all liquids and solids.

Nor are the corpuscles confined to the somewhat inaccessible regions in which cathode rays are found. I have found that they are given off by incandescent metals, by metals when illuminated by ultra-violet light, while the researches of Becquerel and Professor and Madame Curie have shown that they are given off by that wonderful substance the radio-active radium.

In fact, in every case in which the transport of negative electricity through gas at a low pressure (i.e., when the corpuscles have nothing to stick to) has been examined, it has been found that the carriers of the negative electricity are these corpuscles of invariable mass.

Later researches by Thomson, his associates, and others, and by Dr. R. A. Millikan, whose exact measurement of the quantity "e" is described by him in the Smithsonian Report for 1910, page 231, show that the mass of the negative corpuscle, now generally called the electron, is even smaller than Thomson indicates above. It is now accepted as 1/1,848 part of the mass of a hydrogen atom, which throughout the nineteenth century was supposed to be the smallest thing in Nature.

The electron which carries (or perhaps better which *is*) the ultimate single unit of negative electricity, has been proved to be a constituent of every kind of material found in Nature. The hydrogen atom contains only one electron. Atoms of all other substances contain larger numbers of electrons up to 200 or more in the case of very heavy chemical elements like radium or uranium. Since the lightness and smallness of the electron equip it to be the principal actor in the flow of heat and electricity as well as in electric lighting, X rays, and radio, it has seemed proper to give this somewhat long account of its discovery as explained in the original sources.

Regarding other constituents of atoms it will be sufficient to state merely the results and not the methods which have led to present knowledge of the structure of matter. There is another entity called the proton which carries (or perhaps better which *is*) the ultimate single unit of positive electricity. It is electrically equal but opposite in charge to the electron. Its mass is 1,847 times the mass of the electron, so that it is comparatively sluggish in motion and therefore, though sometimes very influential in a quiet way, takes little active part in the transfer of electricity and heat. The hydrogen atom consists of one electron and one proton, and, so far as we know, of nothing else. It is clear that these opposite electric charges must be held apart in the atom by some powerful force, presumably the centrifugal force of rapid orbital motion. Otherwise annihilation would ensue, as the electricities would rush together. It is believed that in the interiors of the sun and stars, where temperatures of millions of degrees and pressures of millions of atmospheres prevail, annihilation of matter is actually proceeding. Thereby the orbital atomic energy which opposes annihilation is being converted into radiation such as light, or rather into the short-wave forms called X rays, which by successive transformations become light at the surface of the stars.

In atoms of all the chemical elements except hydrogen, protons and electrons are agglomerated into very compact central nuclei. Thus far it has proved too difficult for experiments fully to reveal how this occurs. Around the nucleus lie outside electrons at distances which, though far less than can be examined by the highest-powered microscope, are yet, when compared to the sizes of the electrons and the nucleus, somewhat like the distances of the planets from the sun as compared to the sizes of these heavenly bodies. Thus an atom is far from being a solid ball, as some early theories of atoms supposed. It is, on the contrary, a lattice of rather definite total size. In such a lattice free space is almost the exclusive constituent. The electrons and the nucleus which comprise the frame of the lattice are almost as insignificant in size relative to the lattice as are motes compared to the volume of air in a room.

As proved by Moseley, whose untimely sacrifice in World War I must ever be lamented, the number of outside electrons in the atoms increases regularly, step by step.

Hydrogen has one, helium two, lithium three, and so on up to uranium with 92 outside electrons. Uranium stands at the end of the list of chemical elements so far as we yet know. In the larger atoms, the association of these outside electrons with the nucleus becomes very loose. Even the stability of the nucleus itself totters in some very complex atoms. In radium, thorium, and uranium a continual splitting off of fragments of the atoms occurs. This process reduces these broken atoms eventually to the metal lead, with a remainder of several atoms of helium gas. Thus, in a way entirely out of man's control, Nature herself brings true the dreams of the old alchemists who hoped to transmute one element into another. The alchemists, however, worked for gold. Nature is satisfied, like Bassanio in the Merchant of Venice, with base lead. Nevertheless with the cyclotron, invented by Dr. E. O. Lawrence, electric potentials approaching 100,000,000 volts have produced transmutations of the elements by electric bombardments, of both scientific and medical value.

Solids and Electric Conduction

A solid, then, is not a solid, according to the modern view. It is a bounded portion of free space wherein innumerable ultra-ultra-microscopic particles, each carrying a definite electric charge, are huddled together as if constrained by some immutable bond. This bond is so close that during thousands of years the sharp reliefs of ancient coins have still remained distinct. They have not yet parted with enough wandering molecules from their assemblages to change appreciably the contours which delimit their forms. It is then only a definitely bounded region of free space, penetrable by sufficiently small missiles almost without obstruction, that is the real structure of what we call a solid. The ultimate particles which compose it actually fill but an almost inappreciably small proportion of its contour.

In proof of this paradoxical view, many devices now in

constant use in laboratory experiments and commercial arts depend for their operation on the penetration by electrons to and from the interiors of solids. In some apparatus, electrons pass through thin films of metals quite impervious to air. Much stranger than this is the well-known fact that electric energy may be transmitted by wire conductors practically instantaneously for great distances.

Electric conduction by solids appears to depend on the looseness of connection which subsists between some of the outside electrons and the nuclei of atoms of the metals. While the major part of each atomic structure remains bound close to its original position in a wire, some of the outside electrons are often dislodged by collision or outside attraction, and have temporary intervals of freedom before reattaching themselves either to their original atoms or to others from which electrons are missing. Especially is this the case in wires and solids of all sorts at high temperatures. There is, indeed, a continual emission of electrons from hot wires which is of the utmost importance in wireless telephony and radio, because it is the foundation of the indispensable electron tube, also called the thermionic tube.

An astonishing phenomenon is always before us in the conduction of electricity by metallic wires. Electrical effects are produced almost instantaneously at immense distances. With alternating currents such effects are reversed in ordinary circuits 60 times a second, and may indeed be reversed a hundred thousand times a second or even much oftener. Dr. H. M. Barlow of University College, London, contributed in 1929[1] a theory of electric conduction which he modestly describes as "an effort to provide a starting point." Many other scientific men have previously discussed metallic conduction in somewhat similar terms, but Doctor Barlow's paper has some novel features.

[1] London, Edinburgh, and Dublin Philosophical Magazine, ser. 7, vol. 8, p. 289, 1929.

He assumes that the atoms in conducting solids lie so closely together that their outer electron orbits nearly touch. Hence an electron finding itself in that part of its orbit midway between two atomic nuclei requires little expenditure of force to leave the orbit of its own atom and continue along the orbit of the adjacent atom. But no atom can thus give away an electron to a neighbor unless it receives at the same time a replacement electron from elsewhere, because electric attraction forbids. "A current," says Barlow, "consists of a series of electrons passing simultaneously along a chain of atoms. In general the chain will have a zigzag form, but with a resultant direction parallel with the electric force." The astonishing rapidity of electric conductivity is seen to depend on the fact that exchanges go on simultaneously all along the wire. It is not as though each electron carried its charge from one end of the wire to the other. Its path is really infinitesimally short, and yet, short as it is, it is traversed at a velocity above 10 miles per second. These considerations explain the speed of transmission of electricity.

Such interesting speculations as these of Barlow's show us at least a plausible view of how the orbital structure of atoms and their possession of easily-divested negatively-charged electrons may render possible those astonishingly rapid transferences of electric stimuli for hundreds and even thousands of miles in so-called "solid" wires.

The Electron Tube Amplifier

About the year 1884 Thomas A. Edison discovered a curious phenomenon which is the germ of the electron tube now indispensable to wireless telephony and many other arts. He found that if, in an ordinary electric lamp bulb with "hairpin" filament, there is introduced besides the two electrodes a third wire insulated completely from the filament when cold, and charged with positive electricity, then as soon as the filament becomes hot a current flows over from the hot filament to the charged third wire.

The current ceases when the filament becomes cold, and will not flow if the third wire is neutral or negatively charged.

Dr. Irving Langmuir of the General Electric Company, making a long series of experiments on the Edison effect about 1913, showed that what we may call the Simon-pure current effect has very definite laws, but is often masked by other nearly unpredictable effects if small traces of gases are contained in the vacuum tube. With highest vacua and gas-free conductors the phenomenon is represented by Figure 17.

The loose association between outside electrons and the atomic nuclei permits hot wires to emit electrons in all directions. As the electrons are negative charges, their loss from the parent wire must accumulate a positive charge on that wire if it was neutral before. But as the charge, e, of a single electron is only 1.6×10^{-19} coulombs, a very great number of negative electrons must fly away before the positive charge caused by their loss can become measurable by instruments. Meanwhile the space surrounding the wire is becoming populated with negative electrons, which, repelling each other though attracted towards the positively charged wire, tend to check further emission. The surroundings are then said to have acquired a "space charge." This phenomenon may be compared with the evaporation from a hot liquid into a closed space. Evaporation increases until the space above the liquid becomes saturated with vapor. Afterwards the balance of evaporation and condensation keeps the proportions of liquid and vapor constant so long as the temperature is unchanged.

In one respect such a comparison between the hot wire and the hot liquid fails. The electrons are endowed with such high velocities that they frequently knock off other electrons from the molecules of previously neutral surrounding gases. Such molecules are said to be ionized. This leaves the molecular residues positively charged, and therefore in a state tending to capture electrons emitted from the hot wire. When such ionization is going on there may be produced faint glows like the glow of the cathode rays in a discharge tube of moderate evacuation.

The "electron tube amplifier," indispensable in radio receiving sets, has within its evacuated space a tungsten wire heated to white heat by an electric current. This causes the wire to emit negative electrons. Nearby is an electrode, preferably of tungsten or molybdenum, which is charged to a fairly high positive voltage. In this condition it attracts the negative electrons emitted by the hot wire and thus causes negative electricity to flow in a circuit through the hot wire toward the positive electrode. Such a flow of electricity is called a thermionic current.

Between the hot wire and the positive electrode is inserted a grid of fine wire connected to the antenna circuit. The grid therefore fluctuates in its charged condition as the electric waves produced by broadcasting come in. Increasing positive charge or, what is equivalent, a diminishing negative charge, on the grid tends to clear the space around it of negative electrons, and so to increase the thermionic current, and vice versa. In certain sensitive adjustments a very small change of the grid voltage produces a relatively large change of the thermionic current. Such is the operation of the vacuum tube amplifier. A primary thermionic current, thus amplified, may be arranged to influence the grid of a second electron tube, thereby amplifying a second thermionic current, and so on.

These elements were embodied in the "audion" protected by United States patent No. 841,387 granted in the year 1907 to Dr. Lee De Forest on his application filed October 25, 1906. Claims Nos. 1 (in part), 4 and 6 are as follows:

1. In a device for amplifying electrical currents, an evacuated vessel inclosing a sensitive conducting gaseous medium maintained in a condition of molecular activity. . . .

4. In a device for amplifying electrical currents, an evacuated

vessel, three electrodes sealed within said vessel, . . . means for heating one of said electrodes, a local receiving circuit including two of said electrodes, and means for passing the current to be amplified between one of the electrodes which is included in the receiving-circuit and the third electrode.

6. In a device for amplifying electrical currents, an evacuated vessel, a heated electrode and two non-heated electrodes sealed within said vessel, the non-heated electrodes being unequally spaced with respect to said heated electrode, a local receiving-circuit including said heated electrode and that one of the non-heated electrodes which has the greater separation from the heated electrode, and means for passing the current to be amplified between the heated electrode and the other non-heated electrode.

In the earlier use of the electron tube the vacuum was not so high but that considerable ionization of the gases in the tube took place under their bombardment by electrons from the heated wire. This tended to magnify the thermionic current. From one point of view this was desirable. On the other hand, no two tubes were apt to be exactly alike in gaseous content, so that if one tube failed a readjustment of circuits was required when it was replaced. The ionized gas, indeed, acted the part of a second positively charged grid, efficient to reduce negative "space charge" and so to enhance the thermionic current, but not easily replaceable by the ionized gas of a second tube, almost certain to differ essentially from the first.

Dr. Irving Langmuir of the General Electric Company, who studied thermionic currents extensively about 1913, described his researches in 1915 (Gen. Elec. Rev., vol. 18, p. 330, 1915). After quoting findings of previous experiments up to the year 1913 he says:

"We see that there were the best of reasons for believing that it would be impossible to get any electric discharge through a perfect vacuum, because one could not expect to get any electrons from the electrodes." That is, previous experimenters had been led to the view that the emission by the hot wire was of chemical origin— due to the presence of gases—and not thermal.

In summing up his own experiments, in which he used a tungsten lamp filament for the hot wire, he goes on to say:

It was found that the smallness of the [thermionic] current in a lamp was not due to any failure of the filament to emit electrons, but was due entirely to the inability of the space around the filament to carry the currents with the potential available in the lamp. The explanation of this phenomenon was found to be that the electrons carrying the current between the two electrodes constituted an electric charge in the space, which repelled the electrons escaping from the filament, and caused some of them to return to the filament.

. . . . . .

Extremely minute traces of gas however, may lead to the formation of a sufficient number of positive ions to neutralize to a large extent the space charge of electrons, and thus very greatly increase the current carrying capacity of the space. For example, a pressure of mercury vapor of about 1/100,000 mm. has, under certain conditions, been found to completely eliminate the effect of space charge, so that a current of 0.1 ampere was obtained with only 25 volts on the anode, whereas without this mercury vapor, over 200 volts were necessary to draw this current through the space.

Besides this enormous effect on the carrying capacity of the space, many gases have a great influence on the electron emission from the cathode. But in every case where the cathode is of pure tungsten the effect of the gas is to decrease, rather than increase, the electron emission. For example, it is found that a millionth of a millimeter [about a billionth of atmospheric pressure] of oxygen, or gas containing oxygen, such as water vapor, will cut the electron emission down to a small fraction of that in high vacuum.

. . . . . .

Further investigation showed that with the elimination of the gas effects, all the irregularities which had previously been thought inherent in vacuum discharges from hot cathodes were found to disappear.

These experiments of Langmuir's and others have shown that these so-called thermionic currents between heated tungsten filaments and positively charged conductors, all contained in highest vacuum, are subject to definite laws. Knowing the dimensions of the conductors, the temperature of the filament, and the voltage of the positive terminal, the thermionic current can be accurately predicted. Without giving formulae, which may be found in textbooks, we may note that, as shown in Figure 17, in a given tube at fixed positive voltage the thermionic current increases with the temperature of the filament up to a definite value, beyond which temperature no increase occurs. At any given temperature the thermionic current rises with increasing voltage, but not indefinitely. For at any temperature there will be found a critical voltage, beyond which no increase of voltage will increase the current.

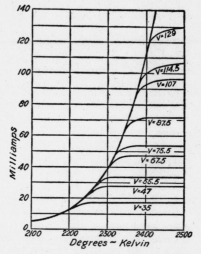

The explanation of these results is as follows: Though the number of electrons emitted by a filament tends to increase indefinitely with the temperature, the presence of a sufficient number of negatively charged electrons, already thrown out into the vacuum, exerts a

FIG. 17. Cathode temperature, voltage, and thermionic current. The strength of thermionic current soon reaches a maximum for any given voltage, owing to space charge. After Langmuir

repelling influence which prevents the escape of more of them from the filament. This is the so-called "space charge" limitation. Again, at any given temperature a sufficient positive charge on the anode will attract *all* the electrons being emitted. Therefore increasing voltage beyond this value will draw no more.

On the basis of his experiments Langmuir applied for a patent on improvements of the electron tube amplifier, filed October 16, 1913. A typical claim is No. 2, as follows:

2. A discharge tube having a cathode adapted to emit electrons and an anode adapted to receive said emitted electrons, the tube walls being fashioned or shaped to permit the direct passage of a useful proportion of said electrons from cathode to anode, the gas content or residue of said tube and the relation of parts of the tube being such that the tube is capable of being so operated in a range below saturation and materially above ionization voltages that the space current is governed or limited by the electric field of said electrons substantially unaffected by positive ionization.

This patent application had a long, rough passage in the Patent Office, but a patent was finally issued on October 20, 1925. Meanwhile, electron tube amplifiers built according to its principles came into use to the exclusion of all others, because they were interchangeable. Such tubes gave uniform results, and were commercially produced to be interchangeable without necessity of special adjustments of the radio circuit on the substitution of one for another.

The De Forest Radio Company, however, contested the validity of the Langmuir patent. It was first held invalid, then reaffirmed in courts of appeal. The case reached the Supreme Court, which decided, May 25, 1931, that the Langmuir patent is "*Held* invalid as not involving invention over the prior art." The Court held that a publication of Lilienfeld, in 1910, and remarks of Fleming, in 1905, indicated that the advantage of a high vacuum was known to persons skilled in the art before Langmuir; that all other elements of Langmuir's tube were contained in the audion of De Forest. "That the high vacuum tube was an improvement over the low vacuum tube of great importance," says the Court, "is not open to doubt. Even though the improvement was accomplished by so simple a change in structure as could be brought about by reducing the pressure in the well-known low vacuum tube by a few microns, still it may be invention. Whether it is or not depends upon . . . whether the relationship . . . was known in the art when Langmuir began his experiments."

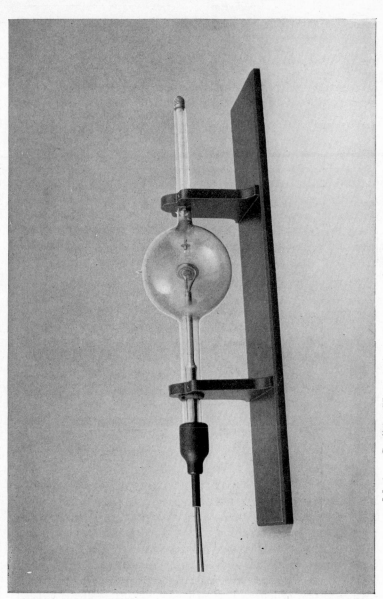

Modern Coolidge X-ray tube. Courtesy of the General Electric Company

PLATE 19

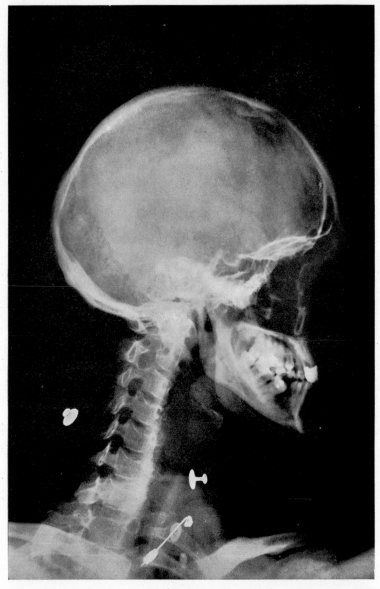

X-ray picture of human head and neck. Courtesy of the General Electric Company

On this question, as we have seen, the Court decided adversely. The legal niceties and the intellectual interest of such a decision may perhaps be appreciated better by quoting a citation by the United States Court of Customs and Patent Appeals in a case decided February 25, 1931, as follows:

PATENTABILITY—INVENTION.

A combination of old elements, in order to be patentable, must involve invention. It must produce not only some useful but some new result which goes beyond what may be achieved by mere mechanical skill in operating the elements disclosed by prior art.

The Supreme Court held that Langmuir did not do this.

Two other General Electric Company devices of great value depending on the properties of the high vacuum electron tube were produced immediately after Langmuir's experiments. These are the Coolidge X-ray tubes famous in hospital practice, and Dushman's "kenotron" alternating-current rectifier.

X RAYS

The Smithsonian Report for the year 1897, among quite a number of extraordinary articles[2] on physical subjects which would well repay reading at the present time, contained a translation of Prof. W. C. Röntgen's original observations published in 1895 on the discovery of X rays and their properties. He was not able in these first experiments to determine what they were, hence he called them "X rays," probably because X is usually an unknown quantity in algebra. Later they were proved to be identical in nature to ordinary light. They are, in short,

---

[2] The evolution of satellites, by G. H. Darwin.
Electrical advance in the past ten years, by Elihu Thomson.
The X-rays, by W. C. Röntgen.
Cathode rays, by J. J. Thomson.
Story of experiments in mechanical flight, by S. P. Langley.
Diamonds, by William Crookes.
An undiscovered gas, by William Ramsay.

waves. But whereas light waves average 50,000 to the inch in length, X rays average 100,000,000. Thus they lie far on the hither side of light rays in the spectrum as compared to radio rays, which are also of similar nature, but whose single waves range from several feet to several thousand feet in length. For lack of proper apparatus to analyze such minute waves, Röntgen did not at first discover these properties, but others have since shown that X rays may be reflected, refracted, diffracted, and polarized, just as light rays can.

Röntgen begins:

If the discharge . . . be passed through a . . . tube . . . containing a sufficiently high vacuum, the tube being covered with a close layer of thin black pasteboard and the room darkened, a paper screen covered on one side with barium-platinum cyanide . . . will be seen to glow brightly and fluoresce . . . even when the screen is removed to a distance of 2 meters from the apparatus. The observer may easily satisfy himself that the cause of the fluorescence is to be found at the vacuum tube and at no other part of the electrical circuit.

It is thus apparent that there is here an agency which is able to pass through the black pasteboard impenetrable to visible or ultra violet rays from the sun or the electric arc, and having passed through to excite a lively fluorescence, and it is natural to inquire whether other substances can be thus penetrated. I have found that all substances transmit this agency but in a very different degree.

He then gives many examples, including glass and several metals, among which he found aluminum very transparent, but lead very opaque. "If," says Röntgen, "the hand is held between the vacuum tube and the screen, the dark shadow of the bones is seen upon the much lighter shadow outline of the hand."

It is of particular importance from many points of view that photographic dry plates are sensitive to X-rays. . . . The retina of the eye is not sensitive to these rays. Nothing is to be noticed by bringing the eye near the vacuum tube although according to the preceding observations the media of the eye must be sufficiently transmissible to the rays in question. . . .

Most substances are, like the air, more transmissible for X-rays than for the cathode rays.

Another very noteworthy difference between the behavior of the cathode rays and the X-rays was exhibited in that I was unable to produce any deviation of the latter by the action of the most powerful magnetic fields.

According to the results of experiments particularly directed to discover the source of the X-rays, it is certain that the part of the wall of the discharge tube which most strongly fluoresces is the principal starting point. The X-rays therefore radiate from the place where . . . the cathode rays meet the glass wall. If one diverts the cathode rays within the tube by a magnet, the source of the X-rays is also seen to change its position so that these radiations still proceed from the end points of the cathode rays. . . . I come therefore to the results that the X-rays are not identical with the cathode rays in the glass wall of the vacuum tube.

This generating action takes place not only in glass, but as I have observed in apparatus with aluminum walls 2 millimeters thick, exists also for this metal [and others also].

Further on, Röntgen examines the differences of penetrating power of X rays, which he found to depend on the voltage used to excite the discharge tube. Tubes very highly evacuated, or which became so by long use, requiring high voltage to force the discharge, sent out, he found, very penetrating X rays. Such tubes he called "hard" tubes and those of a less perfect vacuum "soft." X rays also received the designations "hard" and "soft" according to their penetrating power. We know now that the "hard" X rays are of shorter wave length than "soft" ones.

Röntgen also constructed tubes in which the cathode rays struck a target of metal placed at an angle of 45° to the direction of the cathode rays. From such a target the X rays could be taken out at right angles to the cathode rays. He also used tubes in which a concave mirror of aluminum was employed as the cathode, in order to focus the cathode rays upon the target.

Thus, although he did not know the real nature of X rays, their discoverer within a few months conducted such a fruitful series of experiments as to adequately explore their properties, and he invented excellent means for their production. The new rays sprang at once into hospital practice. Röntgen's discovery has been one of the greatest boons to surgery and medicine ever found, ranking perhaps with Pasteur's discovery of the roles of bacteria and other germs.

The Coolidge X-ray tubes, by furnishing a great increase in intensity and available penetrating power, shortened photographic exposures, and made it possible to examine satisfactorily deep-lying human tissues which before were difficult or impossible to portray. Plate 18 shows a modern Coolidge X-ray tube, capable of using a potential of 200,000 volts, owing to the extremely high vacuum and to the considerable length of path employed. Plate 19 shows an X-ray photograph, made with a Coolidge tube, of the head and neck of a man.

PRACTICAL USE OF PROPERTIES OF ATOMIC STRUCTURE

For purposes of transmission, alternating current is far superior to direct current, as we noted in Chapter II. But for certain uses only direct current is available; hence, methods have been devised to procure direct from alternating current. One of these consists of the split commutator, as used on direct-current dynamos. The same method is also applied in the rotary transformer, which is an alternating-current motor operating a direct-current dynamo, usually on the same shaft.

There are, however, two methods of procuring direct current from alternating current which depend on the properties of atomic structure. One is the Dushman "kenotron" rectifier above mentioned. This device is illustrated in Figure 18. In the high-vacuum tube, *A*, spiral spring connections, *a*, carry taut the hot cathode wire of tungsten, *b*, *b*, through the axis of the surrounding molybdenum cylinder, *c*, *c*, which, supported firmly by connectors, *d*, *d*, forms the anode. Since the cylinder walls lie close to the tungsten filament, only a small drop of

[68]

voltage occurs in forcing a thermionic current across the vacuum gap. If now an alternating current is connected from B to C, whether single or polyphase, only those intervals during which the point B is a negative pole can provide any current, for the cylinder c, c, is so thick as to be always cool and therefore unable to emit electrons. Thus the current which passes, though intermittent, is direct. Nor is there any loss of energy except that due to the small resistance in the wire and the vacuum gap. For during the instants when the unfavorable phases occur, it is as though a switch in the circuit had been opened. There is then zero current and zero loss. Thus the efficiency of the Dushman kenotron rectifier is high, even at voltages as low as 100 and becomes even higher with voltages exceeding 1,000. The intermittent character of the current

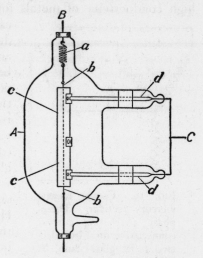

FIG. 18. Dushman's "kenotron" thermionic rectifier. Only at those instants when the alternating current is of proper sign can thermionic currents pass

may be smoothed out by the use of a condenser. As very high voltage currents may be rectified, the kenotron is available for penetrating X-ray tubes, when joined to a step-up transformer line. Many kenotrons can be used in parallel circuit together to carry large currents.

Another device for extracting direct from three-phase alternating current is the mercury-arc rectifier of Cooper Hewitt. The electric arc differs from the high-vacuum tube discharge in that vapors and gases ionized by the

electric discharge, and containing not only negative electrons but positive ions also, form the conducting medium.
The arc persists only when its cathode is at a very high
temperature. Its anode may be quite cool.

Hence it is not as easy to maintain even a direct-current
arc between metals as it is between carbons, because the
high conductivity of metals for heat tends to keep the

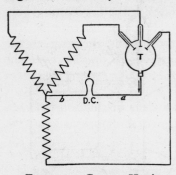

FIG. 19. Cooper Hewitt
mercury rectifier. Three-
phase alternating current
connected to three iron electrodes in glass bulb, *T*.
When any one of them be-
comes positive the current
flows to the mercury electrode at the bottom, and
passes as a direct current
from *a* to *b* through circuit, *l*

cathode cool. Much more
difficult is it to maintain an
arc with alternating current
between metals, because the
poles are alternated, and
therefore the cathode has
twice as long to cool. In a
vacuum the ordinary arc
can not be maintained with
alternating current, except
with carbon poles, and then
only with difficulty. Cooper
Hewitt, however, conceived
the ingenious device shown
in Figure 19.

The three-phase current
is brought to the three iron
poles within the vacuum
tube, *T*, at the bottom of
which is a pool of mercury.
Having once started an
arc with the mercury as cathode, by the use of a high-
voltage direct current for instance, the arc continues to
be maintained by the three-phase alternating current
because one of the three poles is always positive. But the
iron poles, being too cool, are never able to act as cathode,
so that only a direct current is passed.

Cooper Hewitt also invented a very simple direct-
current mercury arc sometimes used for illumination,
though imparting a ghastly hue to the human face. Its

light comes from three green lines in the mercury vapor spectrum at wave lengths 5,791, 5,770, and 5,461 Angstroms. There are also many mercury-vapor spectrum lines in the ultra-violet which strongly affect the photographic plate. Hence the mercury arc is used very extensively in photography and for experimental purposes. The Cooper Hewitt mercury arc is contained in a long, inclined glass tube with electrodes at the bottom and top. It is started by merely tipping the vacuum tube till the liquid mercury makes contact from one electrode to the other. Afterwards the arc continues to operate over the entire tube even though the electrodes are long distances apart.

There is, perhaps, not a very clear distinction between the operation of the Cooper Hewitt mercury arc and the operation of the glow tubes now coming into general use for illumination and advertising. Yet there is this difference, that whereas the mercury-arc tube becomes hot and is thereby filled with mercury vapor at considerable pressure, the long glow-tube illuminators operate always at low pressure, though not at high vacuum conditions. In both cases the conductor of electricity consists of a mixture of negative electrons and ionized molecules.

In Chapter V we shall see some applications of the properties of atoms to wireless signaling.

CHAPTER IV

TELEGRAPHY AND TELEPHONY

WHILE still a young teacher at Albany Academy, Joseph Henry, later to be the first Secretary of the Smithsonian Institution, made valuable inventions. He constructed electromagnets far more powerful than any that had been made before. They were of two kinds, which he called "quantity magnets" and "intensity magnets," respectively. In the former the soft-iron core was wrapped with a few turns of wire carrying a strong electric current. In the latter there were very many turns of fine wire about the core, and a feebler current could then produce a powerful effect. To enable him to superpose many layers of wire without short-circuiting, he wound the copper wire with silk thread, for insulated wire as we purchase it now commercially was then unknown. Henry constructed an electromagnet for Yale College in the year 1831 (Plate 20, upper) which sustained 2,063 pounds, and later another for Princeton which sustained 3,500 pounds.

EARLY WORK ON ELECTRIC SIGNALING

He was interested in the application of magnets for both the electric motor and the electromagnetic telegraph. The United States National Museum has a model of Henry's electromagnetic oscillating motor of 1831 (Plate 20, lower). An iron core shaped like an inverted U was pivoted centrally and wound in opposite directions with two coils, whose ends could dip into mercury cups connected to two battery cells. Two permanent bar magnets were placed beneath the ends of the iron core, each with

PLATE 20

Upper: Henry's Yale magnet, which supported 2,063 pounds. Lower:
Henry's electromagnetic oscillating motor

its north pole uppermost. When the iron core was tilted so as to make contact of the ends of one coil through the mercury cups with one of the cells, it became magnetic and was immediately repelled so as to tilt toward the other cell and make contact there. So the rocking motions continued indefinitely with about 75 tilts per minute.

More important than this electromagnetic engine was Henry's telegraphic experiment. He connected an electric

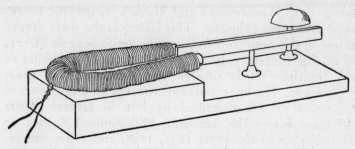

FIG. 20. Henry's electromagnetic telegraph operated at Albany, N. Y., as early as 1831, through a mile of line wire

battery by means of a wire a mile long to one of his horse-shoe intensity electromagnets. A permanent pivoted magnet had one of its ends between the poles of the electro-magnet, as shown in Figure 20. The other end tapped a bell when the circuit was completed. This experiment Henry made successfully while still at the Albany Academy. He used a similar device after his removal to Princeton University to communicate from his laboratory to his house.

Said Henry in his statement on the early history of the telegraph[1]:

Previous to my going to Princeton in November, 1832, my mind was much occupied with the subject of the telegraph, and . . . I introduced it in my course of instruction to the senior class in the Academy. I should state, however, that the arrangement I have described was merely a temporary one, and that I had no idea at the

[1] Ann. Rep. Smithsonian Inst. for 1857, pp. 99–106, 1858.

time of abandoning my researches for the practical application of the telegraph. Indeed, my experiments on the transmission of power to a distance were suspended by the investigation of the remarkable phenomena (which I had discovered in the course of these experiments) of the induction of a current in a long wire on itself, and of which I made the first mention in a paper in Silliman's Journal in 1832.[2]

Joseph Henry's discoveries on electric induction and self-induction are so important for telegraphy, telephony, and wireless, that we may well summarize them before going on to Wheatstone's and Morse's telegraphic inventions and other subjects. This course is the more appropriate in this Smithsonian Scientific Series because Henry, as its first Secretary, laid the foundations of the policy of the Smithsonian Institution and established its great reputation. His important experiments on induction and self-induction are described by him in several papers delivered before the American Philosophical Society at Philadelphia in the years 1835, 1838, and 1840, and republished in the Smithsonian Miscellaneous Collections, Volume 30, pages 92–188, 1887.

First of all, in his paper read February 5, 1835, he quotes the passage already cited announcing his discovery of 1831 as follows:

In the *American Journal of Science* for July, 1832, I announced a fact in Galvanism which I believe had never before been published. The same fact however appears to have been since observed by Mr. Faraday, and has lately been noticed by him in the November number of the *London and Edinburgh Journal of Science* for 1834.

The phenomenon as described by me is as follows: "When a small battery is moderately excited by diluted acid, and its poles, terminated by cups of mercury, are connected by a copper wire not more than a foot in length, no spark is perceived when the connection is either formed or broken; but if a wire thirty or forty feet long be used instead of the short wire, though no spark will be perceptible when the connection is made, yet when it is broken by drawing one end of the wire from its cup of mercury, a vivid spark is produced. If the action of the battery be very intense, a spark will be given by a short wire; in this case it is only necessary to wait a few minutes until the action partially subsides, and until no more sparks are given from the wire;

[2] Silliman's Amer. Journ. Sci., vol. 22, p. 408, July, 1832.

if the long wire be now substituted a spark will be again obtained. The effect appears somewhat increased by coiling the wire into a helix; it seems also to depend in some measure on the length and thickness of the wire. I can account for these phenomena only by supposing the long wire to become charged with electricity, which by its re-action on itself projects a spark when the connection is broken." [3]

The above was published immediately before my removal from Albany to Princeton, and new duties interrupted for a time the further prosecution of the subject. I have however been able during the past year to resume in part my investigations, and among others, have made a number of observations and experiments which develop some new circumstances in reference to this curious phenomenon.

In his experiments on electric induction Professor Henry used batteries in which copper and zinc plates were dipped in acid. In some experiments he employed a large number of battery cells. The electric current was conducted into wires and flat ribbons of copper, insulated when necessary to prevent short-circuits by windings of silk thread or ribbons of silk which separated the convolutions of his coils. His accounts of his experiments are very clear and interesting but quite too voluminous to reproduce here in his own words except in a few specially important instances. Summarizing them he found the following valuable results:

1. When the poles of the battery are connected by a short wire there is no spark on making or breaking circuit unless the battery has many cells. But when a long wire is substituted, although there may be no spark on making circuit, a considerable spark occurs on breaking circuit. This is Henry's original discovery of self-induction. His name is used for its unit.

2. If the long wire is wrapped to form a coil, the spark on breaking circuit is augmented, and still more augmented if the coil contains an iron core. But if the wire is first doubled and then wound into a coil there is no spark.

3. Employing a little spiral in which could be thrust a sewing needle, Henry readily magnetized needles by the

[3] Silliman's Amer. Journ. Sci., vol. 22, p. 408, July, 1832.

current, and used this device to indicate currents and their directions in succeeding experiments.

4. Having a current readily made or broken in one coil, he laid thereon a sheet of glass on which he laid a second coil in no wise connected with the first coil by a metallic connection. This secondary coil could be connected with a galvanometer or the magnetizing spiral.

5. At the instant of making circuit and at the instant of breaking circuit in the primary coil, currents were produced in the secondary coil. But while a current was flowing steadily in the primary coil there was no current in the secondary.

6. Two primary coils and also two secondary coils of different lengths but equal weight were employed. With the long coil of one and a quarter miles of wire as secondary, the secondary current on breaking the primary circuit was so feeble that it gave no sensible magnetizing or galvanometric action, but when 56 students joined hands to complete its circuit they received a smart shock when the primary current was broken. On the other hand when the short secondary coil was used the galvanometer and magnetizing coil showed strong current effects. By exchanging primary coils it was found that a long primary could induce large currents in a short secondary, and a short primary could induce heavy shocks in a long secondary. In Henry's own words: "This experiment was considered of so much importance, that it was varied and repeated many times, but always with the same result; it therefore establishes the fact *that an 'intensity' current can induce one of 'quantity'*, and, by the preceding experiments, the converse has also been shown, that *a 'quantity' current can induce one of 'intensity'*." These are the principles of the step-down and step-up transformers so important in modern engineering.

7. Henry found that secondary induction could be detected at considerable distances. He was also able to demonstrate tertiary and higher orders of induction. Thus

when the terminals of his secondary coil were brought out to a distance of several feet, he joined them to the terminals of another coil. Upon this he placed a glass plate, which supported a fourth coil. To this he connected a galvanometer or the magnetizing spiral and found tertiary induced currents. The same principle he extended to show induction of the fifth order. In these experiments he determined by aid of the magnetizing spiral the directions of the currents of induction. He found the inductions which occur at breaking the primary circuit took the following directions:

Primary current . . . . +
Secondary current . . . . +
Current of the third order . . . . . . −
Current of the fourth order . . . . +
Current of the fifth order . . . . . . −

These signs alternate except the first two. It is therefore to be concluded, in the words of Henry: "During the continuance of the primary current in full quantity, no inductive action is exerted. But when the same current begins to decline in quantity, and during the whole time of its diminishing, an induced current is produced in an opposite direction to the induced current at the beginning of the primary current."

8. Henry found that when he substituted a metal plate for the glass plate between his primary and secondary coils the shock from the secondary on breaking the primary circuit disappeared. But if he cut a radial slot in the metal plate there was no such screening effect. Nor did it return when he placed a second glass plate on the metal plate and a second slotted metal plate on the second glass with the two slots not superposed. Although shock could be screened from the secondary by a full metal plate, nevertheless the galvanometer still responded to the secondary, showing that the screening was not complete.

9. He discovered the oscillatory character of the discharge of a Leyden jar, of which he states as follows:

The discharge, whatever may be its nature, is not correctly represented (employing for simplicity the theory of Franklin) by the single transfer of an imponderable fluid from one side of the jar to the other; the phenomena require us to admit *the existence of a principal discharge in one direction, and then several reflex actions backward and forward, each more feeble than the preceding, until the equilibrium is obtained.* All the facts are shown to be in accordance with this hypothesis, and a ready explanation is afforded by it of a number of phenomena which are to be found in the older works on electricity, but which have until this time remained unexplained.

Henry foreshadowed wireless, for he says:

In extending the researches relative to this part of the investigations, a remarkable result was obtained in regard to the distance at which inductive effects are produced by a very small quantity of electricity; a single spark from the prime conductor of the [frictional electrical] machine, of about an inch long, thrown on the end of a circuit of wire in an upper room, produced an induction sufficiently powerful to magnetize needles in a parallel circuit of wire placed in the cellar beneath, at a perpendicular distance of thirty feet with two floors and ceilings, each fourteen inches thick, intervening.

We shall see presently the important applications of these discoveries of Henry in connection with telegraphy, telephony, and wireless.

The First Commercial Telegraph

Sir Charles Wheatstone, that great English experimental genius, took out a patent for the electric telegraph in 1837. With his partner, Mr. Cooke, he first worked a railway telegraph circuit on July 27, 1837, for a distance of 1½ miles between Euston and Camden Town, stations near London. Though successful, neither the railway officials nor the public were at first favorably impressed, so that for several years after this the railway signals were preferably transmitted between Euston and Camden by whistling through a tube. But the Great Western Railway, more favorably impressed by the telegraph, erected a line from the Paddington terminus to West Drayton, 13 miles, in 1839, and continued it to Slough in 1841. Fortunately this line had an early piece of sensational advertising by the capture of the murderer, Tawell. This man, dressed in Quaker garb, killed a woman named Sarah Hart at Salt Hill, and was observed to take a slow train to London. The police telegraphed Paddington, but the word Quaker nearly baffled the telegraph, for the Wheatstone five-needle instrument had no sign for Q. Several times the operator got as far as "Kwa" only to be asked to repeat. But a boy at Paddington said, "Let him finish the word." When it was spelled out as "Kwaker" they understood, and shadowed Tawell as he got down from the train. He was arrested, tried, and executed, and as the case showed in a spectacular way the merit of the telegraph, it hastened the spread of telegraphy in England.

While Wheatstone's telegraph was probably the first ever used for commercial purposes, many inventors had employed electricity previously to transmit signals. Suggestions were made indeed as early as 1753 for employing the influence of the Leyden jar, operating through many conductors, to attract small pieces of paper and thus indicate the letters of the alphabet. Sömmering, Schweigger, and Coxe all worked out methods based on the chemical action of the electric current prior to 1820. Following Oersted's discovery in 1820 of the deflection of the magnetic needle by the electric current, there came investigations by Ampère, Triboaillet, and Schilling. Cooke, Sir Charles Wheatstone's partner, was interested by the work of Schilling and invented a three-needle instrument in 1836. Wheatstone's first modification of Cooke's device employed five vertical needles, each influenced by a separate electric coil, and made to point out letters on a dial. This telegraph required six line wires. Steinheil in Germany invented in 1837 a telegraph employing Faraday's principle of electromagnetic induction, and also produced an ink-printing recorder of the messages.

The English Postal Telegraph system is founded largely on the work of Wheatstone, who in 1868 was knighted for his invention of the automatic telegraph, by means of which as many as 500 words may be transmitted per minute. By a development of the invention of Bain in 1846, the letters are indicated by holes punched in definite relations through a moving ribbon of paper and are printed in accord therewith by an inking device invented by Thomas John, an Austrian engineer, in 1854. In operating this telegraph, positive and negative currents are sent alternately into the line. The mechanisms used in punching, sending, receiving, inking, etc., are naturally very complicated.

The American commercial systems of telegraphy developed, as is well known, from the work of Prof. Samuel F. B. Morse (1791–1872). He was the son of a Congregational minister, and grandson of Samuel Finley, President of the College of New Jersey. He graduated from Yale College in 1810, but studied art with Washington Allston, and accompanied him to England where he had considerable success as a painter. Becoming a founder of the National Academy of Design, he was its first president from 1820 to 1845. He takes a high place among American artists. It was not until 1832 that he began to work upon the electromagnetic telegraph. The idea occurred to him while in Paris, and became his absorbing preoccupation until his success in 1844. He completed a working invention in 1836 which he exhibited at the University of the City of New York, operating a circuit of 1,700 feet. Judge Stephen Vail, of Morristown, N. J., and his son Alfred Vail, became deeply interested and associated themselves with Morse.

At this time Morse was in sore straits of poverty, denying himself the necessities of life in order to purchase parts for his apparatus. After applying for his patent, April 7,

PLATE 21

Samuel F. B. Morse, who commercially developed the telegraph in
America

PLATE 22

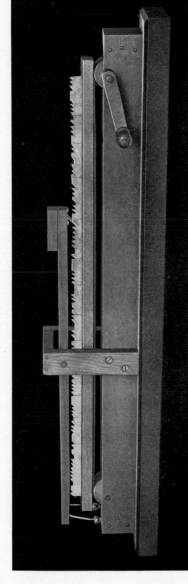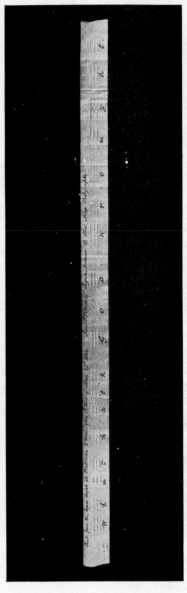

Upper: Model of Morse's sending device. Lower: First Morse telegraphic message, May 24, 1844. Baltimore to Washington

1838, which was granted June 20, 1840, he endeavored to obtain an appropriation from Congress to test the telegraph on a considerable scale. Though favorably reported from committee, Morse's bill did not pass until 1843. A telegraph was constructed from Washington to Baltimore, and first publicly used by him on May 24, 1844. Its first message was: "What hath God wrought?"

Reissues of Morse's patent, clarifying its specifications and claims in more terse and precise form, were granted January 15, 1846 and June 13, 1848. The following claims 1, 4, 5 and 8, which were allowed, are of primary interest as expressing the extent of Morse's invention.

1. Making use of the motive power of magnetism when developed by the action of such current or currents, substantially as set forth in the foregoing description of the first principal part of my invention, as means of operating or giving motion to machinery which may be used to imprint signals upon paper or other suitable material, or to produce sounds in any desired manner for the purpose of telegraphic communication at any distances. (The only ways in which the galvanic current had been proposed to be used prior to my invention and improvement were by bubbles resulting from decomposition and the action or exercise of electrical power upon a magnetized bar or needle and the bubbles, and the deflections of the needles thus produced were the subjects of inspection, and had no power, or were not applied to record the communication. I therefore characterize my invention as the first recording or printing telegraph by means of electro-magnetism. There are various known modes of producing motions by electro-magnetism; but none of these had been applied prior to my invention and improvement to actuate or give motion to printing or recording machinery, which is the chief point of my invention and improvement.)

4. The combination of two or more galvanic or electric circuits with independent batteries, substantially by the means herein described, for the purpose of obviating the diminished force of electro-magnetism in long circuits, and enabling me to command sufficient power to put in motion registering or recording machinery at any distances.

5. The system of signs consisting of dots and spaces, and of dots, spaces, and horizontal lines, for numerals, letters, words, or sentences, substantially as herein set forth and illustrated, for telegraphic purposes.

8. I do not propose to limit myself to the specific machinery or parts of machinery described in the foregoing specification and claims, the essence of my invention being the use of the motive power of the electric or galvanic current, which I call "electro-magnetism," however developed, for marking or printing intelligible characters, signs, or letters at any distances, being a new application of that power of which I claim to be the first inventor or discoverer.

Thus it appears that Morse recognized the existence of various other forms of telegraph in the prior art, but particularly insisted on his priority as the inventor of a printing or embossing recording telegraph. He also claims the relay, a feature indispensable to any long distance line. But the device which, far more than any other, has perpetuated the influence of Morse, is the system of dots and dashes to represent letters and numbers and code words. This feature has penetrated into every telegraphic system in all countries, excepting the limited A.B.C. telegraphic system of Wheatstone, wherein the letters themselves are indicated by a pointer upon a dial, and the needle system of Wheatstone wherein the direction of displacement, not the time of displacement, of a needle is observed. The International Morse code differs a little from Morse's original code, so as to make provision for those letters or letter combinations, very common in foreign languages, but not in English. In the most modern practice, messages are printed in ordinary letters, so that the use of the code has diminished.

Claim 8 was overthrown in one of the most important patent decisions ever rendered by the Supreme Court of the United States. In substance the Court held that no man may patent a law of nature. Certain passages from the decision follow.

O'Reilly et al. v. Morse et al.

We perceive no well-founded objection to the description which is given of the whole invention and its separate parts, nor to his [Morse's] right to a patent for the first seven inventions set forth in the specification of his claims. The difficulty arises on the eighth.

It is in the following words:

[82]

"Eighth. I do not propose to limit myself to the specific machinery or parts of machinery described in the foregoing specification and claims; the essence of my invention being the use of the motive power of the electric or galvanic current, which I call electro-magnetism, however developed, for marking or printing intelligible characters, signs, or letters, at any distances, being a new application of that power of which I claim to be the first inventor or discoverer."

It is impossible to misunderstand the extent of this claim. He claims the exclusive right to every improvement where the motive power is the electric or galvanic current, and the result is the marking or printing intelligible characters, signs, or letters at a distance.

If this claim can be maintained, it matters not by what process or machinery the result is accomplished. For aught that we now know some future inventor, in the onward march of science, may discover a mode of writing or printing at a distance by means of the electric or galvanic current, without using any part of the process or combination set forth in the plaintiff's specification. His invention may be less complicated—less liable to get out of order—less expensive in construction, and in its operation. But yet if it is covered by this patent the inventor could not use it, nor the public have the benefit of it without the permission of this patentee.

Nor is this all, while he shuts the door against inventions of other persons, the patentee would be able to avail himself of new discoveries in the properties and powers of electro-magnetism which scientific men might bring to light. For he says he does not confine his claim to the machinery or parts of machinery, which he specifies; but claims for himself a monopoly in its use, however developed, for the purpose of printing at a distance. New discoveries in physical science may enable him to combine it with new agents and new elements, and by that means attain the object in a manner superior to the present process and altogether different from it. And if he can secure the exclusive use by his present patent he may vary it with every new discovery and development of the science, and need place no description of the new manner, process, or machinery, upon the records of the patent office. And when his patent expires, the public must apply to him to learn what it is. In fine he claims an exclusive right to use a manner and process which he has not described and indeed had not invented, and therefore could not describe when he obtained his patent. The court is of opinion that the claim is too broad, and not warranted by law.

Plate 22 shows a photograph of a model of the Morse sending device which he called the port rule, and a copy of the first message sent between Baltimore and

Washington, "What hath God wrought?" Figure 21 shows how the Morse alphabet was arranged, and some later changes which have come into it. Figure 22 shows a diagram of the sending and receiving arrangements of Morse. The original receiving instrument is on exhibition in the United States National Museum. The message to

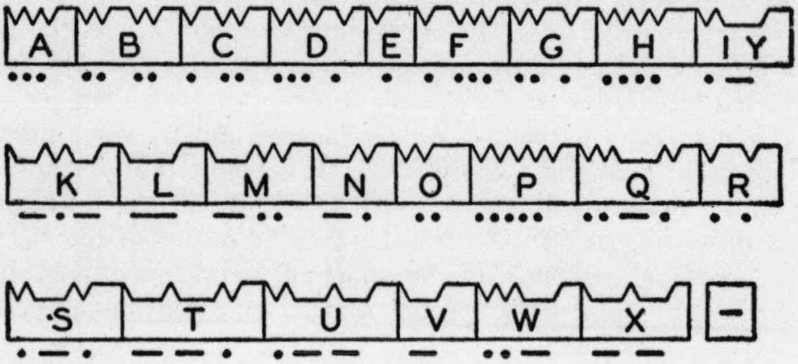

A···	IS THE PRESENT	S	M —··	IS THE PRESENT	D
B··· ··	· · ·	Y	N —·	SAME	
C· ···	· · ·	R	O ··	IS THE PRESENT	1
D···· ·	· · ·	Z	P ·····	SAME	
E·	SAME		Q ···— ·		
F· ···	IS THE PRESENT	&	R ··	IS THE PRESENT	O
G···	· · ·	C	S ·—·	· · ·	F
H····	SAME		T ——·	· · ·	G
I ·—	IS THE PRESENT	A	U ·——	· · ·	W
J···	· · ·	C	V —	· · ·	T
K ·—·	SAME		W ··—	· · ·	U
L —	·		X ——	· · ·	M

Fig. 21. Morse code alphabet and later changes in the international code. Morse's "port rule" arrangement is shown above

be sent was first set up on the port rule, *m*. By turning the wheel, *L*, the port rule vibrated the lever, *P*, thereby making and breaking contacts, *K*. The line current thus made and broken operated electromagnets, *h*, which vibrated the pendulum, *F*, thereby marking with pencil or embossing the paper rolling from *A* over the wheel, *B*, to *C*, as drawn along by the clockwork, *D*.

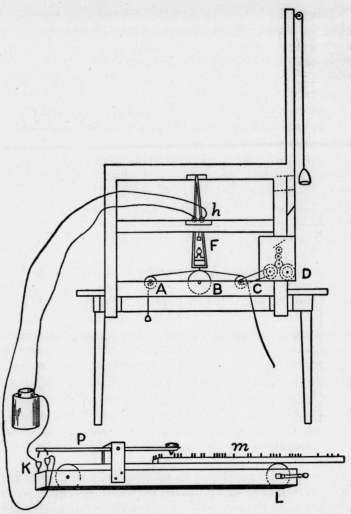

FIG. 22. Diagram of Morse sending and receiving instruments. The "port rule" for sending, shown below, produces intermittent currents in the line. These operate a magnet, which draws over a pendulum carrying a point that embosses the paper record fed along by clockwork. A relay may be interposed to strengthen the action

GREAT INVENTIONS

Telegraphy is a good example of our common experience
that the complex leads frequently to the simple. For the
embossing recording telegraph of Morse yielded generally,
after the operators got experience, to the simple sounder
which has held a large place in American telegraphic
practice, though recently largely superseded by the
type-printing telegraph. The dot and dash signals of the
Morse code can be easily recognized by the experienced
ear in the chattering of the lever of the simple electro-
magnet as it vibrates between its stops, though these
sounds are quite unintelligible to the uninitiated. The
exclusively Morse features in this ordinary application of
telegraphy are his dot-and-dash code and his relay.[4]
The electromagnets of intensity and quantity employed
in the modern telegraph come to us from Joseph Henry's
earliest inventions, and back of them lie the discoveries
of Oersted, Arago, and Sturgeon.

In the A.B.C. system of Wheatstone, the principle of
induction, as discovered by Faraday, is employed directly
to produce the line current instead of a battery or other
independent current generator. Bain in 1846 employed
the chemical action of the electric current to print signals
by conducting the line current directly through moving
sensitized paper. His recording system, though mechanically far simpler than those of Morse and of Wheatstone,
and though it could dispense with the relay owing to its
extreme sensitiveness, has never come into general use,
and is employed now, if at all, only in laboratory experiments.

A principal item of cost in telegraphy is, of course, the
line. But it was early discovered that the earth, even
without lakes or streams, is a return circuit of practically
zero resistance. Yet the cost of a long single line is so
great that ingenious devices were invented whereby first
two (duplex), then four (quadruplex), and finally numer-

---

[4] Henry was early acquainted with the principle of the relay, but no description of
it appears in his publications.

ous (multiplex) messages could be transmitted over the same circuit at the same time. A system of duplexing is indicated in Figure 23. The electromagnets are doubly wound in opposite directions with equal coils. Also a second circuit is provided at each station with a resistance r, r', equal to that of the line, l. Then when the operator

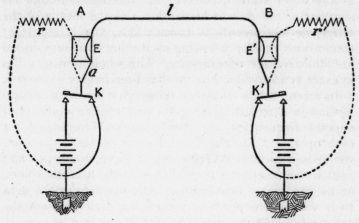

FIG. 23. Duplex telegraph diagram

at A presses the key, K, it produces no effect on his own instrument, E, because two equal currents in opposite directions are being sent. Not so, however, with the electromagnet, E', at B, where the line only is furnishing current. If at both A and B the operators are sending, then the current in the line is stopped by equal and opposite impulses, leaving operative the local circuits only. Therefore the instrument, E, is affected just as long as the key, K', at B is held down, not, to be sure, by the battery at B, but by that at A, which, however, answers the same purpose. Similarly with the instrument at B.

Multiplex telegraphy was perfected from an invention by Meyer in 1873. It depends on quite different principles from duplexing. If two disks at the distantly separated stations can be caused to rotate in exact unison or synchronism, these disks may be subdivided into a considerable number of segments, each of which is given to one sending operator, who can send to the line while his segment is in contact. His partner, the receiving operator at the other station, receives the messages through his segment of the disk at his station. As the inertia of the telegraph instruments is considerable, the intermittent connections rapidly following each other thus established are sufficient for telegraphing. The whole difficulty lies in exact synchronism, but this has been largely overcome.

In recent times multiplex telegraphy has been accomplished in a still different way. Alternating currents of various frequencies are employed, one frequency for each operator. On the line all of these frequencies are superposed to form a very complex wave, much as white light is composed of a combination of the rainbow colors, or as the many broadcasting stations constantly send their various frequencies at the same time through the same space. At the receiving station the frequencies are again separated by tuning, much as white light is separated into colors by a prism, or, more exactly, as individual radio broadcasting stations are isolated at pleasure by the listener. In this way the numerous messages are unraveled and taken by separate operators or recording instruments. By thermionic tube amplifiers the alternating current may be rectified into direct currents and amplified as desired so as to be received by ordinary telegraph instruments. The system has sometimes been described as "wired wireless." It is duplexed and as many as 10 messages each way may thus be transmitted at once by one wire.

Within the last 25 years the printing telegraph has largely superseded all others in America, so that about 70 per cent of all telegraphy is printed out in ordinary letters without the use of dots or dashes. Plate 23 shows

PLATE 23

The printing telegraph sender. Courtesy of the Western Union Telegraph
Company

PLATE 24

Cyrus W. Field. Portrait by Daniel Huntington. Photograph lent
by the Metropolitan Museum of Art

the complicated instrument employed. In direct printing, the paper ribbon usually employed is punched with a central line of holes, making it in effect a chain to be carried without slip, like a bicycle chain. On either side of this central line are spaces of sufficient width so that the paper may be punched with any desired number of holes, up to five, along lines at right angles to its length. Each such line of holes represents a letter or symbol. According to the number of such holes and their position

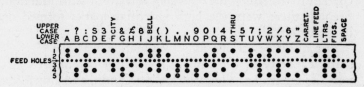

FIG. 24. A code-punched paper ribbon used in the modern printing telegraph

above or below the center of the ribbon, the different letters of the alphabet are indicated. The message is thus punched on the ribbon of paper by the operator using the typewriter keyboard. As thus coded the message is sent by the automatic telegraph. From the order of the punched holes the instrument at the distant station writes out the message in ordinary letters on a ribbon of paper which may be pasted on a telegraph blank. Many inventors have contributed to this improvement, but prominent among them were Hughes, who secured the synchronous operation of the sending and receiving apparatus, and Baudot, who invented the five-punch code of letters and symbols shown in Figure 24.

THE CABLE

When the telegraph had become established in many countries, there arose a desire to connect the continents. But when cables began to be laid under the narrower bodies of water, various difficulties that were not very serious on land lines began to take on a new importance. Among the most serious were those depending on the great length between stations. First of all, as Joseph Henry's experiments had shown, the self-induction of a conductor increases with its length, and with it the time required to build up a current and also the intensity of the shock on breaking circuit. Thus a twofold obstacle arose from self-induction. First, there was a great slowing up of each signal in the making by reason of the time required for the current to overcome the opposing current of self-induction. Second, there were the high potential sparks formed on breaking circuit.

But quite as serious as self-induction was the electro-static capacity of the cable. A century before, in 1745, von Kleist, dean of the cathedral at Kamin, and Cuneus, a rich burger of Kamin, and Musschenbrock, a professor at Leyden, had all independently conceived the idea that electricity could be stored. Holding a glass jar of water in the hand, each had led into it the discharge of a frictional electric machine. Happening to touch the conducting wire with the other hand, the dean, the burger, and the professor had each received a disagreeable shock. Later, a Doctor Bevis discovered that it was not the water but the glass jar that was the storer of the electricity. All that was needed was a conductor without, a conductor within, and a thin layer of nonconductor separating them. Once charged, the conductors could both be removed, leaving the electricities of opposite sign on the outer and inner surfaces of the nonconducting layer. Thus the Leyden jar was invented. It is a glass jar with tinfoil coatings outside and inside, and a conductor leading to the inner coating. The property of storing electricity possessed by such an instrument is called capacity. Instruments of measured capacity are now made with mica, air, glass, oil, or other substances as insulators between plate conductors.

An ocean cable has great capacity. For the water outside and the wires within are conductors separated by rubber insulation. Accordingly, each time a signal is in the making, the cable has to be charged as a condenser. This constitutes another hindrance to cable telegraphy. A third electrical difficulty resides in the difference of electric potential existing between widely separated stations on the earth. This produces strong earth currents through any conductor laid between them. Finally, there occurs considerable leakage of electricity in such a very long line as the Atlantic cable, surrounded as it is by salt water—a good conductor.

In addition to these electrical difficulties there were encountered immense mechanical and financial difficulties in laying a 2,000-mile cable upon the mountainous ocean floor from ships tossed by great waves upon the surface. The electrical difficulties eventually yielded to the great ingenuity and technical knowledge of Sir William Thomson (Lord Kelvin), C. F. Varley, and others. The costly mechanical ones were overcome, after several failures, owing to the undismayed enthusiasm of Cyrus W. Field of New York, Sir Charles Bright, Sir John Pender, and others in England. Millions were spent in organizing company after company, and enlisting the cooperation again and again of the governments of Great Britain and the United States. Mr. Field crossed the ocean 64 times in this enterprise, suffering severely from seasickness on each occasion. We may well pause a little to recall the plucky story of the Atlantic cable, which has meant so much in bringing the nations together, conducting international business, and on countless occasions softening the anxieties of families separated by the great ocean.

Cyrus West Field (1819–1892) was the son of the Reverend David Dudley Field of Stockbridge, Mass., and brother of the eminent jurist, David Dudley Field. As a boy and young man he served as a clerk, but in 1840 he engaged in making paper in partnership with E. Root & Company in New York. The firm failed, however, and

Field then formed a partnership with his brother-in-law, made money, paid off the debts of Root & Company, and retired in 1853, a fairly wealthy man. In 1854 he became interested in the project of F. N. Gisborne, an able English engineer, for a telegraph from America to Newfoundland. Then he conceived the idea of a transatlantic cable, and after obtaining the favorable reports of Prof. S. F. B. Morse and of Matthew F. Maury, the astronomer and navigator, he acquired all the advantageous cable-landing sites available, and organized the first of his cable companies in 1854. Then he went to England and made an agreement in 1856 with J. W. Brett and Mr. (afterwards Sir Charles) Bright as follows: "Mutually and on equal terms we engage to exert ourselves for the purpose of forming a company for establishing and working of electric telegraphic communication between Newfoundland and Ireland, such company to be called the Atlantic Telegraph Company, or by such other name as the parties hereto shall jointly agree upon."

The enterprise proved far more attractive to English than to American subscribers. Although Field exerted himself to the utmost he could raise in America only about one twelfth of the capital sum of £350,000 thought necessary for the first venture. Similarly in the subsequent attempts, which finally won out in 1866, the funds subscribed were almost wholly raised in Great Britain. For although Field aroused great enthusiasm in various American cities, the enthusiasm was backed by very few subscriptions. The governments of both nations aided extensively by furnishing naval vessels for long periods to lay cable and act as tenders and guards. For the successful cables laid in 1866, however, the *Great Eastern* of 22,000 tons burden, an enormous ship for those times, was employed to lay the cables from coast to coast. The cable-laying ships were attended by a warship, which on several occasions proved of great service in firing shots to warn off merchantmen who came near to causing disasters through ignorance of the necessity of the cable ship going steadily ahead.

The first cable was begun in England in February, 1857, and its halves were loaded on board the British warship *Agamemnon* and the American warship *Niagara* in July, 1857. It was intended as an act of international good will that the *Niagara*, beginning at Valencia in Ireland, should lay to the ocean's center, and the American end should there be spliced on and laid to Newfoundland by the *Agamemnon*. The cable was landed at Valencia on August 5, and everything went well until the cable snapped in about 2,000 fathoms at 3:45 o'clock, August 11. The disaster was attributed to inexpert handling of the brake mechanism. Three hundred and eighty miles of cable had been laid.

It was not so easy to raise £100,000 additional capital for the second trial. The chorus of pessimism and ridicule had become very loud. However, the company went on, improved its machinery for paying out the cable, constructed a large additional supply of cable, made a trial cable-laying trip in the Bay of Biscay, and finally left Plymouth on June 3, 1858. It was now intended that the vessels should proceed together to mid-ocean, splice the cable there, and lay both ways at once.

But on the way a frightful storm arose. The heavily loaded *Agamemnon*, smaller than the *Niagara*, suffered greatly, and on many occasions during the 10-day gale was in extreme danger of foundering. At one time it seemed almost necessary to heave overboard a large coil of the cable. A great length of it was snarled. A hundred tons of coal was carried away from its storage and slid to and fro upon the decks, injuring many. Forty men were in hospital. Water flooded the ship. But at last all the vessels reached the rendezvous in calm weather.

The splice was made, but a break came before 10 miles of cable had run out. A second trial was made at once, but after 40 miles had been laid a new break came. For the third time the ships returned, respliced the cable, and agreed that if more than 100 miles should have been laid by either ship, and a new break should then come, they would return to Great Britian. This time things went for a time more successfully, but the fatal break came again after 146 miles had been paid out by the *Agamemnon*. She feared the *Niagara* might not return to England on so close a margin to 100 miles as this, and though short of coal beat back to the rendezvous. But the *Niagara* was not there, and after several days of waiting all the ships returned to England.

At the meeting of the board of directors there was evinced a feeling of despair. The chairman of the board recommended liquidation. But bolder counsels prevailed. The chairman resigned, and was succeeded by Mr. Stuart Wortley. As it was still summer and there was still enough cable, the ships were dispatched once more on July 17, 1858.

The rendezvous was reached on July 28, and cable-laying was begun at 12:30 o'clock on July 29. Electrical communication was suspended a little while at about 8 o'clock owing to trouble with the apparatus on the *Niagara*. This caused great consternation on the *Agamem-non*. The cable was cut and respliced in attempting to locate the break, but in the midst of the excitement communication returned, and the voyages continued. Plate 25 shows the *Agamemnon* engaged in cable laying in 1858.

A gale sprung up on July 31, and only by the most un-remitting care could the cable be preserved during the next few days. With various disturbing incidents, but no disasters, the ships proceeded, until on Thursday, August 5, the ends of the first successful cable were landed in the Old World and the New. Its total length was 2,022 miles. The chief engineer, Charles Bright, telegraphed the directors: "Valencia, August 5th. The *Agamemnon* has arrived at Valencia, and we are about to land the end of the cable. The *Niagara* is in Trinity Bay, Newfoundland. There are good signals between the ships."

PLATE 25

H.M.S. *Agamemnon* laying the Atlantic cable in 1858. A whale crossing the line. Painting by Robert Dudley

PLATE 26

The 1866 cable fleet, including the *Great Eastern*. Painting by Robert Dudley

Great Britain and America went wild with rejoicing. Bright was immediately honored with knighthood. Preparations were begun for intercommunication by public officials between the two countries. Unfortunately the chief electrician, Mr. Whitehouse, thought it necessary to work with high-potential currents, and even used 2,000 volts ineffectually. After a week of these experiments, during which the cable was ruined, a return was made to the delicate methods of Sir William Thomson which had been used during the cable-laying. In this way the following messages, the first ever to be communicated officially by telegraph between America and Europe, were transmitted.

August 16, 1858. From the Directors in England to those in the United States:

Europe and America are united by telegraphy. Glory to God in the highest, on earth peace, good-will toward men!

Then followed:

From her Majesty the Queen of Great Britain to his Excellency the President of the United States:
The Queen desires to congratulate the President upon the successful completion of this great international work, in which the Queen has taken the greatest interest.
The Queen is convinced that the President will join with her in fervently hoping that the electric cable, which now already connects Great Britain with the United States, will prove an additional link between the two nations, whose friendship is founded upon their common interest and reciprocal esteem.
The Queen has much pleasure in thus directly communicating with the President, and in renewing to him her best wishes for the prosperity of the United States.

This message was shortly afterward responded to as follows:

Washington City.

The President of the United States to her Majesty Victoria, Queen of Great Britain:
The President cordially reciprocates the congratulations of her Majesty the Queen on the success of the great international enterprise

accomplished by the skill. science, and indomitable energy of the two countries.

It is a triumph more glorious, because far more useful to mankind than was ever won by a conqueror on the field of battle.

May the Atlantic Telegraph, under the blessing of Heaven, prove to be a bond of perpetual peace and friendship between the kindred nations, and an instrument destined by Divine Providence to diffuse religion, civilization, liberty, and law throughout the world.

In this view will not all the nations of Christendom spontaneously unite in the declaration that it shall be forever neutral and that its communications shall be held sacred in passing to the place of their destination, even in the midst of hostilities?

James Buchanan.

But the first successful Atlantic cable had been spoiled by the high voltages that had been used in the first week. Communication grew weaker and weaker and ceased entirely on October 20, 1858, after transmitting 732 messages in all. An inquiry was made into the causes of its failure, which definitely proved the high voltages to have been fatal.

In 1865, after the American Civil War, the cable project was renewed, this time as a contractor's venture. The *Great Eastern* was used by them as cable ship with the same able navigator, Staff Commander H. A. Moriarty, R.N., who had so successfully navigated the *Agamemnon*. Plate 26 shows the *Great Eastern* and the cable fleet and Plate 27 the paying-out machinery on the deck of the *Great Eastern*. A much heavier cable than that of 1858, as recommended by Sir Charles Bright, was constructed. Several times the cable developed faults but was picked up by means of newly invented devices and spliced. But after 1,186 miles had been laid, a new fault developed, and in picking it up from a depth of 2,000 fathoms the cable parted. Several attempts were made unsuccessfully to recover it, but at length the project had to be abandoned for that year.

Yet the promoters were not discouraged. Field secured the support of Sir Daniel Gooch, M.P., of the Great

PLATE 27

Paying-out machinery on the *Great Eastern*. Painting by Robert Dudley

PLATE 28

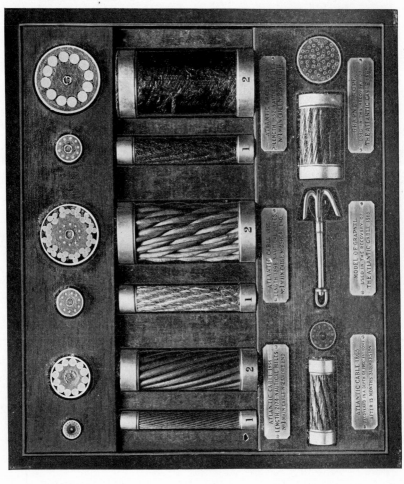

Atlantic cables of 1858, 1865, and 1866. A short length and a section of each

Western Railway, who contributed £20,000. Led by his example other large subscriptions came in, and the Telegraph Construction Company, which had made the cable and undertaken its laying, agreed to take stock in large amounts in compensation. A complete new cable was ordered, and plans were made to recover and splice the cable of 1865. Many new grappling devices were prepared for this purpose.

With minor accidents, all went well this time. Starting on July 13, 1866, from Foilhommerum Bay, Ireland, in 14 days the *Great Eastern* arrived at Heart's Content, Trinity Bay, Newfoundland, having laid 1,852 nautical miles of Atlantic cable. She then put back to sea, and after 24 days of grappling, distressing slips occurring again and again, the cable of 1865 was at last recovered. A signal brought great joy to the patient but downhearted watchers in Ireland on a Sunday morning. The message came: "Ship to shore. I have much pleasure in speaking to you through the 1865 cable. Just going to make splice." On September 8, 1866, the 1865 cable was finished to Newfoundland, with a total length of 1,896 nautical miles.

So much for the triumphant overcoming of the financial and mechanical difficulties. On the electrical side, to avoid disturbing earth currents Varley had introduced the idea of interrupting the cable as it approached the receiving end with a plate condenser, as shown in Figure 25. Under these circumstances, on making a signal the entering current charges the first-met plate of the condenser, which induces across the insulation layer the opposite charge on the other plate, and drives from that plate through the receiving instrument to earth an electric charge equal in quantity and sign to that which the current had brought to the first-met plate. For telegraphy the effect is exactly as though the line were continuous, but the disturbing earth current can not flow at all across the break into the line, after once producing its steady state within the condenser. Indeed, condensers are placed at both ends of the cable, so that no direct current enters the line at all. The cable is duplexed also, so that telegraphy becomes merely the creation of a succession of electric surges against the walls of the condensers.

It was found that owing to induction and capacity the Atlantic cable would be very slow if time were allowed to

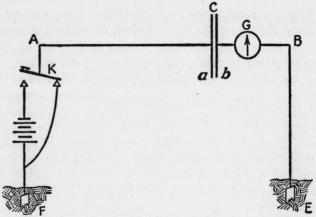

Fig. 25. Cable operation through electric condenser

fully complete each signal. Also the disaster of the cable of 1858 had proved that the cable could not bear currents strong enough to work ordinary telegraph relays. For both these reasons it was necessary to substitute some form of instrument sensitive enough to indicate the first beginnings of an effect at the receiving station. The current could then be immediately reversed to discharge the line, and make a signal by the contrary deflection of the instrument. For this purpose Sir William Thomson invented the reflecting galvanometer. This instrument has no material pointer like the older galvanometers. Its pointer is a beam of light reflected from a little mirror fastened to the system of magnets which hangs between

PLATE 29

Sir William Thomson (Lord Kelvin)

PLATE 30

Alexander Graham Bell

the coils. Such a galvanometer is described on page 80 of Volume 2 of this Series. As it was desirable to make a record of the signals, Sir William Thomson later invented another device called the syphon recorder, in which a fine electromagnetically deflected glass syphon spurts minute droplets of ink upon a moving paper.

THE TELEPHONE

Alexander Graham Bell (1847–1922) was of the third generation of a family of Scotch experts in the science of speech. His father, Alexander Melville Bell, and his uncle, David Bell, published in 1860 a work entitled "Bell's Standard Elocutionist," which has gone to some two hundred editions and is still used in Great Britain as a textbook. Melville Bell also invented a remarkable system called "Visible Speech," according to which any sound of any language may be so accurately described that it can be imitated by an adept even if he has never heard it spoken. Graham Bell and his brother, Melville James, were thoroughly taught in their father's system of "Visible Speech." Says a friend of the family, the Reverend David Macrea:

When Bell's sons had been sent away to another part of the house, out of earshot, we gave Bell the most peculiar and difficult sounds we could think of, including words from the French and the Gaelic, following these with inarticulate sounds as of kissing and chuckling. All these Bell wrote down in his Visible Speech alphabet and his sons were then called in.

I well remember our keen interest and astonishment as the lads— not yet thoroughly versed in the new alphabet—stood side by side looking earnestly at the paper their father had put in their hands, and slowly reproducing sound after sound just as we uttered them. Some of these sounds were incapable of phonetic representation with our alphabet.[5]

At 17 years of age Alexander Graham Bell became a partner in his father's business as a teacher of elocution in London. A little later the family emigrated to Canada,

[5] From Alexander Graham Bell, by Catherine MacKenzie. Houghton, Mifflin Company, 1928.

and Melville Bell gave a series of lectures in Boston. As a result he was invited to extend the series, but being obliged to return to his business in Canada, he recommended his son in his stead. The Boston School Board appropriated $500 for this purpose, and at the age of 23 Alexander Graham Bell came to Boston, in April, 1871, for his first engagement. In October, 1872, he returned to Boston and opened a school of vocal physiology for the correction of stammering and other defects of speech.

A child of Thomas Sanders of Haverhill had been born deaf, and was then 5 years of age. Bell undertook to supervise the education of the boy, who came to live at Bell's boarding house and grew to love him tremendously. George Sanders' father became Bell's financial supporter in the telephone development. Another guiding influence in Bell's life was Gardiner Green Hubbard, a wealthy Boston lawyer, whose little daughter Mabel had lost her hearing at 4 years of age. She was in some degree Bell's pupil, and later became his wife. Hubbard was frequently in Washington in attendance on Supreme Court cases and resided there in later life. He became a Regent of the Smithsonian Institution, February 27, 1895, and served until his death, December 11, 1897. He was succeeded by his son-in-law, Alexander Graham Bell, January 24, 1898, who served as Regent until February 20, 1922, shortly before his death.

There is a particular appropriateness in the fact that the inventor of the speaking telephone and his backer were both Regents of the Smithsonian Institution. On March 1, 1875, Bell had come to Washington in the interest of a patent application for his harmonic telegraph (a device for multiplex telegraphy which did not in the end become adopted). He called on Joseph Henry, then an aged man, who had been for almost 30 years Secretary of the Smithsonian Institution and a leader in American science. Bell told Henry, with that tremendous enthusiasm which always characterized him, of his harmonic telegraph. Then he mentioned a curious experiment which he had made with an intermittent current of electricity and a helix of wire, which produced a sound. Secretary Henry was interested, and asked if he could demonstrate it. Bell made an appointment for the next day. Joseph Henry sat for a long time with the coil at his ear listening to the sound. This so much encouraged Bell that he determined to ask Henry's advice regarding his idea of the electric speaking telephone which he had then been experimenting upon for about a year. He explained the germ of his idea, and then added, "Which would you advise me to do: Publish it and let others work it out, or attempt to solve the problem myself?"

"You have the germ of a great invention," said Secretary Henry. "Work at it."

"I replied," says Bell, "that I recognized that there were mechanical difficulties, and that I felt that I had not the electrical knowledge necessary to perfect the invention. His laconic answer was, 'Get it'. I can not tell you how much these two words encouraged me."

Bell was at that moment particularly discouraged. His multiplex telegraph was dragging. His love affair with Mabel Hubbard seemed hopeless, and the telephone was as yet but a dim idea. Secretary Henry, the leading American scientist of that day, had listened to him cordially, and had given him a tonic of encouraging advice. As long as he lived Bell never forgot his obligation to Henry, or refused to listen to any young inventor in his turn. "But for Joseph Henry," said he, "I should never have gone on with the telephone."

It was on June 2, 1875, that Bell for the first time got a really fruitful idea of how to vary an electric current by the speaking voice. With his instrument maker and admiring friend, Thomas A. Watson, he was tuning certain receiving parts of his harmonic telegraph to the pitch of the transmitting apparatus, operated by Watson 60 feet away. Suddenly Bell rushed over to Watson and exclaimed, "What did you do then? Don't change anything! Let me see." What had happened was that the make-and-break points of the transmitter had stuck together, so that when the spring was snapped the circuit had remained unbroken while the magnetized steel vibrating over the pole of the electromagnet had set up vibratory electrical currents in the circuit which Bell had recognized as sound at the receiver.

"Before we parted that night," said Watson, "Bell gave me directions for making the first electric speaking telephone." The instrument now in the United States National Museum is shown in Plate 31, upper. The

Witnesses:

Ewell stock.

N. J. Hutchinson

Inventor:

A. Graham Bell

Gatty Polska Bailey

FIG. 26. Diagram from Alexander Graham Bell's telephone patent

mouthpiece is covered with stretched goldbeater's skin. Attached to the center of the skin is an iron piece pivoted at the side, and close above the iron piece is an electromagnet connected to the line. Watson strung a wire down two flights of stairs. That night he and Bell tried out the first electric speaking telephone. Bell could not hear Watson, but Watson heard Bell and rushed upstairs. "I could hear you!" he shouted. "I could hear your voice! I could almost make out what you said."

The delay until February 14, 1876, in filing Bell's patent application almost cost him priority, for Elisha Gray filed a caveat on a system of electric speaking telephony only two hours after Bell's application was filed. The delay occurred in this way. Bell went home to his father in Canada in the summer of 1875 and interested a wealthy acquaintance there, George Brown. A contract was made whereby Brown was to apply for foreign patents on the telephone and share 50–50 in their profits. For this he and a friend agreed each to pay Bell $25 a month for six months to promote the experimentation, but stipulated that no patent application should be made

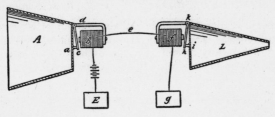

Witnesses

Ewellitosick).

N.J. Oletchinson

Inventor:

a. Graham Bell

by atty Pollok Bailey

FIG. 27. Diagram from Alexander Graham Bell's telephone patent

in the United States until after he had reached England and filed one there. Brown delayed his sailing, and even after reaching England delayed filing. Bell held to his contract. But Gardiner Hubbard, without Bell's knowledge or consent, filed, on February 14, the application which Bell had signed on January 20, 1876. It was allowed almost without change, and the patent issued March 7, 1876.

As this is said to be financially the most valuable patent ever issued, so much of it as is needful to our understanding is here quoted. Two of Bell's illustrations are shown in Figures 26 and 27.

GREAT INVENTIONS

ALEXANDER GRAHAM BELL, OF SALEM, MASSACHUSETTS
IMPROVEMENT IN TELEGRAPHY

Specifications forming part of Letters Patent No. 174,465,
dated March 7, 1876; application filed February 14, 1876.

To all whom it may concern:

Be it known that I, ALEXANDER GRAHAM BELL, of Salem,
Massachusetts, have invented certain new and useful Improvements
in Telegraphy, of which the following is a specification:

. . . . . .

My present invention consists in the employment of a vibratory
or undulatory current of electricity in contradistinction to a merely
intermittent or pulsatory current, and of a method of, and apparatus
for, producing electrical undulations upon the line wire.

. . . . . .

It has long been known that when a permanent magnet is caused
to approach the pole of an electro-magnet a current of electricity is
induced in the coils of the latter, and that when it is made to recede
a current of opposite polarity to the first appears upon the wire.
When, therefore, a permanent magnet is caused to vibrate in front of
the pole of an electro-magnet an undulatory current of electricity is
induced in the coils of the electro-magnet, the undulations of which
correspond, in rapidity of succession, to the vibrations of the magnet,
in polarity to the direction of its motion, and in intensity to the amplitude of its vibration.

. . . . . .

There are many ways of producing undulatory currents of electricity, dependent for effect upon the vibrations or motions of bodies
capable of inductive action. A few of the methods that may be employed I shall here specify. When a wire, through which a continuous
current of electricity is passing, is caused to vibrate in the neighborhood of another wire, an undulatory current of electricity is induced
in the latter. When a cylinder, upon which are arranged bar-magnets,
is made to rotate in front of the pole of an electro-magnet, an undulatory current of electricity is induced in the coils of the electro-
magnet.

Undulations are caused in a continuous voltaic current by the
vibration or motion of bodies capable of inductive action; or by the
vibration of the conducting-wire itself in the neighborhood of such
bodies. Electrical undulations may also be caused by alternately
increasing and diminishing the power of the battery. The internal

PLATE 31

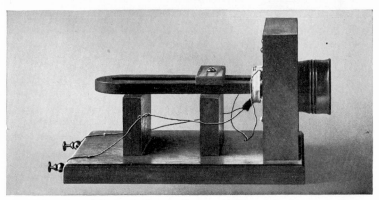

Upper: Bell's original telephone. Lower: Bell's original box telephone

PLATE 32

Upper: Bell's box telephone of 1877 with hammer called "Watson's thumper" used to attract the listener. Lower: Hand telephone receiver of 1877

resistance of a battery is diminished by bringing the voltaic elements nearer together, and increased by placing them farther apart. The reciprocal vibration of the elements of a battery, therefore, occasions an undulatory action in the voltaic current. The external resistance may also be varied. For instance, let mercury or some other liquid form part of a voltaic circuit, then the more deeply the conducting-wire is immersed in the mercury or other liquid, the less resistance does the liquid offer to the passage of the current. Hence, the vibration of the conducting-wire in mercury or other liquid included in the circuit occasions undulations in the current. The vertical vibrations of the elements of a battery in the liquid in which they are immersed produced an undulatory action in the current by alternately increasing and diminishing the power of the battery.

In illustration of the method of creating electrical undulations, I shall show and describe one form of apparatus for producing the effect. I prefer to employ for this purpose an electro-magnet, A, [Fig. 26] having a coil upon only one of its legs b. A steel-spring armature, c, is firmly clamped by one extremity to the uncovered leg d of the magnet, and its free end is allowed to project above the pole of the covered leg. The armature c can be set in vibration in a variety of ways, one of which is by wind, and, in vibrating, it produces a musical note of a certain definite pitch.

When the instrument A is placed in a voltaic circuit, $g\ b\ e\ f\ g$, the armature c becomes magnetic, and the polarity of its free end is opposed to that of the magnet underneath. So long as the armature c remains at rest, no effect is produced upon the voltaic current, but the moment it is set in vibration to produce its musical note a powerful inductive action takes place, and electrical undulations traverse the circuit $g\ b\ e\ f\ g$. The vibratory current passing through the coil of the electro-magnet f causes vibration in its armature h when the armatures $c\ h$ of the two instruments A I are normally in unison with one another; but the armature h is unaffected by the passage of the undulatory current when the pitches of the two instruments are different.

I desire here to remark that there are many other uses to which these instruments may be put, such as the simultaneous transmission of musical notes, differing in loudness as well as in pitch, and the telegraphic transmission of noises or sounds of any kind.

. . . . . .

One of the ways in which the armature c, [Fig. 26] may be set in vibration has been stated above to be by wind. Another mode is shown in [Fig. 27], whereby motion can be imparted to the armature by the human voice or by means of a musical instrument.

The armature *c*, [Fig. 27] is fastened loosely by one extremity to the uncovered leg *d* of the electro-magnet *b*, and its other extremity is attached to the center of a stretched membrane, *a*. A cone, *A*, is used to converge sound-vibrations upon the membrane. When a sound is uttered in the cone the membrane *a* is set in vibration, the armature *c* is forced to partake of the motion, and thus electrical undulations are created upon the circuit *E b e f g*. These undulations are similar in form to the air vibrations caused by the sound—that is, they are represented graphically by similar curves.

The undulatory current passing through the electro-magnet *f* influences its armature *h* to copy the motion of the armature *c*. A similar sound to that uttered into *A* is then heard to proceed from *L*.

* * * * * *

Having described my invention, what I claim, and desire to secure by Letters Patent is as follows:

1. A system of telegraphy in which the receiver is set in vibration by the employment of undulatory currents of electricity, substantially as set forth.

2. The combination, substantially as set forth, of a permanent magnet or other body capable of inductive action, with a closed circuit, so that the vibration of the one shall occasion electrical undulations in the other, or in itself, and this I claim, whether the permanent magnet be set in vibration in the neighborhood of the conducting-wire forming the circuit, or whether the conducting-wire be set in vibration in the neighborhood of the permanent magnet, or whether the conducting-wire and the permanent magnet both simultaneously be set in vibration in each other's neighborhood.

3. The method of producing undulations in a continuous voltaic current by the vibration or motion of bodies capable of inductive action, or by the vibration or motion of the conducting-wire itself, in the neighborhood of such bodies, as set forth.

4. The method of producing undulations in a continuous voltaic circuit by gradually increasing and diminishing the resistance of the circuit, or by gradually increasing and diminishing the power of the battery, as set forth.

5. The method of, and apparatus for, transmitting vocal or other sounds telegraphically, as herein described, by causing electrical undulations, similar in form to the vibrations of the air accompanying the said vocal or other sound, substantially as set forth.

In testimony whereof I have hereunto signed my name this 20th day of January, A. D. 1876.

ALEX. GRAHAM BELL.

A part of Elisha Gray's caveat filed two hours later is also given.

SPECIFICATION

To all whom it may concern:

Be it known that I, Elisha Gray, of Chicago, in the county of Cook, and State of Illinois, have invented a new Art of Transmitting Vocal Sounds Telegraphically, of which the following is a specification:—

It is the object of my invention to transmit the tones of the human voice through a telegraphic circuit, and reproduce them at the receiving end of the line, so that actual conversations can be carried on by persons at long distances apart.

· · · · · ·

To attain the objects of my invention, I devised an instrument capable of vibrating responsively to all the tones of the human voice, and by which they are rendered audible.

· · · · · ·

My present belief is, that the most effective method of providing an apparatus capable of responding to the various tones of the human voice, is a tympanum, drum or diaphragm, stretched across one end of the chamber, carrying an apparatus for producing fluctuations in the potential of the electric current, and consequently varying in its power.

In the drawings, the person transmitting sounds, is shown as talking into a box or chamber A, across the outer end of which is stretched a diaphragm *a*, of some thin substance, such as parchment or goldbeaters' skin, capable of responding to all the vibrations of the human voice, whether simple or complex. Attached to this diaphragm is a light metal rod A', or other suitable conductor of electricity, which extends into a vessel B, made of glass or other insulating material, having its lower end closed by a plug, which may be of metal, or through which passes a conductor *b*, forming part of the circuit.

This vessel is filled with some liquid possessing high resistance, such for instance as water, so that the vibrations of the plunger or rod A', which does not quite touch the conductor *b*, will cause variations in resistance, and, consequently, in the potential of the current passing through the rod A'.

Owing to this construction, the resistance varies constantly, in response to the vibrations of the diaphragm, which although irregular, not only in their amplitude, but in rapidity, are nevertheless transmitted, and can, consequently, be transmitted through a single rod, which could not be done with a positive make and break of the circuit employed, or where contact points are used.

· · · · · ·

The obvious practical application of my improvement will be to enable persons at a distance to converse with each other through a telegraphic circuit, just as they now do in each other's presence, or through a speaking tube.

I claim as my invention the art of transmitting vocal sounds or conversations telegraphically, through an electric circuit.

ELISHA GRAY.

Hubbard had an official position at the Philadelphia Centennial of 1876 and urged Bell to exhibit his telephone. Bell was so late in getting the exhibit ready that it could not be placed in the electrical section, but occupied a very inconspicuous corner in the educational section. Bell himself was occupied with the annual examinations of his speech classes when Hubbard telegraphed him to come to Philadelphia, so as to demonstrate the telephone to the judges. Bell felt it impossible to go, but his fiancée, Mabel Hubbard, and her mother at last persuaded him.

He was present in Philadelphia to meet the judges on a very hot Sunday, June 25, 1876, and had arranged to return to Boston that same night. Among the judges was Sir William Thomson, the great English expert who had made the Atlantic cable work, and accompanying the judges was Dom Pedro, Emperor of Brazil. They were tired and hot, and intended to finish their examinations for the day just before reaching Bell and the telephone. Fortunately the Emperor, Dom Pedro, who had discussed the problems of speech with Bell in Boston, happened to see the inventor, and where the Emperor went the committee of course followed. It was only a moment before their discomfort from the heat was forgotten when they heard for the first time human speech transmitted electrically. Sir William Thomson was especially enthusiastic. He introduced Bell's telephone a little later in a lecture in Scotland as the most astonishing invention of the times. Before he left America he visited Bell in Boston, where a telephone demonstration was made. Plate 31 shows the box telephone in use at that time, now deposited in the United States National Museum.

During the summer of 1876, Bell arranged a demonstration over a 5-mile line at his father's home in Canada. An improvement of Bell's telephone was patented by him in England in November, 1877, and Bell was presented at Court on January 16, 1878, where he demonstrated the telephone to Queen Victoria. Plate 32 shows a box-type telephone and a hand receiver of that period.

Bell's telephone was offered to the Western Union Telegraph Company but was declined. Instead, that company bought the patents of Elisha Gray and engaged Gray, Edison, and Dolbear to design a telephone for them. The American Speaking Telephone Company was formed as a subsidiary of the Western Union, and it entered into competition with Bell and his associates. Edison had invented the variable resistance carbon microphone transmitter, so that for a time the Western Union interests had the advantage in equipment. But the Bell interests brought suit for infringement of the Bell patents and also fortunately secured the microphone invented by Emile Berliner and improved by Francis Blake, which put their instruments fully on a par with those of the Western Union.

Emile Berliner (1851–1929) was born in Hanover, Germany. At the time he invented the microphone he was a dry-goods clerk in Washington. It was in the year of the Philadelphia Centennial that he became interested in Bell's telephone and tried to make one without knowing the details of Bell's devices. From a friend interested in telegraphy he learned that a telegraph key must be pressed down hard to send a crisp message. That led him to the secret of the loose contact microphone. With a soapbox, a screw, and a button he made one that enabled him to talk down the stairs of his boarding house.

Berliner wrote out a caveat covering the loose contact transmitter. It was filed and dated in the United States

Patent Office on April 14, 1877, just two weeks before Edison's application for the loose contact carbon microphone. Berliner applied for his patent in 1877, but it was not finally granted until 1891. As it covered basically all loose contact microphones, including Edison's carbon transmitter, this patent of Berliner's, then owned by the Bell Telephone Company, extended their monopoly from 1891 for 17 years. Suit to annul the Berliner patent was brought by the United States and carried to the Supreme Court. But that court, by a decision of six judges against one, upheld its validity, and dismissed the suit of the Government.

To return to the suit with the Western Union: Making an end of the litigation between the Bell interests and the Western Union, George Gifford, counsel for the Western Union, informed his client that Bell was unquestionably the first inventor and advised a settlement with him. The patent rights of both contestants were pooled, with the ownership vested four fifths in the Bell interests, one fifth in the Western Union. In December, 1879, the Bell stock sold at $995 a share, though up to that time it had never paid a dividend. Many suits involving various claimants were instituted later against the Bell patent, of which several reached the Supreme Court. Bell's position as the original inventor was invariably sustained by the courts.

The telephone, as now constructed, is well shown by a working sectional model donated by the American Telephone and Telegraph Company to the Smithsonian Institution in 1928 for exhibition in the United States National Museum. It is illustrated in Plate 33. The vocal speech is prepared for the line by the loose carbon granule microphone at A. The diaphragm, a, is made to vibrate by the voice, and in vibrating alters the pressure on the carbon particles at b. This alters the electrical resistance offered by these particles. Accordingly the current from the source, c, varies in strength as the electrical resistance of the carbon transmitter fluctuates with the vibrations of the

PLATE 33

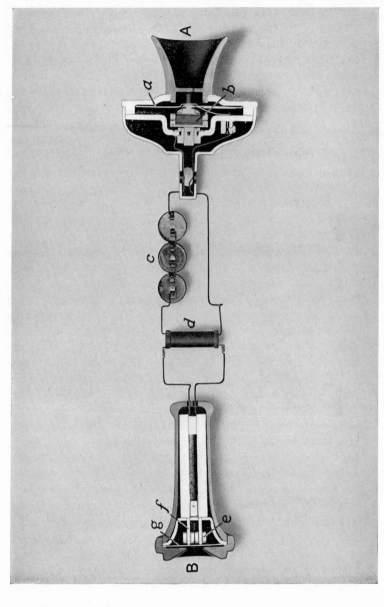

Working model illustrating the modern telephone. In the National Museum

PLATE 34

Interior of a telephone exchange

voice. This fluctuating current, passing through the primary windings of the induction coil, d, induces an alternating current in the secondary windings. The alternating current passes through the line and variably energizes the distant coil, e. As this coil rides upon the pole pieces it alters the magnetic attraction of the magnet, f, for the iron diaphragm, g. In this way the air which adjoins the diaphragm, g, is caused to vibrate so as to reproduce at B the vocal speech spoken at A.

Telephony has advanced with great rapidity, particularly in the United States, with something like 60 per cent of all the telephones in the world. Their numbers in the United States increased from about 50,000 in 1880 to 1,350,000 in 1900, 13,300,000 in 1920, and now more than 20,000,000. The problem of connecting the immense numbers of subscribers in the large cities to the central exchanges is naturally a difficult one. Plate 34 shows the interior of a telephone exchange. Improvements have reached the point where nearly 2,000 wires are enclosed in a single metal-sheathed cable. Cross-talk by induction from one circuit to another is prevented by twisting the wires according to certain patterns. The exchanges, formerly entirely hand-operated, are growing more and more to be automatic. Very nearly all of them are now of this class. The automatic switchboard is far too complicated to be explained here; it was developed from the invention of A. B. Strowger in 1889.

More than 100,000,000 miles of wire are now operated by the Bell system in the United States. Long circuits between the East and the West, such as are now used with perfect clearness, were made possible by Michael I. Pupin's invention in 1900 of the "loaded line." This consists in the insertion at certain computed intervals along the circuit of definite quantities of self-induction, supplied by so-called "loading coils." The invention by G. E. Elmen, of "permalloy" which is an alloy of about 80 per cent of nickel with 20 per cent of iron has been of advantage for the cores of loading coils.

Like a telegraph line, the telephone must be relayed occasionally to produce sufficient volume of speech on very long lines. The early attempts at mechanical relays were not very satisfactory. The invention of the high vacuum thermionic amplifier described in Chapter III has solved the problem, for it can amplify the volume tremendously without much distorting the quality of the voice. This device has even made possible transoceanic telephony. The ocean transmission is accomplished by wireless repeating. It is now possible to carry on telephone conversations from any part of the United States to most of the countries of the world.

CHAPTER V

RADIO TRANSMISSION

In Volume 2 of this Series readers will have found the story that visible and invisible rays tell of the sun and stars. Distance, size, motion, temperature, pressure, magnetic condition, and chemical composition of these immense bodies, millions, trillions, and quadrillions of miles away, are made known to us by the study of their radiation. In this study the leading instrument is the spectroscope, which may be regarded as merely a wireless radiation receiver of exceptional selectivity, operating on rays of 2,000,000 times the highest frequencies now used in short-wave wireless. Light is but a wireless ray of shorter wave length. Whether we meditate on the marvels of the one or the marvels of the other, we must be lost in admiration of that essence, common to them both, which on the one hand reveals the secrets of the universe, and on the other can communicate around the world the voice and features of a friend.

In conversation with the writer, a noted executive, who is an eminent authority in all branches of telephony, remarked that though his position required him to be familiar with every step of progress in communication and to understand fully the details of the apparatus used, nevertheless the present perfection of wireless telephony still seemed to him almost magical, unbelievable. For instance, some one might pick up an ordinary desk telephone in Sweden, get his wire connection to the coast, thence by ocean cable to England, and again by wire to the transatlantic radio station. There his voice is changed and committed to ethereal vibrations and amplified up and up until the soundless waves can carry it across the Atlantic. Again it is retransformed and sent by land lines to the Pacific Coast. Wireless again takes it and flings it across to Hawaii. Another transformation is made, and the person called, seated at his desk with an ordinary telephone, not only understands the message, but recognizes his friend's voice in far-off Sweden, as if he were in the next room.

This is no fortunate discovery of one man. The boon came to the world little by little, as the genius, hard work, and financial sacrifices of many scientists, inventors, experimenters, and business men combined to accomplish the miracle.

We commonly speak of messages "on the air." The air is indeed useful in wireless, but only as a convenient construction material, like iron or copper, for parts of the apparatus. Air is not the conveying medium for wireless, as it really is for ordinary speech. Wireless messages travel like light by ethereal waves, and can travel quite as well in vacuum as in air. In fact wireless waves are very much like light waves in their true nature. They differ only in wave length, or, if we prefer, in frequency, which is the reciprocal of wave length. All waves, both of wireless and of light, travel approximately at 186,000 miles (300,000,000 meters) each second. Hence as a wave of green light is $5/10,000,000$ meter long, it requires $10,000,000/5 \times 300,000,000$ such waves to carry light forward as far as it travels each second. The frequency of green light is therefore 600,000,000,000,000,000 waves per second. Radio waves are immensely longer, those ordinarily used ranging from 1 meter to 15,000 meters in length. Their frequencies are therefore much slower, ranging from 300,000,000 down to 20,000 waves per second.

Yet all of these radio frequencies are too rapid to operate an ordinary telephone. Even if the telephone diaphragm could respond to them, the ear of the listener could not. To bring wireless waves into telephonic reception these rapid wave trains are either modulated or broken up, in sending or receiving, into trains of groups of vibrations. In effect, as indicated in Figure 28, these groups of radio-frequency waves are the individual elements of audio-frequency waves forming parts of a series of vibrations slow enough to move the telephone diaphragm and to impress our ears. Figure 28, I, shows what is called a carrier wave of radio frequency. Figure 28, II, indicates the vibrations of the letter "A" as in "father" spoken in the ordinary telephone. Figure 28, III, shows how, by impressing it on the carrier wave, a modulated wave is produced which can be heard in the telephone.

We referred above to Joseph Henry's discovery in 1842 that

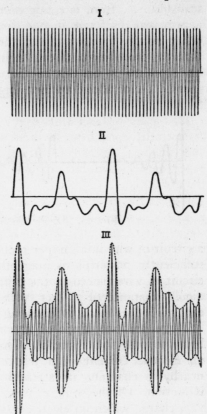

FIG. 28. Carrier and modulated radio waves. A carrier wave of radio frequency is indicated by I, though in waves billions of times the true radio wave length. In II is shown the form of the sound wave of "a" as in "father". In III is shown the modulated wave produced by impressing the telephoned "a" on the carrier wave

the discharge of a Leyden jar (or any other kind of electric condenser) is oscillatory. It is not, he says, "a single transfer . . . from one side of the jar to another, [but] a principal discharge in one direction, and then several reflex actions backward and forward, each more feeble than the preceding until equilibrium is obtained." During his experiments on this subject he found that "a single spark . . . of about an inch long, thrown on the end of

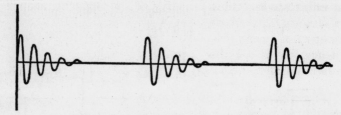

FIG. 29. Discontinuous radio wave

a circuit of wire in an upper room, produced an induction sufficiently powerful to magnetize needles in a parallel circuit of wire placed in the cellar beneath, at a perpendicular distance of 30 feet, with two floors and ceilings, each 14 inches thick, intervening."

There are two kinds of actions which electricity can bring to pass at a distance. The first is such as sets up an electric current in a free coil whenever a current nearby is changing its strength. This is called mutual induction. Of the same nature is the force opposing its own charge which an electric current produces in its own conductor. This is called self-induction. Effects of electric induction fade out rapidly with distance. The fading is proportional in many cases to the inverse cube of the distance. If induction were the only available means to propagate electric action through space, wireless communication could go but short distances.

But electricity produces another effect, capable of traveling great distances. Whenever a high-frequency oscillatory discharge of a condenser takes place it sets up electromagnetic radiation which travels, as we have said, 300,000,000 meters per second. In long paths above the earth this radiation weakens only in direct proportion to the increasing distance, not proportionally to the cube of the distance, as does induction. Electromagnetic waves can not travel in conductors, but only in insulators. The upper part of the earth's atmosphere is an ionized vacuum, and like any high vacuum is a conductor and a reflector of radio waves. This property of the upper atmosphere

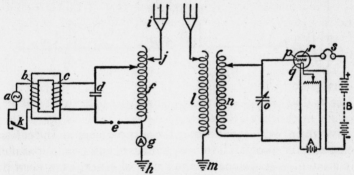

FIG. 30. A discontinuous-wave radio set

was suggested by Heaviside, so that we speak of the "Heaviside layer." Radio waves are reflected by it and by the earth, both being good conductors. Therefore, instead of going out into space and being lost, radio waves travel round and round the earth in the space occupied by the atmosphere between these two conducting layers.

Electromagnetic waves were the effects which Joseph Henry produced by the spark above mentioned. He was dealing then not with induction, but with radiation. It easily leaped the 30 feet of distance from the experimental room to the cellar of his laboratory.

Wave trains of wireless waves may be either continuous or discontinuous. Discontinuous waves comprise successions of similar groupings of highly damped waves as shown in Figure 29. In Figure 30 is shown one kind of apparatus for producing damped discontinuous wave trains. The alternating dynamo, *a*, is connected to the primary of the step-up transformer, *b*. From its secondary, *c*, a high voltage charges the condenser, *d*, alternately positively and negatively as the current alternates. The short spark gap at *e* has not sufficient resistance to hold back the full charge of the condenser, *d*. Hence the spark passes at every plus and at every minus phase of the current wave. But, as Joseph Henry discovered, the spark is oscillatory and goes through several very quick oscillations before subsiding. These oscillations are of radio frequency and may be communicated by a sending antenna to great distances.

The individual groups of waves themselves, like those illustrated in Figure 29, succeed one another only twice as fast as do the cycles of the alternator, *a*. If the alternator is, for instance, of 500 cycles per second, the groups in the wave train will repeat 1,000 times per second. If broadcast and received by antennas, this frequency will produce in a listening telephone a singing note of about the pitch of B natural of the high soprano register. Hence the sender needs only to interrupt the current, according to Morse's dot and dash alphabet, to communicate a wireless telegraphic message, received in the form of singing notes and silences.

The explanation of the action of the antenna in propagating and receiving the oscillations set up by a spark discharge or other high-frequency wave source, leads us to the important subject of resonant electric circuits. A condenser, as we have remarked, is any electric device in which an insulating medium lies between and separates two electric conductors. The earth is a conductor, and so, too, is the antenna, which, as is well known, is insulated from the earth. Between them lies the air. This is the insulating medium, or as it is called, the "dielectric," which completes the group of three necessary parts of a condenser. From the sending antenna to the earth is connected a wire in which is often inserted a low-resistance coil.

This wire and coil, together with the antenna, constitute an electric system which has not only a small resistance, but also, like every extended electric connection, has the property of self-induction discovered by Joseph Henry.

It has been shown both by theory and experiment that in a circuit comprising both a condenser and an inductance, there is an opposition called reactance to the flow of an alternating current. The reactance may easily be millions of times as great as the electrical resistance of the circuit. In such a case it is a complete bar to the current. On the other hand, except for the ordinary ohmic electrical resistance itself, the reactance in the circuit may be reduced to zero. This condition is called resonance. It holds only for waves of a particular frequency. Since this is so, all other waves but those for which the circuit is resonant are excluded by reactance. This constitutes "tuning."

Resonance or tuning is possible because the reactance due to the capacity of a condenser is opposite in nature to the reactance due to induction. To find the total reactance of the circuit one must take account of the reactance of resistance additional to that of induction, but must diminish their combined effect by reason of the reactance of capacity. Now it is true that the reactance of induction increases in direct proportion to the wave frequency, but the reactance of capacity decreases numerically in direct proportion to the wave frequency. To see how the two influences neutralize each other at certain wave frequency, consider the following table, appropriate to a circuit whose capacity is 0.005 microfarads, and whose inductance is 500 microhenrys, and whose resistance is neglected.

Frequency cycles per second	Reactance of induction (ohms)	Reactance of capacity (ohms)	Reactance Total (ohms)
60	0.19	−530,000.	530,000
1,000	3.14	−31,840.	31,837
100,700	316.2	−316.2	0
1,000,000	3,142.	−31.8	3,110

This particular circuit is in resonance for a frequency of 100,700 cycles per second, corresponding to a wave length of 300,000,000/100,700 or 2,980 meters. For any frequencies far removed from this one, the reactance of this circuit becomes very great, and prevents the passage of appreciable currents.

Circuits may be tuned to given frequencies by altering either the inductance or the capacity. The capacity is very simply varied in ordinary radio sets by rotating a handle which carries on its axis a set of parallel metallic plates much longer than they are wide. As they rotate they interlockingly enter between a corresponding set of parallel metallic plates. When the two sets of plates are wide apart the air gap is so large that the capacity of the condenser is very small. As the plates interweave, the air spaces become narrow, and the electric capacity increases. Near the condensers in the cabinet of a radio receiver are coils of wire wound on paper cylinders; these are the induction coils with which the condensers are in tune.

Figure 30 shows a diagram of a simple but complete radio telegraph. The alternating current, of perhaps 500 cycles per second, indicated as originating at a, actuates the primary coil, b, of a step-up transformer. The high voltage secondary coil, c, charges the condenser, d, above the discharging point of the spark gap, e, at each maximum of positive and negative phase in the alternating cycle. Thus there are produced a group of damped oscillations of radio frequency perhaps 100,000 per second, as each spark occurs (see Fig. 29). With the 500-cycle alternator there will be 1,000 such groups of oscillations each second. The induction coil, f, is adjustable in its inductance so that at the radio frequency of the oscillations set up by each spark, the circuit, d, e, f, is in resonance. Similarly the antenna, i, and induction coil, f, together with the ground connection, h, are also adjusted at j to be in resonance for oscillations of this frequency, which, as we suggested, may be 100,000. At g a hot-wire ammeter, or,

PLATE 35

The author examining the General Electric Pliotron vacuum tube and other tubes

more simply still, a glow lamp, indicates by a maximum current when the tuning of the antenna circuit is correct.

The receiving antenna, with its inductance, l, and ground connection, m, is tuned to resonance with the incoming waves. A second resonant circuit is formed by the induction coil, n, and adjustable condenser, o. By the inductive coupling shown, the impulses in the coil, l, induce oscillations in the circuit, n, o. These oscillations vary the charge on the grid, p, of the electron tube (see Chapter III), q, p, r, whose filament, q, is heated by an auxiliary battery, A. Through the circuit of the plate, r, go amplified trains of groups of oscillations of audio-frequency 1,000, as the successive sparks pass at e. These are suitable to produce a singing note in the telephone, s. The energy of the current which actuates the telephone, s, is given by the battery, B, but is governed by the oscillatory voltage on the grid, p. This voltage in turn is governed by the distant key, k. As they key in the transmitting circuit ticks off its Morse code language, the telephone in the receiving circuit responds by singing notes and silences.

Nature has provided and men have discovered a truly remarkable combination of elements which unite as just stated to make extensive wireless communication possible: First, the ethereal waves which travel 300,000,000 meters each second. Second, the rapid vibratory electric discharge of any instrument adapted for storing electricity. Such a discharge, like the pendulum, is not quieted at the zero status, but carries on past zero to a negative departure almost as great as the original positive one, and so continues a whole train of oscillations until the gradual effects of damping bring quiescence. Third, the ability of such oscillatory electric discharges to set up ethereal waves. Fourth, resonance made possible by the counter-acting influence of inductance against capacity, whereby the opposition to the current, created by that electric capacity without which waves could not be produced, is reduced to zero. Fifth, the narrow range in wave lengths to which this compensation of reactances called resonance extends, thereby making it possible to extract a single message undisturbed from space filled simultaneously with other messages carried by waves of other frequencies. Sixth, the constant discharge of negative electrons from a heated wire, which is the basis of the electron tube, the soul of modern radio. Seventh, the ingenious device of the grid between the heated wire and the positively charged plate. For the easy modification of the voltage of the grid, in association with the feeble, inconceivably rapid oscillations of the wave trains received, produces a faithfully copied fluctuation on a highly amplified scale in the flow of electrons to the plate, which we call the plate current. Eighth, and finally, the ingenious but relatively simple devices of the telephone, which, in combination with these other elements, produce and carry to receptive ears the messages of this wireless age.

Thus far we have dealt with damped waves, but ocean telephony and broadcasting are founded on systems of continuous undamped wave trains. As inventions have occurred, three principal sources of continuous wave trains have come into wide use. These are the mercury arc, often called the Poulsen arc, after a noted Danish inventor; the high-frequency alternator, often called the Alexanderson alternator, already mentioned; and the electron tube, also already mentioned. At the present time the electron tube has outdistanced the others completely in the extent of its application, though formerly it was the mercury arc which held the field. We shall restrict our description of continuous-wave generation to the electron tube. This instrument has an enormously wide range of possible frequencies, from one to several hundred million cycles per second.

Plate 35 shows three different types of vacuum tubes, representing extremes reached in modern development. The large tube in the center is a Pliotron, generating

100,000 watts of radio-frequency power, sufficient to supply the output of a modern high-power broadcasting station. The copper cylinder (cut open to show the interior structure) is the anode, and is surrounded by a water jacket for cooling when in operation. The small tube on the right is a split-anode magnetron capable of generating several watts of ultra-high-frequency power, operating readily at 400,000,000 cycles per second. The small tube at the left is a low-grid-current Pliotron, used in the amplification and measurement of extremely minute direct currents, being capable of detecting a current of $\dfrac{1}{100,000,000,000,000,000}$ ampere—a flow of only 60 electrons per second. In an ordinary household electric lamp about 3,000,000,000,000,000,000 electrons pass in a second.

The use of an electron tube as an oscillating generator depends on the principle of regeneration. This principle bears a close analogy to the clock. In the clock we have a weight which furnishes abundant power to move the wheels and hands and a pendulum or balance wheel which restrains the action by making a certain number of vibrations per second. The pendulum or balance wheel would soon stop, owing to friction and air resistance, and the weight would then be unable to move the hands if it were not arranged that a very small amount of power from the weight is diverted from the hands to keep the pendulum or escapement moving at the required rate.

Figure 31 shows the principle of the regenerative oscillating circuit applied to continuous-wave generation, and with it a device to modulate the wave train by a microphone, so as to transmit speech. All to the right of the dotted line XY is the radio-frequency circuit, that to the left of XY is the audio-frequency circuit. Beginning at the lower center of the figure, a is a direct-current generator or battery, whose negative pole, at the left, is directly connected to the junction, b, of which we shall make mention repeatedly. From the positive pole of the generator the connection passes through the iron-cored induction coils, *c* and *d*, and the "choke coil," *e*, to the plate, *f*, of an electron tube. Thence the connection continues to the condenser, *g*, and the inductance, *h*. To the latter is attached the antenna, *i*, through an ammeter,

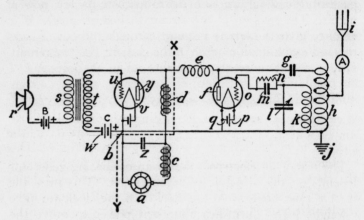

FIG. 31. A regenerative oscillating radio circuit with modulated continuous wave propagation

A, and also the ground, *j*. Tracing the connection further, we come to the oscillating circuit including the inductance, *k*, and variable condenser, *l*. The regenerative impulse is provided here. It will be noted that the inductance, *k*, is so near the inductance, *h*, that when currents are made in *h* they produce by induction currents in *k*. The inductance, *k*, and the condenser, *l*, are adjusted to be a tuned circuit of the desired frequency. Oscillating in harmony with them is the antenna circuit. From the condenser, *l*, the connection branches. One branch goes through the condenser, *m* (about which is shunted the large resistance, *n*, called a "grid leak"), and ending with the grid, *o*, of the electron tube. The other connection from *l* continues to the junction point, *b*, but on the way throws off the hot-filament circuit, *p*, of the electron tube, which has a small battery, *q*, of which the negative pole is on the left. Being directly connected to the junction, *b*, this pole of the battery, *q*, is at the same potential as the negative pole of the generator, *a*.

Confining our attention at first to the radio-frequency part of the diagram, just described, let us see how it works. The making of the circuit to furnish power at *a*, at once gives a current impulse through the coil, *h*, and this induces a small current in the coil, *k*. But the circuit, *k*, *l*, is resonant, so that this sets up in the circuit *k*, *l*, an oscillation of the desired frequency, which is communicated through the condenser, *m*, to produce an oscillating voltage on the grid, *o*. Thereby an amplified oscillation of the same frequency is produced in the current from the filament, *p*, through the plate, *f*. This oscillating high-frequency current can not pass through the choke coil, *e*, or the iron-cored induction coils, *d* and *c*, to set up surges in the generator, *a*, which might spoil its insulation. However, the condenser, *g*, offers little impedance to it and it builds up oscillations in the antenna circuit. By induction these oscillations strengthen the feeble oscillations in the tuned circuit, *k*, *l*. Thus the oscillations intensify more and more, at the expense, of course, of power furnished by the generator, *a*. At length (and though it takes long to tell it, and the time "at length" measured by number of oscillations is enormous, yet the time "at length" measured by the clock is only a fraction of a second), the intensity of oscillation reaches a maximum, and continues unchanged thereafter, so far as the radio-frequency circuit is concerned.

To complete the story of the radio-frequency circuit, the grid, *o*, which is of the same average potential as the junction, *b*, and the filament, *p*, captures negative electrons in the positive half of every oscillation. Thus it tends to become more negative. But this tendency, which if unchecked would stop the oscillation, is nullified by the grid-leak resistance shunt, *n*, which allows the excessive negative charge on *o* to be dissipated. The ammeter, *A*, is merely for the purpose of noting when the circuit is so attuned as to give the maximum antenna current.

Turning now to the audio-frequency circuit, the microphone, *r*, of the ordinary telephone type, when spoken into, sets up current changes in the primary, *s*, of the step-up transformer, whose secondary, *t*, impresses the accompanying voltage fluctuations on the grid, *u*. This grid is normally more negative in potential than the junction, *b*, and the hot filament, *v*, by the whole voltage of the battery, *w*, whose negative pole is on the left. Hence, without capturing any negative electrons itself, the fluctuations of the grid voltage cause amplified fluctuations of streams of negative electrons to pass between the filament and the plate, *y*. Owing to the iron-cored choke coil, *d*, the voltage changes thus produced on the plate, *y*, are hindered from being freely dissipated in plate-current changes. These audio-frequency fluctuations go over as surges of voltage through the air-cored coil, *e*, effective as a choke coil only at the much higher radio frequencies, and so modulate the voltage of the plate, *f*. Accordingly the oscillations in the antenna change from a uniform continuous wave train like I of Figure 28 to a modulated wave train as shown at III.

The generator, *a*, it will be seen, plays a part in the audio-frequency circuit. It maintains a high positive potential on the plate, *y*. As rapid fluctuations of voltage of the generator would introduce disagreeable modulations in the antenna current, the iron-cored coil, *c*, and condenser, *z*, are introduced as a filter. They smooth out rapid fluctuations of the direct-current generator which might arise from inequalities of the commutator.

Heterodyne and superheterodyne reception are terms often heard. It is not possible to perceive with a telephone a uniform continuous radio-frequency train of waves, nor are irregular breaks made by telegraphic signals of the

Morse dot and dash system directly recognizable in such waves. But if at the receiving station a local uniform continuous wave train of equal amplitude but differing slightly in frequency is superposed on that coming from a distance, beat waves, comparable to the beats listened for by piano tuners, are produced, having a frequency equal to the difference in frequencies of the two original sets of waves. If, for instance, the distance wave is of 300 meters, or 1,000,000 cycles in frequency, and the local wave of the frequency 1,001,000 cycles, a third wave of audio frequency of 1,000 cycles will be produced by the beats. If now, the wave train from the distant station is interrupted by dots and dashes of the Morse code, then the audio-frequency beat wave will be interrupted by silences every time the sending is interrupted. This is called heterodyne reception, but is unnecessary in wireless telephony, because the modulation of waves produced by the microphone take its place.

However, it is found unsatisfactory to amplify greatly the exceedingly high frequencies, up to 20,000,000 cycles per second, or more, now used in ocean telephony. These may first be reduced to moderate radio frequencies by heterodyne methods before amplifying. After amplification in this intermediate radio frequency, the message may be reduced to audio frequency and again amplified. The same device is used in some broadcasting receiving sets to improve the tone quality. It is called super-heterodyning.

It would be too complex to trace the improvement of radio communication further. Crystals that expand and contract in unvarying rhythmic vibration are used as master oscillators to standardize the frequency of broadcasting stations. Amplifying electron tubes are applied in cascades to step up the intensities of radio-frequency and audio-frequency waves. The resources of the theory of sound and of electricity are applied by expert mathematicians and experimenters to improve the quality of the sounds received and to eliminate disagreeable blemishes.

It is said that the eminent conductor of the Philadelphia orchestra, Stokowski, finds the broadcasting of his music so perfect that he is unable to distinguish at the broadcasting station whether the sound comes to him directly through the air or indirectly by radio transmission. It is not to be supposed that a perfection so complete at the source is retained in the many receiving sets in distant States where his concerts are enjoyed. Yet more and more, in rapid advance, the art of radio transmission and reception is being improved. Even now it must be a critical musical ear that fails to receive great pleasure from radio rendition of a symphony.

When we trace the steps of radio development, we find that the number of discoverers and inventors is so great and their contributions so outstanding that it is impossible in a brief space to do justice to them. Starting from the experiments which led Henry to infer the oscillatory character of the spark in 1842, we should note that in 1853 Sir William Thomson (Lord Kelvin) demonstrated it from theory and gave formulae suitable for computing the frequency of oscillation. His work was beautifully confirmed by the experimental demonstrations of Feddersen a few years later. At nearly the same time, 1864, Clerk Maxwell predicted from theory that electric waves must radiate from every system whereby such oscillations are produced and must travel in all dielectric media with the velocity of light and with other characteristics analagous to those of light.

Maxwell's theory incited Heinrich Hertz, in the decade 1880–90, to a brilliant series of world-renowned experiments. Hertz was able to demonstrate Maxwell's waves experimentally, and to measure their reflection, refraction, polarization, diffraction, and wave lengths by experimental means analagous to those which show similar properties of light. Hertz used mainly the principle of resonance

PLATE 36

Guglielmo Marconi. Courtesy of Maj. William J. Hammer
of New York

PLATE 37

Radio transmitting station, Lawrenceville, N. J. Courtesy of the American Telephone and Telegraph Company. Photograph by Fairchild Aerial Surveys, Inc.

for detection. Then came Branly and Lodge with the coherer, a tube of metal granules which, under the influence of waves, arranges its particles so as to become more highly conducting. This instrument was improved by Marconi, and made the basis of his earlier successes in developing Hertzian waves for wireless signaling.

For a man so famous, unusual difficulty is encountered in finding an adequate biography. The following sketch of Signor Marconi's early career is translated and abridged from *"Nuova Antologia,"* pages 482–487, January–February 1916.

Guglielmo Marconi, a senator of the Kingdom of Italy by virtue of a statute which includes those who "by eminent services or merits will have made the country famous," was born at Bologna on April 25, 1874, of an Irish mother, Annetta Jameson, whom his father, Giuseppe Marconi, had taken as his second wife in 1864. Having spent his childhood in Bologna, he completed his first studies at Florence in the Cavalleri Institute and at Leghorn in the Ferrini Institute, where he had Professor Vincenzo Rosa as teacher of physics.

"In reviewing the history of my improvement of radiotelegraphy," said Marconi in a lecture delivered before the Royal Academy of Sciences at Stockholm when in 1909 the Nobel Prize for physics was conferred upon him, "I desire to mention that I have never studied physics or electricity in a regular manner, although from my youth I have always been intensely interested in those sciences.

"Moreover, I took a course of lessons in physics under the lamented Professor Rosa at Leghorn, and I believe I can say that I was very well acquainted with the publications of that time which treated of scientific subjects, including the work of Hertz, Branly, and Righi.

"In my house near Bologna, I began early in 1895 to make trials and experiments with the object of determining by means of the Hertzian waves the possibility of transmitting telegraphic signs and symbols to a distance without the aid of connecting wires.

"After some preliminary experiments with the Hertzian waves, I very soon became convinced that if those or similar waves could really be transmitted and received at considerable distances, a new system of communications would be possible, which would present enormous advantages over the luminous and optical methods of signaling, that are dependent upon the clearness of the atmosphere for their success."

The house was the Villa Grifone near Pontecchio about 10 kilos from Bologna, the property of his father. His father had assigned to him for his experiments a room located in the upper part of the house, and there Guglielmo Marconi worked, "trying and trying again," and with very moderate means constructed apparatus conceived by him. As the first support of his antenna he employed a "broom handle" which is still preserved as a valuable relic. With a rudimental antenna he at last succeeded in transmitting a signal from one end of his laboratory to the other. He repeated the experiment over a greater distance between the Villa Grifone and the Mountain of the Cross near Montechiaro in the Tenuta Malvasia about one kilo distant. A cross which stands upon that hill served him as a support for the antenna. . . .

In September, 1910, a little more than 15 years after his first experiments in which he succeeded in transmitting to a distance of a few meters, he was able to receive signals at a distance of 10,000 kilometers on the Italian liner *Principessa Mafalda* in port at Buenos Aires.

In February, 1896, Guglielmo Marconi went to England, making his first experiments at Westbourne Park. On June 2 of the same year, he made his first application for a patent for radiotelegraphy, which was granted a few months afterwards under the number 12,039 of 1896.

In July, 1896, Guglielmo Marconi was introduced to the Chief Engineer of the English Telegraphs, Sir William Preece, who listened attentively to the young man, assisted in his experiments, and was a great help to him. It was in fact at the desire of Preece that Marconi made some successful experiments between the Central Post Office in London and the distant Thames. In December, 1896, Preece delivered a lecture in Toynbee Hall, London, on "telegraphy without wires," which Marconi illustrated by experiments. New records were made in May, 1897, in the canal of Bristol between Lavernock and Flatholm, and then between Lavernock and Brean Donn. across the canal to a distance of about 15 kilometers.

In July, 1897, Marconi, called to Italy by the Ministry of the Marine, gave the first demonstration of his invention to the Italian authorities in the Ministry of the Marine, and then in the Quirinal in the presence of their Majesties King Humbert and Queen Margaret. On July 18 experiments were made between the arsenal of Spezia and the cruiser *San Martino*, reaching a distance of 16 kilometers. At the arsenal of Spezia a station was erected on the land and two warships were kept in constant communication with the coast.

On his return to England, Marconi tried new experiments between Salisbury and Bath, reaching a distance of 55 kilometers. That led to the organization of a financial company to utilize the Marconi patent. It took the name of "Wireless Telegraph and Signal Company, Ltd.," changed in March, 1900, to that of "Marconi's Wireless Telegraph Company, Ltd." To that company Marconi ceded all his patents for all the countries in the world, except for Italy and the Italian colonies, desiring to reserve liberty of action regarding his own country, in order to be able to yield his patents on preferential conditions whenever they might be able to serve in the defense of Italy.

At that period two permanent stations were erected on the Isle of Wight and the experiments were happily continued in very stormy weather as his birthday approached.

In May, 1898, a demonstration of apparatus for wireless telegraphy took place in the House of Commons. A little while afterwards, in July, what was probably the first experiment in its practical application took place. The newspaper "Express" of Dublin published every day the report of the Kingstown yacht regattas by means of radio telegrams, which demonstrated the utility and the facility of using the new system for commercial purposes. Later on, Marconi established a communication between the Osborne residence of Queen Victoria and the royal yacht *Osborne*. In 1899, after a lecture at the Institute of English Electrical Engineers, he visited the United States. That year is noteworthy from the fact that the Marconi apparatus was installed on some warships of the English navy. Two years later, in 1901, a distance of more than 400 kilometers was attained, and soon afterwards the first signals were transmitted between Poldhu in Cornwall and St. John's, Newfoundland. After numerous experiments between Nice and Corsica, in February, 1902, Marconi received good messages on board the steamboat *Philadelphia* at a distance of about 2,500 kilometers. In December, 1902, the station established at Cape Breton, Nova Scotia, by the Government of Canada was put in communication with the station of Poldhu in Cornwall, England, and on its inauguration messages were sent from America to the King of England, to the King of Italy, to the "Times" and to the warship *Carlo Alberto*, which by the courtesy of the Italian Government had aided Marconi in his experiments.

The great English steamship *Lucania* successfully made the first trial of permanent communication in the passage between Europe and America in October, 1903, and every day a bulletin of radio-telegraphic news was published on board. That service was then regularly adopted beginning with June 4, 1904. At the same time the stations of Bari in Italy and Antivari in Montenegro were established with a view to instituting a public telegraphic service between Italy and the Balkan peninsula. Finally, in 1907 the great station of Clifden was erected on the west coast of Ireland, but had to be reconstructed in 1910 on account of a fire. Since April of that year it has worked regularly in the service between Europe and America and every day sends and receives messages for the whole world, corresponding with the station at Glace Bay in Canada.

GREAT INVENTIONS

The great inventor did not fail to encounter both struggles and difficulties; but now the glorious discovery has been confirmed in history and the name of Marconi will go down to posterity with the admiration and the gratitude of the most remote generations. In the meantime the greater universities of Europe have conferred academic degrees upon him, the principal governments have accorded him the highest honors. and in 1909 the Nobel Prize for physics was awarded him.

Sir William Preece, the eminent English telegraph engineer, observed: "It is said that Marconi has not found anything new. It is true that he has not discovered any new rays and that he has made use of the Hertzian waves, that his transmitter is the oscillator of Righi, and the essential part of his receiver is a coherer; but even Columbus did not make the egg and taught only how to make it stand upright."

During his long residence in other countries Marconi has never forgotten that he is an Italian, nor has he ever given up his Italian citizenship. He has also served his country, like all his fellow-citizens, by rendering military service in the *Royal Navy*, and he has reserved for Italy unconditionally the use of his patents for military purposes.

Marconi has the credit of having saved, thanks to his invention, thousands and thousands of human lives, persons who without the desperate appeal for help thrown out by the radiotelegraphic apparatus of the ships in danger, would have perished miserably. The English Prime Minister justly remarked before Parliament after the wreck of the *Titanic* that the safety of the 700 persons rescued was due to a single man—Guglielmo Marconi. The same thing may be said of the *Republic* (January 23, 1909), of the *Slavonia* (1909), of the *Delhi* (December 13, 1911), of the *Veronese* (January 1, 1913), of the *Templemore* (September 30, 1913), of the *Volturno* (October 10, 1913), to mention only the earlier, more important ones.

So the work of Guglielmo Marconi displays a cnaracter not only economic but highly humanitarian and his name will be revered and blessed in all the generations. We still remember the great emotion with which a traveler, accustomed to crossing the ocean, related to us the impressions of his first voyage on a steamship equipped with the Marconi telegraph. He felt as if connected with his family, with his business, with terra firma, and with all ships sailing in the entire world; and it seemed that a new sense of security and of pleasure accompanied him across the seas. As Italians we must feel particularly proud of him, of his name, of his work, endorsing the general and enthusiastic approval with which the senate received the words of Major Ferraris, who in the meeting of December 16, 1915, calling to mind the recent discourse of Marconi, thus expressed himself: "To him I convey the sentiment of my devotion as an Italian, because wherever

PLATE 38

One of the buildings of the Lawrenceville radio station.   Courtesy of the American Telephone and
Telegraph Company

PLATE 39

Cape Spencer Light Station, Alaska. Photograph by the United States Navy Department

and under whatever quarter of the heavens I may find myself, his name today is the symbol of an Italy which works, studies and produces for the benefit of humanity."

The progress of radio in this century is so wide-ranging and technical that it is not possible to give a fair account of it without extensive use of the principles of mathematics and physics. We must, therefore, be content here to name without further explanation some of the great inventions and their makers.

Lee De Forest, who invented the three-electrode tube, also applied it as a generator of high-frequency oscillations, in which use it is now preeminent over the arc and the alternator. De Forest and E. H. Armstrong independently invented the feed-back or regenerative vacuum-tube receiver. Litigation on priority eventually reached the Supreme Court, where De Forest was finally adjudged the first inventor.

I. Langmuir and H. D. Arnold independently discovered the properties of the high-vacuum electron tube. Priority was decided in favor of Langmuir by the Court of Appeals of the District of Columbia. Eventually the Supreme Court held there was no invention in the patentable degree over the prior art.

E. F. W. Alexanderson invented the tuned cascade radio-frequency tube amplifier.

F. A. Kolster invented the coil direction finder.

L. A. Hazeltine introduced neutralization of tube capacity in the radio-frequency amplifier.

J. H. Hammond, Jr., developed distant control by radio.

E. H. Colpitts introduced modulation of high-frequency oscillations for voice transmission.

W. G. Cady proposed the use of piezo-electric crystal vibrations as a control for oscillator frequency.

J. H. Rogers invented underground antennas.

P. D. Lowell and F. W. Dunmore jointly introduced alternating-current energization of radio receivers.

GREAT INVENTIONS

G. Marconi developed directive or beam radio transmission.

Many other valuable improvements should perhaps be mentioned, but the list is already long. We must close here this brief account of the principles and progress of the most astonishing of the arts which the discoveries of modern times have made possible.

Plates 37 and 38 show the great installation for short-wave radio telephone transmission at Lawrenceville, N. J. The general view in Plate 37 shows in the short line of towers running approximately east to west, the supports of three antennas employed in the South American telephone service. The longer line of towers, running approximately northwest and southeast, supports nine antennas employed in the three short-wave circuits to Europe. The two buildings shown inside the antenna "V" each contain transmitters—one for South America and three for Europe. Three antennas each for different wave lengths are provided for each transmitter. Since this photograph was taken the foreign services have been greatly extended, and new antennae and transmitters have been installed for them. The receiving stations for these circuits are located at Netcong, N. J. In order to give a more just idea of the enormous magnitude of this installation, we show in Plate 38 one of the two transmitting stations barely visible in the general view.

Plate 39 is a view of the Cape Spencer Light Station, Alaska, where is located one of the radiobeacons that add so greatly to the safety of travel at sea.

CHAPTER VI

THE ELECTRIC LIGHT

WHEN Abraham Lincoln educated himself by the light of the flickering fire and of the tallow candle, these were the common light sources. The scholar's "midnight oil," furnished by the sperm whale, was a luxury. Kerosene had hardly come into use, and gas lighting, though used in cities, was not generally available. All of these kinds of light, which in their times have lighted the composition of some of the greatest poems, speeches, and books that the world has ever known, and have helped the ambitious boys of former days to become great lawyers and statesmen, are now largely discarded. Electric lighting, based upon the fundamental discoveries in electromagnetism of Faraday and Henry, is now well-nigh universal.

Some use was made of electricity for arc lighting as early as 1850, but little real progress in the modern sense came until about 1875, when the Jablochkoff candle and William Wallace's arc lights came into use. Shortly after this, both Edison's incandescent lighting system and electric arc lighting began to make rapid progress.

It is true that Sir Joseph Swan as early as 1860 became convinced that the most practicable source of illumination for the future would be the incandescent carbon filament glowing within a glass bulb that had been evacuated, thus depriving it of air to prevent combustion of the filament. He constructed such a lamp in 1860, in which carbonized strips of paper were caused to glow by electric current from primary batteries. At that time, however, there were no air pumps that could produce even an approximate vacuum, so that the life of such a filament was short. In 1865 Sprengel's mercury pump for producing high vacua appeared. Swan continued his experiments, but not until February, 1879, did he exhibit his improved glow lamp at a meeting of the Newcastle Chemical Society. In October, 1880, he conducted a demonstration of incandescent lighting by this method, and a month later read a paper on "The Subdivision of the Electric Light," showing its suitability for domestic lighting.

Sir Joseph Swan continued in the lighting field, and invented a method of squirting cellulose by hydraulic pressure through a die, thereby producing the raw material for the fine, regular lamp filaments which gave place to tungsten early in this century. He was, besides, a fruitful inventor in other fields. His addition of gelatin in the copper-plating bath made possible far greater rapidity and improved quality in the electrolytic deposition of copper. He also made great improvements in photography, including the invention of the first really fast dry plates, and he devised methods of photographic reproduction still used. Sir Joseph, who came of a family of inventors, early showed a taste for chemistry and was apprenticed in the chemical business of Mawson in Newcastle. He became a partner in that firm, and after a long and useful life, in the course of which he received many honors, he died, at the age of 86 years, on May 27, 1914.

Thomas A. Edison (1847-1931) was born at Milan, Ohio, but spent most of his boyhood at Port Huron, Mich. He was a very enterprising boy, highly interested in chemistry. To earn money for his chemical experiments, he obtained a concession for a paper route on the Grand Trunk Railway. He also started two stores in Port Huron, one for periodicals, the other for vegetables, and hired a newsboy to work the Detroit train. All this before he was 15 years old! To report the battle of Shiloh in 1862, he borrowed enough money of the editorial office of the Detroit Free Press to buy a thousand papers, and sold them all from the train, some at 25 cents a paper. He fixed up a part of a baggage car for chemical experiments, and also set up there a small printing press. As reporter, editor, printer, and news agent he himself published a sheet called "The Weekly Herald," and sold over 400 copies a month. Unfortunately a stick of phosphorus among his chemicals took fire one day and threatened to burn the baggage car, whereupon the conductor of the train ejected boy, laboratory, and printing plant. The deafness that affected Edison throughout his whole life was caused about the same time by his being lifted into his box-car laboratory by his ears by a well-meaning friend.

That same year, 1862, young Edison was so fortunate as to save the life of a little son of Mr. Mackenzie, a station agent. Out of gratitude, the father taught Edison more of the art of train telegraphy, of which he already knew something. His first job in telegraphy was at Port Huron, and soon after, at 16 years of age, he was made night operator at Stratford Junction, on the Grand Trunk Railway in Ontario. Owing to a narrow escape from an accident, which was thought by officials to involve some blame on Edison's part, he left Canada and soon after obtained work as a night operator at Adrian, Mich. Thence he went from place to place, working up speed and experience, till at length he entered the employ of the Western Union Telegraph Company at Indianapolis. Edison became an exceptionally fast telegraph operator, but again by his chemical experiments he caused trouble and was discharged.

He next went to Boston and there got telegraphic work which kept him from starving while he began his inventive career. His first considerable invention was a stock ticker, to dispose of which he removed to New York. His ingenuity attracted attention, and he soon formed the partnership of Pope, Edison & Company to develop some of his inventions. For his improvements on the stock ticker, Edison was paid $40,000 by the Western

Union Telegraph Company, and then, in 1870, he opened a large shop in Newark, N. J., to make stock tickers for the Western Union. Thus, at only 23 years of age Edison was a successful inventor and manufacturer.

His telegraphic experience gave the bent to his early inventions. Improvements on the printing telegraph and duplex and quadruplex telegraphy occupied him till 1873. His quadruplex invention was bought by Jay Gould for $30,000.

After his first marriage in 1871, Edison removed in 1876 to Menlo Park, N. J., a little town ever to be celebrated as the scene of his famous demonstration of the practicability of the incandescent electric light. Despite the skeptical attitude of many able physicists and engineers, Edison was firmly convinced that the future of electric lighting lay not in the powerful and unwieldy arc, but in the small incandescent lamp, adapted to replace gas lighting in dwellings and offices, and like the gas jet, capable of being turned on and off at pleasure. After familiarizing himself with the whole state of the art of lighting, both by electricity and gas, and the best means of furnishing electric power, he began his experiments.

Edison had gathered about him a devoted band of young assistants, whom he did not hesitate to drive day and night by his own example. Of powerful and enduring physique, he seemed able to go almost without sleep, yet could sleep instantly at any time he pleased. For many years his working schedule averaged more than 18 hours a day. Many a night he merely lay down upon a table top for a few minutes, and then pressed on with his work. His indefatigability in experimentation, in the course of which he would try everything that could be tried, was finally rewarded by success.

Edison first tried innumerable experiments with fibers of carbonized wood and other organic substances in evacuated glass bulbs. But these fibers proved in this series of experiments to be so short-lived as to be worthless.

THE ELECTRIC LIGHT

Then he went over to refractory metals—platinum, iridium, and alloys. In association with them he tried bobbins of rare earths, and in this series he made 1,600 tests of various materials. He gained experience in producing high vacua, but no real success in lamps, and finally he went back to carbon. On October 21, 1879, a carbonized cotton thread in high vacuum attained a life of 40 hours. This was hopeful, but the lamp was too fragile to be commercially successful.

He went on carbonizing substance after substance. Filaments of Bristol board cut to form, and carbonized by prolonged baking at high temperatures, gave so great a measure of success as to bring out the famous news article in the New York Herald of Sunday, December 21, 1879.

EDISON'S LIGHT

The Great Inventor's Triumph in
Electric Illumination

A SCRAP OF PAPER

It Makes a Light, Without Gas or
Flame, Cheaper Than Oil

TRANSFORMED IN THE FURNACE

Complete Details of the Perfected
Carbon Lamp

FIFTEEN MONTHS OF TOIL

Story of His Tireless Experiments with Lamps,
Burners and Generators

SUCCESS IN A COTTON THREAD

The Wizard's Byplay, with Bodily Pain
and Gold "Tailings"

HISTORY OF ELECTRIC LIGHTING

The near approach of the first public exhibition of Edison's long looked for electric light, announced to take place on New Year's Eve at Menlo Park, on which occasion that place will be illuminated with the new light, has revived public interest in the great inventor's work.

and throughout the civilized world scientists and people generally are anxiously awaiting the result. From the beginning of his experiments in electric lighting to the present time Mr. Edison has kept his laboratory guardedly closed, and no authoritative account (except that published in the HERALD some months ago relating to his first patent) of any of the important steps of his progress has been made public—a course of procedure the inventor found absolutely necessary for his own protection. The HERALD is now, however, enabled to present to its readers a full and accurate account of his work from its inception to its completion.

A LIGHTED PAPER

Edison's electric light, incredible as it may appear, is produced from a little piece of paper—a tiny strip of paper that a breath would blow away. Through this little strip of paper is passed an electric current, and the result is a bright, beautiful light, like the mellow sunset of an Italian autumn.

"But paper instantly burns, even under the trifling heat of a tallow candle!" exclaims the sceptic, "and how, then, can it withstand the fierce heat of an electric current?" Very true, but Edison makes the little piece of paper more infusible than platinum, more durable than granite. And this involves no complicated process. The paper is merely baked in an oven until all its elements have passed away except its carbon framework. The latter is then placed in a glass globe connected with the wires leading to the electricity producing machine, and the air exhausted from the globe. Then the apparatus is ready to give out a light that produces no deleterious gases, no smoke, no offensive odors—a light without flame, without danger, requiring no matches to ignite, giving out but little heat, vitiating no air, and free from all flickering; a light that is a little globe of sunshine, a veritable Aladdin's lamp. And this light, the inventor claims, can be produced cheaper than that from the cheapest oil. . . . . . .

The Herald's account of "lights strung on wires" so caught the public fancy that the fame of the "Wizard of Menlo Park," already noted for his phonograph, was greatly enhanced.

The Pennsylvania Railroad ran special trains to Menlo Park to see Edison's marvel of the incandescent electric light. Plate 41, left, shows one of the earliest forms, now on exhibition in the United States National Museum. Yet carbonized paper did not seem to be quite the thing for filaments, and it occurred to Edison that the bamboo

PLATE 40

Thomas A. Edison. Courtesy of F. A. Wardlaw, Secretary, Edison
Pioneers

PLATE 41

Left: Edison's basic patented incandescent electric lamp. Facsimile now exhibited in the National Museum. Patented January 27, 1880. Right: General Electric monster and pygmy incandescent electric lamps of 1931

rim of the ordinary palm-leaf fan might furnish the lamp fiber he had so long sought. Upon being tested, it proved to be much superior to all preceding substances. Not content, he ransacked the world's original sources for the species of bamboo most suitable for his lamps. He spent $100,000 in expeditions and tests. A Japanese farmer got a contract to supply the kind of bamboo finally chosen.

One of Edison's emissaries named McGowan, who searched Peru, Ecuador, and Colombia for vegetable fibers, after traveling for 98 days through jungles swarming with wild beasts, venomous snakes, and insects, at length returned at the end of 15 months to New York. After giving his friends an account vivid with adventure, he bade them good night at a New York restaurant and vanished, never again to be seen. The following extract from the New York Evening Sun of May 2, 1889, gives a glimpse of McGowan's experiences.

Going up the Amazon you meet nothing but yellow water and dense forests. The banks of the river are lined with alligators. Fifty-two alligators were shot one morning from the steamer's deck. In former years grape shot was sometimes fired on Indians assembled on the river banks. Now matters are much reversed. The Indians amuse themselves by making a target of the Brazilian gunboats and literally deluge them with showers of arrows. The Indians shoot these arrows with such terrific force as to send them through the steamship's hull. I shall never forget my own experience. It was like peril dropping out of a clear sky. We were lazily engaged one sunny afternoon in dragging out an existence on the steamship's deck, when suddenly from out of the forest came a volley of arrows. Some of these arrows penetrated the woodwork. Their bows are at least eight feet long and at the middle are as thick as my wrist. I could not bend one of them. The strings are made of the bark of trees. The arrows are about five feet in length and are invariably tipped with poison.

. . . . . .

From Iquitos I struck out on foot across the country accompanied by three Inca Indians. I carried 300 South American silver dollars under my arm in a tin box that weighed about twenty-five pounds. Every time those coins jingled I noticed the Indians exchange significant glances, and I was in mortal dread to go to sleep nights. Once I was suddenly awakened by a fierce growl.'"" Dancing about me I saw one of the Indians, who pulled and tugged at me roughly, and pointing into the forest said in Spanish, "Big tiger!" The following morning we reached the Napo river and poled up the stream in canoes many miles. At night we camped on the shore, sleeping on the wet banks. Twelve times during our journey the river rose so high that our party was washed off the banks while sleeping.

In going down the River Santiago we encountered river snakes fifteen feet long and six inches in diameter. It was now the rainy season and we could not sleep at night, for every two hours or so we had to bail out the canoes. The temperature was 100 to 102 and our clothes fairly steamed from moisture. We encountered millions of sand flies which got in our eyes, ears and hair. The river is full of fish, and frequently in the morning we found fish in the bottom of the canoe which jumped in during the night.

I struck out on one trip for the Western Cordilleras, where I went into camp for twenty-seven days. A party of Peons accompanied me. I had the greatest difficulty in holding them, as they were terribly afraid of wild animals, and the woods were full of them. At night we were obliged to keep an immense fire blazing to keep them off, and even then we could hear them roaring uncomfortably near us. At midnight June 29, 1888, we were rudely shaken in our sleep by an earthquake. It made the mountains tremble. The Peons were instantly up and on their knees praying to their patron saint. Much of my valuable material which I collected for Mr. Edison was found in the Cordilleras, and I do not begrudge the hardships I endured.

In Edison's first successful lamps, the oval loops of carbonized paper were secured by little platinum clamps to platinum wires sealed through the glass. The early lamps were of uneven life but averaged 300 hours. The first considerable installation of them was made at the request of Henry Villard on the steamship *Columbia* for the Oregon Railway and Navigation Company, of which Villard was president. She carried 115 lamps of 10 candlepower, and made the journey round the Horn to Oregon, arriving July 26, 1880, with the new illumination proved to be a great success. The first lamps required 4.9 watts of energy per candle. A modern Mazda C lamp, gas filled, uses from 3/10 watt per candle upwards, depending on the power, and has a life of 1,000 hours. We shall trace some of the steps in this improvement.

THE ELECTRIC LIGHT

Among the most perfect accessories of the incandescent lamp was the Edison screw socket, which became nearly universal not only for lamps, but for all sorts of electrical appliances. Various other lamp-supporting devices were invented by other makers to avoid the Edison patents, but they have nearly all disappeared. In later constructions, cheaper metals and welded joints were substituted for the costly platinum lead wires and screw clamps. The carbonized bamboo filaments continued till 1894, when carbonized squirted cellulose replaced them. These, in turn, were replaced about 1908 by tantalum and later tungsten, of which another story must be told.

Hardly had the search for a fiber reached success before Edison and his band of workers turned with the same untiring ardor to prepare the means for providing and subdividing the current. Not content with the direct-current dynamos then available, Edison constructed a type characterized by very long electromagnets for the field, as shown in Plate 42. He obtained a high efficiency for that time, though greatly improved dynamos came from other inventors about the same time.

He had preferred fibers of high electric resistance for his lamps because that made possible economy in copper. His idea was to provide a central electric power station, from which would go out conductors to convey the current to the lamps in houses and offices. In order to avoid relatively great loss of power in long transmission lines, the resistance of such lines had to be small compared with the resistance of the lamps. If the lamps had small resistance, the copper wires would have to be of large diameter and costly. On the other hand, if the lamps had a very high resistance, a dangerously high voltage would be required to make them incandescent.

As a compromise, Edison fixed on 110-volt circuits, which voltage has remained the standard to this day. The device of the three-wire system occurred to him as another means of saving copper. It was, of course, necessary for practical reasons to have the lamps connected in parallel as the rounds of a ladder are connected to its two sides. For if in series, like a ring of people joining hands, all the lamps would have to burn at once—if one failed the whole series would be in darkness. In the three-wire system, the two outside mains were 220 volts apart. The middle wire acted both as negative pole for one bank of lights and positive pole for the others. If the lights were of equal numbers in the two banks, no current at all would flow in the middle wire. Even if the numbers of lights were not quite equal, the current in the middle wire was so much less than those in the two outside mains that a much smaller middle copper wire would serve.

During 1880 and 1881, Edison was assembling engines, dynamos, lamps, underground feeders and mains, switches, meters, sockets, and the thousand and one accessories for the first central lighting station in New York. This he located on Pearl Street, and arranged to supply from it a square mile extending from Spruce to Wall Street and from the East River to Nassau Street. On September 4, 1882, the current was turned on for the first regular distribution of light. Thirty-five years later a bronze tablet was placed on the building at 257 Pearl Street bearing this inscription:

1882   1917
IN A BUILDING ON THIS SITE AN ELECTRIC
PLANT SUPPLYING THE FIRST EDISON
UNDERGROUND CENTRAL STATION SYSTEM
IN THIS COUNTRY AND FORMING THE ORIGIN
OF NEW YORK'S PRESENT ELECTRICAL SYSTEM
BEGAN OPERATION ON SEPT. 4, 1882
ACCORDING TO PLANS CONCEIVED AND
EXECUTED BY
THOMAS ALVA EDISON
TO COMMEMORATE AN EPOCH-MAKING EVENT
THIS TABLET IS ERECTED BY
THE AMERICAN SCENIC AND HISTORIC
PRESERVATION SOCIETY
THE NEW YORK EDISON COMPANY

PLATE 42

Edison dynamo used on the S. S. Columbia, 1880. Now in the
National Museum.

PLATE 43

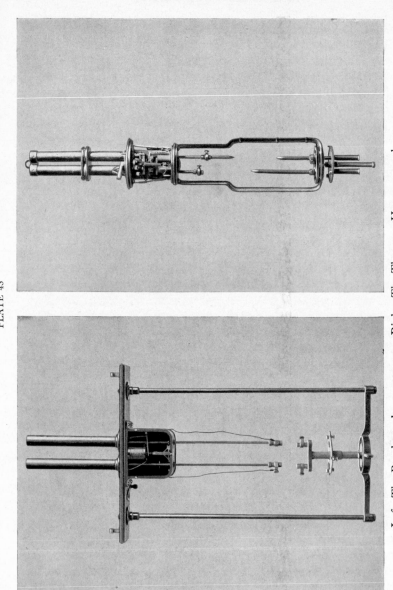

Left: The Brush arc lamp support. Right: The Thomson-Houston arc lamp support

THE ELECTRIC LIGHT

At the present time nearly a billion incandescent electric lamps are in use in the United States, and they have nearly driven arc lighting from the field. But the tremendous increase of incandescent lamps in late years has been due to the improvements in tungsten filament lamps, to which we will now turn.

From Edison's manufacturing enterprises grew the General Electric Company with headquarters at Schenectady, N. Y., and many branches and connections in the United States and abroad. This company established a great laboratory where many improvements in electrical appliances and discoveries in pure science have been made under the inspiring direction of Dr. Willis R. Whitney. It was Dr. William D. Coolidge of the General Electric Laboratory who made tungsten available for electric lighting.

It will be recalled that Edison in 1878 and 1879 had made many experiments with wires of the platinum group, including osmium, iridium, and others. The metal tungsten does not fall in the group with platinum but is, next to uranium, the heaviest element of that group of chemical elements which contains oxygen and chromium. Tungsten melts at 3400° C. while platinum melts at 1755°. Hence as a lamp filament, tungsten runs none of the danger of melting when brightly incandescent, which, together with costliness, made platinum impossible.

Tungsten had been known since about 1780, but had been little used except in alloys of steel. As a metal it was known to be extremely hard, but so brittle that it seemed quite impossible to draw it into wire. Two Austrian chemists, Just and Hanaman, had indeed prepared incandescent tungsten filaments in 1904, by mixing tungsten dust with organic matter, carbonizing the latter, and sintering the tungsten particles together by heat and pressure in presence of hydrogen. These lamps, though very fragile, were of high luminous efficiency, and immediately became popular after their general introduction in 1907 and 1908.

W. D. Coolidge, assistant director of the General Electric Laboratory, after several years of experimenting, aided by his associates, succeeded about 1912 in producing ductile tungsten which could be drawn into the finest of wires, and wound in close spirals. As nearly all modern incandescent lamps and electron tubes are constructed with ductile tungsten filaments and grid wires, this discovery is one of the most useful of recent times. The process invented by Coolidge and his associates of the General Electric Company is as follows:

First of all, it is desirable to begin with exceptionally pure tungsten. The ductility of tungsten is greatly diminished by very slight admixtures of impurities. This also holds true with other metals. Gold, for instance, that when pure may be beaten almost inconceivably thin, is rendered brittle by as little as 0.05 per cent of lead, bismuth, or tin, and is no longer malleable when it contains no more than 0.0003 per cent of antimony. Hence the first step toward ductile tungsten is purification. Tungsten may be prepared from its ores by first converting them to tungstic acid, a heavy yellow powder. From this substance is prepared ammonium tungstate, which must be purified to the highest degree by recrystallization. When this product is heated to a certain degree, the ammonia is driven off, and tungstic acid in purest form remains. By heating this for five hours in a crucible of the proper composition, alumina and silica as desirable impurities are added to the extent of about one per cent. The tungstic acid is then reduced to metallic tungsten by heating gradually to redness in a current of hydrogen. The metal has normally a bright metallic luster like platinum, but when finely powdered, it is black.

The material is made up into rods by pressing the powdered metal into molds and raising it in a hydrogen atmosphere to a bright red heat. This consolidates the powder so much that it can be heated electrically in a hydrogen atmosphere to blinding white heat, and thus sintered firmly into a billet for mechanical working. The metal can now be worked mechanically at high temperatures. As the working process proceeds by the forcing of the billet through swaging dies, the ductility increases. At length, at lower and lower temperatures, the metal may be drawn out into fine wires. The die used for this process is drilled diamond. The wires produced are so pliable that they may be wound in small spirals and used for any kind of bends. Indeed, the tensile strength of tungsten in this form is as great as that of steel.

Some time after the general introduction of tungsten filaments for incandescent electric lamps, Langmuir discovered the advantage of introducing nitrogen or argon gas into the bulb. Either gas is inert and does not destroy the filament as atmospheric oxygen would destroy a carbon filament, for instance. In such a gaseous medium the evaporation of the tungsten filament is diminished. Hence, the time when the lamp bulb is darkened by deposited tungsten is postponed and the life of the lamp extended. On the other hand, the amount of current required to maintain a certain brilliance is increased, because the gas carries away the heat by convection. Langmuir's device is most efficient for high-candlepower lamps, because with filaments of larger diameter, other losses are greater in proportion to convective losses than with small filaments. In small lamps with fine filaments, the loss in light efficiency tends to overbalance the gain in longer life.

As remarked above, the advent of the high-candlepower gas-filled incandescent tungsten lamp greatly reduced the field of arc lighting, which at the beginning of the century monopolized the illumination of streets, stores, factories, and large halls. From 1877, when the arc system of Charles F. Brush appeared, and in 1878 when the Thomson-Houston arc was introduced, the electric arc for illumination was more and more improved in its regulation and efficiency by numerous inventors. Plate 43 shows the Brush and Thomson-Houston arc supports. The tight enclosure of the arc in a glass globe, introduced by L. B. Marks in 1893, increased manifold the duration of the carbons and decreased accordingly the care of maintenance. Prior to that time the carbons were rapidly burnt away by the free attack of the oxygen of the air. In Germany, Bremer in 1898 produced the flaming arc, in which the carbons were impregnated by calcium fluoride. Other chemical salts have been used to increase the luminosity of the arc, and with particularly notable success by the Sperry Company. For searchlights, the arc will probably never be displaced, and at the present time very high efficiency in this field is obtained.

CHAPTER VII

PRIME MOVERS

THE machine age is an age of power. Man power, horse power, the leisurely overshot water wheels found here and there in brooks and small rivers a couple of generations ago, and even the reciprocating steam engines of those days are largely superseded. Swifter and stronger genii such as the gasoline engine, the water turbine, and the steam and mercury turbines have been called forth to excite the master spirit, electricity, that does nearly all things in our time.

Some think machinery is a curse, and praise the good old days. The curse is found in three aspects of the wide-spread use of machinery, which no doubt will be removed in the future. These are: the noisy rush; the subdivision of labor into partial operations, senseless by themselves, which take away the pride of craftsmanship; and the suffering which comes when labor-saving machines throw workers out of employment. Inventions and the segregation of noisy operations can mitigate the hubbub. The evils of the subdivision and of the superseding of labor will both be cured sometime by social reorganization. Progress is needed more in this field than in any other at the present time.

The machine age has advanced too rapidly to allow the required changes in social organization to keep pace with it. Evils grow to large proportions before their cure is discovered and applied. A century hence, the historian may be able to trace the steps which led society from the difficulties attending the first rapid rush of the introduction of new forces in our time to their happy solution by the following generations. In principle, the progress of invention and the bounty of nature, both tending to diminish necessary labor, are good. We do not work for work's sake, but for the sake of the comforts it brings, the mental pleasure it affords, and the physical well-being it promotes.

If invention and nature's fertility together could relieve the world of nine tenths of the present work, interesting occupations might still be retained. Handicrafts, for instance, could be preserved, not because they are indispensable, but because they are enjoyable exercises of skill, productive of exceptionally fine artistry. Athletic occupations would be retained because they develop health. But under a proper social system for the distribution of goods to all who need them, the abolition of nine tenths of the world's work ought not to produce suffering. Nor in the society of the future ought individuals to be forced to do one sort of drudgery throughout their working lives. A rotation of occupations ought to be provided. Other societies have existed happily with all their wants supplied without much labor. Consider, for instance, the birds that sing and frolic in the air. Man ought not to be so dull that a plentiful supply of good things merely multiples poverty and suffering for a large portion of his race.

Before the war mechanical energy amounting to about 100,000,000 horsepower was produced in the United States, of which one third was hydroelectric and two thirds came from the combustion of coal and oil. Of the larger fractional part produced by fuel, about nine tenths came from coal and one tenth from oil and gas. These immense quantities of power were produced mainly by the water turbine, the reciprocating steam engine, the steam turbine, and the internal combustion reciprocating engine.

Prime movers may use energy of position or energy of

PLATE 44

Impulse water turbine. Bucket wheel for 56,000 h.p., 2,200-feet head, 250 r.p.m. Courtesy of the Allis-Chalmers Manufacturing Company

PLATE 45

Single steel casting, 52½ tons, the runner for 70,000 h.p. turbine. Courtesy of the Niagara Falls Power Company

motion or both. To illustrate, in the old overshot water wheel a very large diameter was used. The water from the surface of the pond came over the top of the wheel into its buckets, which were gradually lowered to the bottom as the wheel turned. Practically all the energy of the high position of the water was thus given over to turning the wheel and its connected machinery. In the old undershot wheel, on the other hand, the water spurting out at the bottom of the dam gave up most of its energy of motion to the paddles of the wheel.

WATER POWER

Power from flowing water is now produced principally either by the Pelton wheel or by impulse or reaction water turbines. There is little difference in principle between the Pelton wheel and the impulse turbine, though the latter has a plurality of nozzles for the impinging water. The Pelton wheel is particularly adapted to small streams falling great distances. In Switzerland there are found such installations with a head of more than a mile in the fall of water. A pipe to confine the water brings it to the wheel, where the pipe is constricted to a nozzle out of which the water issues with great velocity. It then impinges on shovel-like blades or buckets of specially designed curvature set radially on the outside of the wheel.

Plate 44, illustrating an impulse turbine wheel, shows the peculiar shape of the buckets. The area of the buckets is about 10 times the area of the cross-section of the water jet. The curvature of the buckets is such that the water does not splash or spatter excessively but is gradually slowed up nearly to zero velocity as it turns the wheel. A rule usually followed is to make the diameter of the wheel in feet not less than the diameter of the nozzle in inches. Theoretically, the speed of the wheel at its circumference should be one-half the speed of the jet. In practice, a well-designed Pelton wheel has a peripheral speed of 0.47 of the jet velocity. From 75 to 85 per cent of the energy of the jet is made available by a modern Pelton wheel.

The regulation of the water to suit variations in the load is somewhat difficult. The flow can indeed be checked by screwing forward a needle valve so as partially to close the nozzle. But a quick reduction of flow would be apt to produce a dangerous water hammer in the pipe, somewhat similar in nature to the water hammer often heard in steam radiators in which water is condensed, but far more powerful. To avoid this, the jet is often arranged to be deflected so as not to impinge centrally upon the wheel buckets. The deflection and the valving are made to co-operate so that the rapid adjustment to suit a quick diminution of load is first made by deflecting the jet, and then the appropriate reduction of the water flow by the valve is made slowly, with a simultaneous gradual restoration of the jet till it again impinges centrally.

When the head of water is more moderate and the volume of the flow is large, as at Niagara, some other form of water turbine is usually preferred. Turbines are classed as reaction or impulse, according to whether they operate by steady pressure, or (like the Pelton wheel) by the energy of the flow of water. In reaction turbines the water is deflected by a complete encirclement of curved fixed guides onto curved vanes fastened to the circumference of a rotating wheel called the runner. The runner and deflectors are encased in a steel casing tightly fitting so that all the water must flow past the vanes. In most machines the axis is vertical, and the water may either flow vertically down the axis or radially inward or radially outward to produce its effect on the curving vanes. In the first case the shape of the vanes is somewhat like that of a screw propeller. In certain mixed types the water flow enters radially inward from the fixed vanes, is curved downward by the upper rotating vanes, and leaves the runner nearly vertically between screw-shaped lower rotating vanes.

PLATE 46

Niagara Falls.   Butterfly valve to control water flow.   Courtesy of the
Niagara Falls Power Company

PLATE 47

Niagara Falls. 70,000 h.p. turbine runner. Courtesy of the Niagara Falls Power Company

PLATE 48

Niagara Falls. Castings being assembled to form wheel casing. Diameter of left-hand opening 15 feet. Whole diameter 47 feet. Penstock shown in the background. Courtesy of the Niagara Falls Power Company

PLATE 49

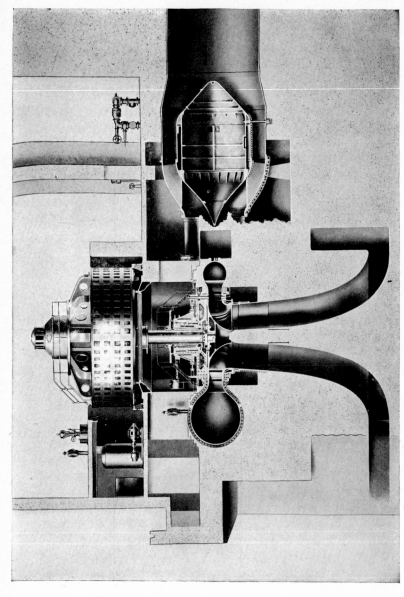

Niagara Falls. Sectional view of 70,000 h.p. turbine. Courtesy of the Niagara Falls Power Company

The inward-flow turbine is preferred on account of the greater compactness of construction of its runner.

In the vertical-reaction turbine the passages are filled with water at all times. However, the outflow tube, called the draft, is of enlarged size and of a downward curving siphon form, so that a partial vacuum may be produced beneath the runner. Yet the machine works nearly as efficiently when fully submerged. Thus it is adaptable to great differences in the water level of the discharge, such as occur with the spring freshets.

The impulse turbine differs from the Pelton wheel only in that it operates by the impinging of many jets of water from fixed guides onto curved vanes all around the circumference of the runner. It can not work submerged but must be so high that it is never reached by the level of the discharge. In the United States the impulse turbine is little used, for under the circumstances most favorable to it the Pelton wheel is preferred.

Among the great hydroelectric power installations the most interesting on account of location is at Niagara Falls. The Governments of the United States and Great Britain, solicitous to preserve the grandeur of the Falls and the navigation of the Great Lakes, prohibited any increase in the volume of water diverted for power purposes for several years after 1905 until an international committee should report on the subject. In accord with the findings of the International Waterways Commission in the Boundary Water Treaty of 1910 between the United States and Great Britain, "the high contracting parties agree that it is expedient to limit the diversion of waters from the Niagara River so that the level of Lake Erie and the flow of the stream shall not be appreciably affected." Having regard for vested rights in diversions already made, the treaty provides that the limit of diversions for power purposes shall be 20,000 cubic feet per second from the American side and 36,000 cubic feet per second from the Canadian side.

These limitations tend to keep the operation of the power plants at considerably below their combined capacity. The Edward Dean Adams plant on the American side, with a capacity of 105,000 horsepower, is at times held in reserve for emergencies. The total capacity of all the active plants is now: American side, 452,500 horsepower; Canadian side, 1,098,950 horsepower. A considerable part of the power manufactured in Canada is used in the State of New York.

The active American-side power plants are the three units of the Schoelkopf Station of the Niagara Falls Power Company, named after Jacob F. Schoelkopf. He, with associates, organized the Niagara Falls Hydraulic and Manufacturing Company, the forerunner of the present company, and purchased in 1877 the hydraulic canal which had been constructed by Woodhull, Bryant, and others about 1853. This canal, starting near Port Day, above the American Falls, runs across the country about a mile to a point on the Gorge about a mile below the Falls. Originally a small canal, it has been broadened and deepened to 100 feet wide and 20 feet deep. In addition, a tunnel 32 feet in diameter runs from Port Day to Schoelkopf 3C station. Inclined penstocks lead down to the bottom of the Gorge to the turbines of the three Schoelkopf stations. They contain, respectively, thirteen 10,000-horsepower units, three 37,500-horsepower units, and three 70,000-horsepower units. The turbines are double-runner Francis type, horizontal-axis machines, operating under about 210-feet head. They actuate direct-connected generators furnishing 12,000-volt, three-phase, 25-cycle alternating current. Power from American and Canadian sources is transmitted as far south as Bradford, Pa., and as far east as Syracuse, N. Y.

On the Canadian side the Toronto Power Company, the Ontario Power Company, and the Hydro-Electric Power Commission of Ontario have a combined capacity of 869,-350 horsepower. The Hydro-Electric Power Commission

PLATE 50

Niagara Falls. Interior of Schoelkopf Station. Three 37,500 h.p. generators in the foreground, three of 70,000 h.p. at the rear. Courtesy of the Niagara Falls Power Company

PLATE 51

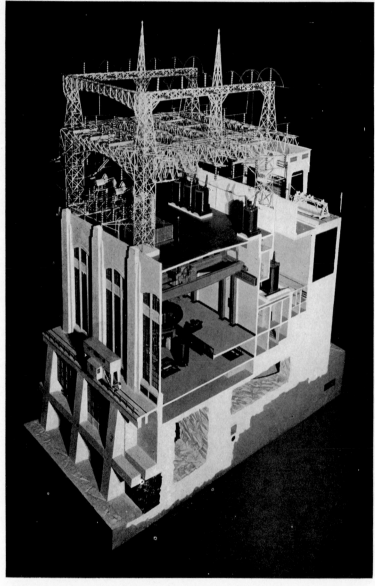

Conowingo power and distributing station. Model in the National Museum of 378,000 h.p. hydroelectric station on the Susquehanna River has the latest and by far the most powerful of all the plants. They take the water from near the mouth of the Welland River and transmit it by canal 8 miles to a point on the lower Niagara Gorge only 2 miles above Queenston. In this way they obtain a head of 305 feet. Their installation comprises five 55,000-horsepower units and four 58,000-horsepower units of vertical shaft, single-runner Francis turbines, driving five 45,000 and four 55,000 KVA direct-connected generators of 12,000 volts, three-phase, 25 cycles. The voltage is stepped up to 110,000 volts, and current is supplied to municipalities in Western Ontario under public ownership auspices.

Plates 45–50 illustrate some of the interesting features of the hydroelectric power installations at Niagara Falls.

Plate 51 shows a model in the United States National Museum of the Conowingo hydroelectric installation on the Susquehanna River.

HEAT POWER

The conversion of heat energy into mechanical energy is accomplished through the expansion of gases. Heat may be developed by an outside boiler, or within the engine by explosion. Water heated by coal is used principally in the former case, and fuel oil or gasoline in the latter. Water boils at higher and higher temperatures as the pressure upon it increases, as is shown by the following table which starts with atmospheric pressure.

Pressure, lbs. per sq. in.	15	23	35	52	75	106	145	196	258	336	430
Boiling temperature F.	212°	236°	260°	284°	308°	332°	356°	380°	404°	428°	452°

Steam in presence of boiling water at whatever temperature is called saturated steam, and it contains droplets of water thrown up by ebulition. Engine boilers usually have special pipes in which the steam is superheated to evaporate the contained water, and the steam freed from

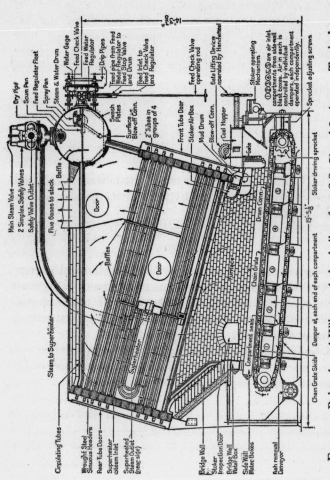

FIG. 32. Babcock and Wilcox tubular boiler; from S.S. *City of Saginaw.* Typical installation of 1929. Chain grate stoker, 5,190 square feet boiler surface, 315 pounds working steam pressure

water is called dry steam. Condensation by cooling within the engine is one of the difficulties in steam engineering.

Steam boilers are of two types, called water-tube and fire-tube boilers. In the former the water to be boiled is contained in part in the bottom of a nearly horizontal cylinder, in which the steam occupies the top. The remainder of the water is contained in a circulatory system of numerous inclined pipes which are bathed by the heated air and other gases from the fire. Figure 32 shows a Babcock and Wilcox tubular boiler of this type photographed from the collection of the United States National Museum.

In the fire-tube boiler there are no water tubes. The heated gases are drawn by strong draft through and through tubes which honeycomb lengthwise the cylinder containing the water and steam. This type is used on locomotive engines.

Steam under the high pressure produced by the high temperature of the boiler contains much potential mechanical energy. It is like a drawn bow ready to let fly the arrow. When a fixed quantity of steam is admitted and allowed to expand against a piston within a cylinder, the useful work is measured by the product of the pressure into the change of volume. But since the pressure continually falls as the steam expands, the measurement of work is not a simple matter of arithmetic, but involves calculus. We shall, therefore, refer interested readers to treatises on thermodynamics for the demonstration of the curious and important formulae which lie at the basis of steam engineering, and indeed of internal combustion engineering also. Yet there are certain conclusions of great interest which we can hardly pass over.

All heat engines are subject to the law proved a century ago by the distinguished French physicist, Nicholas Leonard Sadi Carnot, who died in 1832 at the early age of 36 years. His "Reflexions sur la puissance motice du feu," published in 1824, contained the demonstration of his famous "cycle," wherein he shows what is the maximum possible efficiency for the absolutely perfect heat engine, which, of course, is not reached by actual heat engines of any kind. In a later expression of it, after Sir William Thomson had introduced his absolute temperature scale, the maximum efficiency is stated as the difference between the temperatures of heat received and heat rejected divided by the absolute temperature at which heat is received by the working medium used in the engine.

To illustrate, suppose a steam engine receiving steam at 600° F. or 1060° Abs. F. rejects its steam by condensation at 100° F. or 560° Abs. F. Then if the engine were absolutely without losses by friction or mechanical inefficiency of any sort, its highest possible efficiency in the use of the steam to produce mechanical work would be $\frac{1060-560}{1060}$, or 47 per cent. It might be supposed that internal combustion engines would not be subject to Carnot's principle, but actually they are. All heat engines of whatever nature are limited in their maximum efficiency by this consideration of temperatures.

It is clear, therefore, that the higher the temperature from which an engine can work, and the lower the temperature of its exhaust, the greater its possible efficiency. High initial temperature of their exploded gases is one cause of the high efficiency of gasoline and oil engines. Another favorable factor for the economy of fuel in these engines is the combustion of fuel within the engine itself, instead of in a separate boiler, so that no loss occurs in heat transportation. The late Doctor Emmet of the General Electric Company devoted much time and thought to the successful development of a new form of turbine engine in which mercury vapor is employed instead of steam and used at a much higher initial temperature than will ever be possible with steam, because steam dissociates at 700° F. In this way Doctor Emmet obtained an efficiency practically as high as that of the gasoline engine, or even the Diesel oil engine.

Good bituminous coal produces about 14,000 British thermal units of heat per pound, and gasoline and heavy fuel oils produce from 18,500 to 20,500 of these heat units per pound. This is equivalent to saying that to burn completely a pound of coal will produce heat enough to warm 14,000 pounds of water 1° F. It was shown by the experiments of Prof. H. A. Rowland, of Baltimore, about the year 1875, that 1 British thermal unit of heat is produced by the expenditure of 777.5 foot-pounds of work. A horsepower is equal to 550 foot-pounds of work per second. The best recent engine practice employs a combination of the mercury turbine and steam turbine so as to use advantageously for steam the heat rejected from the mercury. A mercury steam installation has recently produced mechanical energy at the rate of 2,600,000 foot-pounds per 7,000,000 foot-pounds mechanical equivalent combustion value of coal. This gives 37 per cent efficiency—comparable, as we shall see, with the Diesel oil internal combustion engine.

Steam Engines

Prior to the inventions of James Watt the steam engine (then called fire-engine) had been constructed by Thomas Newcomen for pumping. In Newcomen's device, steam at about atmospheric pressure pushed upward a piston in a vertical cylinder. At the top of the cylinder a jet of cold water was thrown into the steam within the cylinder under the piston, thus condensing it, and the weight of the atmosphere brought the piston down. At the bottom, steam was again allowed to enter, driving out the water and raising the piston a second time.

James Watt (1736–1819), having been engaged to repair a Newcomen engine, perceived the great waste of heat involved by cooling the cylinder and piston with water each time the steam was condensed. His patent of 1769 is so revolutionary and so clearly expressed that it will be of prime interest to quote from it the first four and the last claims.

My method of lessening the consumption of steam, and consequently fuel, in fire-engines, consists of the following principles:—

First, That vessel in which the powers of steam are to be employed to work the engine, which is called the cylinder in common fire-engines, and which I call the steam-vessel, must, during the whole time the engine is at work, be kept as hot as the steam that enters it; first by enclosing it in a case of wood, or any other materials that transmit heat slowly; secondly, by surrounding it with steam or other heated bodies; and, thirdly, by suffering neither water nor any other substance colder than the steam to enter or touch it during that time.

Secondly, In engines that are to be worked wholly or partially by condensation of steam, the steam is to be condensed in vessels distinct from the steam-vessels or cylinders, although, occasionally communicating with them; these vessels I call condensers; and, whilst the engines are working, these condensers ought at least to be kept as cold as the air in the neighbourhood of the engines, by application of water or other cold bodies.

Thirdly, Whatever air or other elastic vapour is not condensed by the cold of the condenser, and may impede the working of the engine, is to be drawn out of the steam-vessels or condensers by means of pumps, wrought by the engines themselves, or otherwise.

Fourthly, I intend in many cases to employ the expansive force of steam to press on the pistons, or whatever may be used instead of them, in the same manner in which the pressure of the atmosphere is now employed in common fire-engines. In cases where cold water cannot be had in plenty, the engines may be wrought by this force of steam only, by discharging the steam into the air after it has done its office. . . .

Lastly, Instead of using water to render the pistons and other parts of the engine air and steam tight, I employ oils, wax, resinous bodies, fat of animals, quicksilver and other metals in their fluid state.

Thus we see that Watt introduced the separate, cooled condenser, and the vacuum applied thereto. He also introduced the insulated steam jacket to retain the heat of the cylinder. He also suggests the use of steam to force back the piston after it has made its upward stroke, i.e., the double-acting engine, and proposes both condensing and noncondensing engines. We still see in the modern locomotive a noncondensing engine. He also avoided

PLATE 52

James Watt

PLATE 53

George H. Corliss

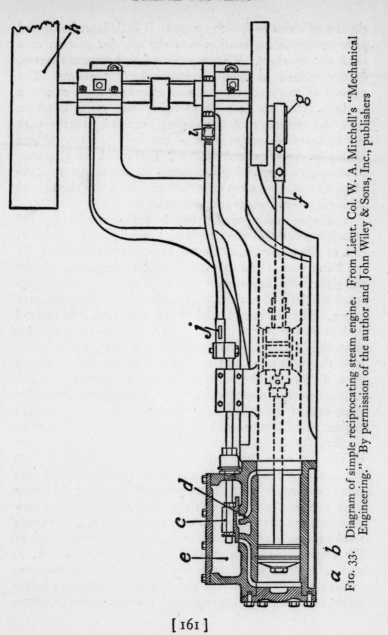

FIG. 33. Diagram of simple reciprocating steam engine. From Lieut. Col. W. A. Mitchell's "Mechanical Engineering." By permission of the author and John Wiley & Sons, Inc., publishers

the use of water to seal the piston. A little later he turned pure reciprocating motion into the circular motion of a shaft and flywheel. Watt never used high pressure steam, hardly indeed as high as atmospheric pressure. The science of thermodynamics was unknown until nearly a century later, so that he probably was quite unaware that the efficiency of the engine increases greatly with the increase of temperature of the boiler steam. Oliver Evans in America and Richard Trevithick in England, however, employed high pressure steam about 1795 to 1800, though of course unacquainted with the theoretical basis on which its advantage rests.

A simple reciprocating steam engine works on the principle shown in the diagram, Figure 33. At the position of the piston, *a*, as shown, steam is just entering the left-hand end of the cylinder to drive the piston toward the right. At the point, *b*, the slide valve, *c*, moving toward the left, closes the port and stops further entry of steam. That already in the cylinder continues to expand and push the piston toward the right. During all this time, the steam has been escaping to the vacuum condenser from the right-hand end of the cylinder out of the exhaust port, *d*. But as the valve moves farther to the left, the exhaust port is closed to communication with the right-hand end of the cylinder, and the residue of steam there begins to be compressed, tending to slow the piston to prepare for stopping. Still further motion of the valve to the left opens the right-hand end of the cylinder to the live steam from the steam chest, *e*, and at about the same time opens the exhaust port for the escape of steam from the left-hand end of the cylinder. The piston now reverses, and the valve presently reverses also. The return stroke is made after a similar manner. The remainder of the engine, including pitman, *f*, crank, *g*, flywheel, *h*, and valve linkage, *i*, *j*, is clearly indicated in the diagram.

Such an engine is about four times as wasteful of steam as the best reciprocating engines. The slide valve develops much friction owing to the heavy steam pressure upon its back; the steam wasted into the exhaust still contains most of its power; the compression of residue steam at the ends of the stroke takes energy, and many other losses occur. George H. Corliss (1817–1888) in 1849 invented valuable improvements in the steam-engine valve mechanism, which added greatly to its efficiency. He is regarded as the third great contributor to the improvement of the reciprocating steam engine, following James Watt and Richard Trevithick.

Unlike most of the discoverers and inventors mentioned in this book, George H. Corliss had no occasion for a youthful struggle with poverty. His father, Dr. Hiram Corliss, was a skillful and successful physician and surgeon, intellectual in his tastes and of strong religious character. His son George was born at Easton, N. Y., but Doctor Corliss removed to Greenwich, N. Y., when George was 8 years old. Though the family was in good circumstances, George Corliss obtained employment in a general store as soon as he had completed his common school education. He soon considered it desirable, however, to carry his studies further. This he did for three years at Castleton, Vt., but with rugged independence, he preferred to earn his way there by his own work.

At 21 years of age he became the proprietor of a general store at Greenwich, where he sold clothing, groceries, hardware, etc., for some years. The failure of the seams in a pair of boots he had sold led him to attempt the invention of a boot-sewing machine. This he developed and patented in 1843, some years before the famous sewing machine invention of Elias Howe. Corliss' machine involved more complex devices than Howe's and did not come into general use.

It was his attempt to construct and dispose of his sewing machine which led Corliss into the engine field. Having spent much time and money fruitlessly in this effort, he accepted work as a draftsman and designer in the shop of

GREAT INVENTIONS

Fairbanks, Bancroft & Company at Providence, R. I. Within a few years Corliss bought a share in the business, and, on reorganization, the firm became Corliss, Nightengale & Company. At 40 years of age, in 1857, he became sole owner, and the company became known as the Corliss Steam Engine Works. After this, Corliss lived 21 years, a man of the highest integrity, honored and trusted by all, kindly to men and animals, deeply religious, and prominent in good works and liberal benefactions.

The Corliss valve mechanism, patented March 10, 1849, led to an improvement of about 25 per cent in steam-engine efficiency. Its construction ensured perfect control of the steam consumption by the engine governor without waste of steam, which prior to that time had been prodigal. Instead of rigidly coupling the steam valves to the exhaust valves as in the simple slide-valve device shown in Figure 33, Corliss provided four separately operating valves at the four corners of the cylinder section. Moreover, he used a linkage of such a character that each valve remained nearly stationary during the comparatively long part of its cycle when there was no occasion to move it. This reduced greatly the friction loss produced by the heavy steam pressure on the backs of the valves. Also his linkage was adapted to move each valve very quickly when the time arrived to move it. This gave definite, quick cut-offs of steam with proper timing. Finally, the engine governor, whose balls rise by centrifugal force when the engine runs too fast, was connected by a linkage with the steam valves in such a manner that the higher the balls rose the earlier the cut-off, so that less steam was admitted to the cylinder. The mechanism was further improved, as specified in the Corliss patents of July 29, 1851, and July 6, 1859. The Corliss engine mechanism would require more space to make its action and advantages fully clear than we can well allot to it in this book.

So certain was Corliss of the advantage of his engines that he sometimes consented to install them under contract to accept nothing in payment but the amount saved in a certain number of months through their economical use of fuel. In one instance a purchaser who had made the contract to pay the amount saved during two years was glad to settle for twice the market price of the engine, instead of the much larger sum demanded by his contract.

At the international exhibition held in Vienna in 1873 George H. Corliss received for his engine the Grand Diploma of Honor, although he had made no exhibition there of machinery of any kind. While others were making great fortunes out of war contracts, he constructed at exact cost for the United States Government the great iron ring on which the turret of Ericsson's *Monitor* revolved in its famous fight with the *Merrimac*. For the Centennial Exposition of 1876 at Philadelphia, he constructed gratuitously at a cost to himself of about $100,000 a 1,400-horsepower steam engine which furnished the entire power for the exposition. He stipulated, however, that the exposition should not be open on Sundays, as he considered that a desecration of the day.

We may conclude our notice of George H. Corliss with the following quotation from London Engineering in 1888, only 40 years after Corliss' first engine patent. The quotation shows how very quickly the merit of the Corliss engines brought out in the fifties forced the recognition of foreign engineers.

By the death of George H. Corliss, America has lost the best known engineer she ever produced. In all the countries of the world where steam engines are employed, the name of Corliss has been heard, and ranks next in familiarity to that of Watt. Indeed it has become so much a part of our technical vocabulary that many engineers will learn with surprise that little over a month ago the owner of it was not only alive, but was the active head of the Corliss Steam Engine Works, of Providence, R. I. Many men verging on middle age found the Corliss engine an established fact when they entered on their apprenticeships, and hence they have been disposed to class its invention with the events of ancient history, and its inventor with those who are dead or superannuated.

GREAT INVENTIONS

The device of multiple expansion in the reciprocating
steam engine is very old. J. C. Hornblower constructed
and patented in England an engine of two cylinders, in
which the steam entered first a smaller cylinder in which
it was partially expanded, and from the exhaust passed
over into the larger cylinder and was further expanded.
Hornblower, however, could not compete successfully
with the Watt and Boulton Company. Later on, in
1804, A. Woolf employed a two-cylinder engine. These
inventors recognized the mechanical advantage of distributing the thrust of the piston more uniformly during
the cycle by the use of two cylinders. But a principle on
which the advantage of multiple expansion over single
expansion mainly rests could not have been known until
after the development of the science of thermodynamics
by Joule, Clausius, Sir William Thomson, and Rankine,
after 1849.

As we have stated above, expansion is necessarily
attended by cooling, and cooling of the steam draws heat
from the walls of the cylinder and piston. Accordingly,
after the exhaust occurs these walls are much below the
temperature of the incoming high-pressure steam. But
if that steam is saturated, then any lowering of its temperature by contact with cooled metal produces condensation to the form of water, with loss of expansive
force. By subdividing the expansion between several
cylinders, the difference of temperature between the
metal and the entering steam in all the cylinders is
diminished, and consequently the condensation is reduced.
Two other devices to reduce losses by condensation are
the steam jacketing of cylinders introduced by Watt,
and the superheating of steam by exposure to the furnace
gases, in pipes well separated from the water circulation,
before conveying the steam to the engine. Furthermore,
a part of the gain in efficiency in the Corliss engines came
about from locating the steam valve well apart from the

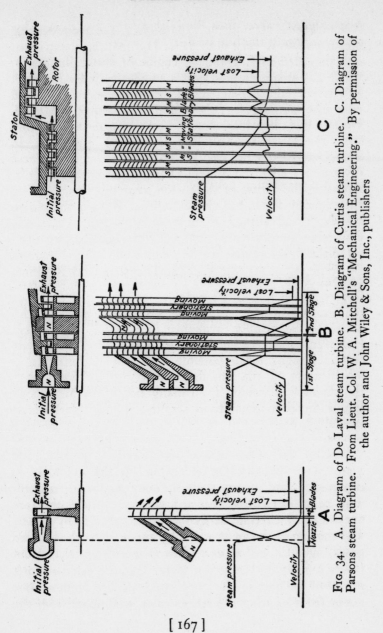

FIG. 34. A. Diagram of De Laval steam turbine. B. Diagram of Parsons steam turbine. C. Diagram of Curtis steam turbine. From Lieut. Col. W. A. Mitchell's "Mechanical Engineering." By permission of the author and John Wiley & Sons, Inc., publishers

cold exhaust valve, thus diminishing the loss caused by condensation of the hot steam.

Many inventors have attempted to avoid the reciprocating motion of the piston in its cylinder, but the development of rotary steam engines did not advance until the application of the turbine principle. As there are reaction and impulse water turbines, so are there reaction and impulse steam turbines. Applying the principles of thermodynamics, Gustaf de Laval about 1889 computed the form of nozzle which would cause steam to issue at maximum velocity from a chamber at given pressure and temperature. He then employed this high-speed steam issuing with a velocity of some 4,000 feet per second to drive an impulse wheel with numerous curved blades upon its circumference, much after the method of the Pelton water wheel as shown in Figure 34 A. Several such jets may be situated opposite different sectors of the wheel. This device has for most purposes the disadvantage that it produces too high speeds of the wheel to be readily available for driving machinery. However, relatively small losses in reduction gearing of certain designs make possible such applications. In a modification of the impulse steam turbine by Curtis the steam first issuing from many nozzles in high-speed jets is directed tangentially against moving blades of a special crescentlike curvature. Thence the jets issue in a contrary direction against oppositely curved crescent-shaped fixed blades, which again reverse the jets toward a second set of moving blades. The same device is again repeated. The issuing stream, now at lower pressure, may be collected and directed through a new series of nozzles upon a second series of movable and fixed blades. The scheme is shown in the diagram, Figure 34 B. The advantage of it is that much less speed is imparted to the rotor, and the friction of the steam on the blades is much less than with the De Laval turbine. In large sizes, Curtis turbines are much used to drive electric generators,

PLATE 54

Steam turbine, Parsons type. Top view. Capacity 30,000 kilowatt, 1,800 r.p.m. Courtesy of the Allis-Chalmers Manufacturing Company

and they have an efficiency quite equal or perhaps even superior to the best triple-expansion reciprocating engines.

The reaction turbine invented in 1884 by Sir Charles A. Parsons (1854–1931) antedated the De Laval impulse turbine by about six years. Sir Charles inherited his engineering genius. He was the fourth son of William Parsons, third Earl of Rosse, whose seat, Birr Castle, Parsonstown, Ireland, is famous as the site of his 6-foot reflecting telescope, which he completed and mounted there in the year 1845. Sir William Herschel had been the principal maker of reflecting telescopes of speculum metal before Lord Rosse, but his largest useful one was of 18 inches diameter. He left no account of his methods of casting and figuring specula. Lord Rosse, therefore, began anew about 1825 working out experimentally the best composition of the metal, which he fixed at four atoms of copper to one of tin, or by weight 126.4 parts copper to 58.9 parts tin. He then invented and developed a grinding and polishing machine which he described in 1828, and in 1839 completed and mounted a 3-foot reflecting telescope in which he built up the mirror of many thin plates backed by brass of equal expansibility. Not satisfied, he improved the methods of casting speculum metal, and after casting a solid 3-foot mirror in 1840, he accomplished the casting of the great one of 6 feet diameter in 1842. It was completed as a telescope in 1845, and was used with great success to reveal the forms of excessively distant nebulae, till then unknown. All the work of this difficult metallurgy and engineering was performed under Lord Rosse's direction by the tenants and laborers on his estate.

Less spectacular than his father's great telescope, but of immense practical value to industry, was Sir Charles Parsons's invention of the steam turbine. As stated by his son, Robert H. Parsons, in the London Times of September 21, 1931: "To any engineer conversant with power station practise the statement that without the steam turbine the electrical supply industry as we know it today simply could not exist is a mere truism." He goes on to point out that the Parsons turbine exceeds the best multiple-expansion large reciprocating engine in coal efficiency; that in London 185,000-kilowatt turbo-generator capacity had been installed in space intended for a maximum of only 55,000-kilowatt capacity with reciprocating engines; that turbines are adaptable to any steam pressure from the very highest to the very lowest, their range far exceeding the possible range of pressures adaptable to reciprocating engines; and finally that while the largest reciprocating engine units do not exceed 10,000 kilowatts capacity, steam turbines in units of 150,000 kilowatts are already in use, and no limit to their capacity is yet reached.

Figure 34C gives a sectional diagram showing the principle of the Parsons steam turbine. Steam, entering at high pressure, flows through alternate rows of moving and fixed oppositely curved blades, fastened circumferentially in the rotor and the casing. Clearance is only about 30/1,000 inch, so that leakage of steam is not large. As the steam expands, larger and larger passages are provided by a combination of two expedients. The diameter of the rotor grows larger, and the radial extension of the blades grows greater.

To balance the tendency always to push the rotor toward the exhaust end, as many equal enlargements of the rotor diameter are provided at the left as there are enlargements of the rotor at the right, and steam passages are provided between the balancing enlargements. Thus the pressures are equalized in opposite directions. On account of the smallness of the clearance, exact end-thrust devices must, of course, be prepared at the ends of the axis to prevent the rotor from touching the casing.

These machines, contrasting with the De Laval impulse turbine, may be constructed for comparatively low speeds, that they may be direct-connected with the propellers in steamships. In order to back the ship, however, auxiliary turbines running oppositely are provided. Turbines may be used at any steam pressure and have been employed with great success to save the steam rejected by the exhaust of reciprocating engines, working at pressures from below one atmosphere downward. Double the output for the same amount of coal may thus be obtained in association with a noncondensing reciprocating engine, and 50 per cent additional power may sometimes be produced by the combination of a turbine with a condensing engine. The Parsons turbine operates with from 75 to 90 per cent of the coal required for the same power in the best reciprocating engines, and gives a total efficiency in the best installations of about 36 per cent, equaling the Diesel internal-combustion oil engine.

Plate 54 shows a top view, with casing removed, of a 30,000-kilowatt capacity steam turbine of the Parsons type, driving 1,800 revolutions per minute.

Internal Combustion Engines

We have been considering engines for which the working gas is prepared under high pressure in separate devices, generally in boilers. We take up now those in which liquid or gaseous fuel is sprayed or sucked, together with the proper amount of air for complete combustion, into the engine cylinder itself. Pressure is developed within the engine cylinder by the explosion of the mixture. In their earlier history such engines operated generally with explosive mixtures of illuminating gas and air. In modern practice it is more common to use as fuel either gasoline or some heavy oil prepared from the crude oil products of the wells. Gas distilled from coal is also used.

A pioneer gas engine was devised by W. Cecil in 1820, but the earliest gas engines used to any extent commercially in England were those of Samuel Brown, beginning about 1823. A very valuable improvement was made in 1838 by William Barnett, who discovered the importance of compressing the explosive charge before ignition. Yet Barnett's plan was not generally followed. As late as 1860, Lenoir, in France, began to build gas engines operating without preliminary compression. The more efficient Otto and Langen engine, though mechanically inferior, drove Lenoir from the field.

Gas engines are generally, though not always, single acting—that is, all the gas expansion takes place on only one side of the piston. Almost immediately after Lenoir's first constructions, Beau de Rochas in Paris in 1862 enunciated the fundamental order of events of the ordinary gas engine, which is the famous four-stroke cycle, often called the Otto cycle. This cycle comprises: (1) Suction of a charge of the explosive mixture into the cylinder during the first out-stroke; (2) compression of the mixture to several atmospheres pressure in the first in-stroke; (3) ignition accompanied by sudden pressure increase near the dead point, followed by expansion in the second out-stroke, which is the working stroke; and (4) expulsion of the burnt and expanded gases in the second in-stroke, which is the fourth and last of the cycle.

Many gas engines have only a single cylinder, open at one end, and the connecting rod connects directly from the piston to the crank pin. Thus it vibrates through a considerable angle within the open end of the cylinder instead of being attached to a piston rod sliding in fixed guides to and fro, as is usual in steam engines. In the four-stroke cycle there is but one working stroke in four. The crank shaft makes two full rotations impelled by only one explosion in each cycle. To make the rotation of the crank shaft nearly uniform, despite the wide separation of the driving impulses, a heavy flywheel is fixed to it, or sometimes two such wheels.

Two valves are provided in the closed end of the cylinder, one for the entrance of the charge, the other for the expulsion of the burnt and expanded gases. These

PLATE 55

First gas engine built in America, 1878

PLATE 56

Dr. N. A. Otto

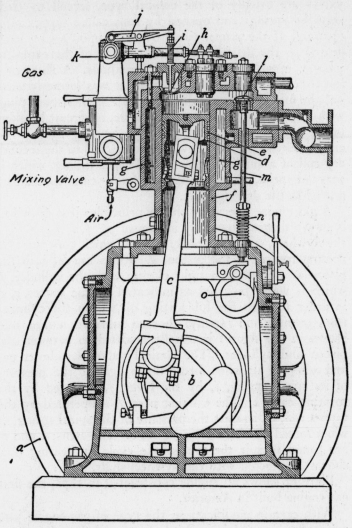

FIG. 35. Sectional view of a vertical gas engine. From Lieut. Col. W. A. Mitchell's "Mechanical Engineering." By permission of the author and John Wiley & Sons., Inc., publishers

valves are usually of the conical type, forced to their seats by springs and opened by rods called tappet rods, operated at the proper times by cams upon a cam shaft geared to the driving shaft. The firing of the explosive mixture may be done by several methods. A flame or a hot tube connecting with the cylinder was formerly used, but the firing now is usually electrical. Either spark plugs with a spark gap, as in an automobile, or circuit breakers inside the cylinder head give the igniting sparks. In either case the igniting device is connected to the secondary coil of a small transformer. Proper timing, which is very essential, is accomplished by a cam mechanism geared to the driving shaft.

A gas engine operating on the principles just described is shown diagrammatically in Figure 35. On the shaft of the flywheel, a, is the crank, b, from which goes the connecting rod, c, to the piston, d. Rings are let into the piston at e to make a tight closure with the cylinder, f, which is water jacketed as indicated by the spaces, g, g, in order to keep the lubricating oil within the cylinder from burning too rapidly. Forced lubrication (not well shown in the figure) is usually resorted to between the piston and cylinder. The conical valve, h, admits gas and admixed air when forced down against the pressure of its spiral spring, i, by the lever, j, operated by the rotating cam, k. The exhaust port, l, is operated by the tappet rod, m, against the pressure of the spiral spring, n, when forced by the rotating cam, o. The cams, k and o, are timed to suit the four-stroke cycle by gearing (not shown) connected with the flywheel shaft.

Plate 55 shows an engine constructed in 1878, the first gas engine built in America.

With certain modifications the type of gas engine just referred to is used in multiple form with liquid fuel for automobiles and airplanes. These applications involve the use of the carburetor, a device to produce a proper mixture of liquid fuel and air. More elaborate timing devices are also required to ignite the explosive mixtures in all the cylinders at the right instants, and cooling devices, combining air and water as cooling agents, are arranged to prevent injurious effects of the waste heat. Otherwise, these gasoline engines follow closely the type of the four-stroke cycle gas engine just explained, which was devised by Dr. N. A. Otto (Plate 56), of Cologne, Germany, about the year 1876.

There is, however, another type of internal-combustion engine suitable for employing both light and heavy oils without the use of a carburetor or sparking device. It was invented in 1892 by Dr. Rudolph Diesel (1858–1913). It will be recalled that oils such as kerosene and heavier distillates from the cruder oils of the wells have a critical temperature known as the "flash point." If heated in air above that temperature they take fire spontaneously. In the Diesel engine, temperatures above the flash point of the oil used as fuel are obtained by high compression of the air introduced for combustion.

A four-stroke cycle in such an engine would run as follows: On the first out-stroke air is drawn into the cylinder. By the first in-stroke the air is compressed to perhaps 500 pounds per square inch. Near the end of the stroke or dead point, oil is forced by very high pressure through atomizer nozzles into the compressed air. The jets of oil are placed so as to set up in the air a great turbulence which thoroughly mixes the fuel spray with the air. Owing to its high compression, the air is very hot and the fuel spray therefore ignites. On the out-stroke the cut-off of fuel is a little delayed so that during part of the working stroke the spray still continues to be forced into the air, burning as it enters. Thus the expansion continues through the remainder of the working out-stroke. At the end of it the exhaust port opens, and the products of combustion begin to escape. The exhaust port still remaining open, the in-stroke begins and the products of combustion are nearly all swept out of the cylinder. The cycle is thus completed and then repeats itself.

There are several variations from the Otto and Diesel cycles. Two-stroke cycles are sometimes used instead of four. In such cases the piston overruns the ports for the entrance and escape of gases, so that the piston acts like a slide valve in a simple steam engine. In certain engines two pistons, working in opposite directions, are used in a single cylinder. The mixture is exploded between them when they are nearest together. Several cylinders are frequently employed instead of one.

Internal combustion engine cylinders must be cooled in order that they may be lubricated, and the cooling is usually accomplished by water circulation. For this purpose the cylinder is often cast with a hollow wall to contain the water. Some engines are double acting, the cylinder being closed at each end. In that case the piston rod is made hollow, and the piston itself is provided with canals through which water is forced. It is shown by thermodynamics that the efficiency increases with compression. As the advantage of high compression is very great, the pistons must fit without sensible leakage, and for this purpose they are encircled by expansive rings. Since no water is present on the cylinder walls, in contrast with steam engines, adequate provision must be made for oiling the parts. For this purpose either a forced circulation or a splash circulation of oil is provided, so that at every cycle the piston and cylinder are well lubricated.

Although internal combustion engines are much used in manufacturing, their greatest applications, of course, are in automobiles and airplanes. Special forms have been invented for these purposes, in which extraordinary lightness has been combined with extraordinary durability and certainty of action. As it was found unpleasant to ride with an engine of one cylinder, the automobile engines were very early constructed with four, then with six, and now with eight, twelve, or sixteen cylin-

PLATE 57

Liberty airplane engine. In the National Museum

PLATE 58

Packard-Diesel airplane engine

ders, so as to give a steady motion with a flywheel of only moderate inertia. The same multicylinder practice, even accentuated, was carried over into airplane engineering,

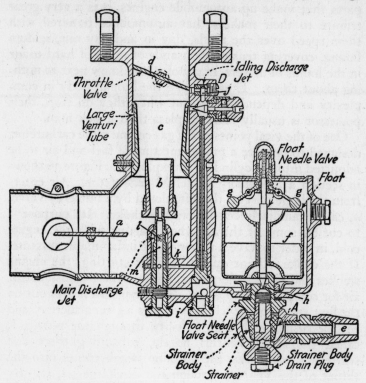

FIG. 36. Sectional view of the Stromberg carburetor. From Streeter, "Internal Combustion Engines." Courtesy of the McGraw-Hill Book Company, New York

where no flywheel is permissible because of the necessity of lightness.

In engines having up to six cylinders it is convenient to arrange them in a single row, all connected to a common crank shaft. But with more than six cylinders the V arrangement is introduced in automobiles and in the

[177]

Liberty airplane engine. Plate 57 is a view of the V-type Liberty engine in the United States National Museum.

When we consider the multitude of delicately adjusted parts that make up automobile engines, it is a very great tribute to their makers that automobiles powered with them speed over the roads, day in and day out, seldom failing, covering tens of thousands of miles of hard usage in the hands of drivers, many of whom know next to nothing about them. They are like the human body in complexity and dependability, but when they do stop, their possessor is usually more helpless than a sick man.

One of the vital points of the gas engine is the carburetor, designed to prepare a proper mixture of fuel and air to be admitted into the cylinders for explosion. Figure 36 shows in section a Stromberg model M carburetor. Air enters from the large port on the left, closed by a butterfly valve, a, called familiarly by drivers the choke. Its purpose is to cut off some of the air when starting with the engine cold, in order to have a richer, more inflammable mixture. If the choke is kept operative after starting, the engine smokes and gives little power, because there is insufficient air for complete combustion. As the piston moves out on the first stroke of a cycle it produces a strong suction, and the air rushes with high velocity through the nozzle, b, called the small Venturi nozzle, entraining there and scattering into spray the gasoline which comes into the throat of the Venturi through the discharge jet, m. By turbulence, the spray is well mixed into the air above in the large Venturi, c, where more air is added to the spray. The quantity of the mixture admitted at a stroke is governed by the throttle butterfly valve, d, which is operated by the hand or foot feed as governed by the driver.

The gasoline from the supply tube, e, enters the float valve, f, on the right. When the little tank is full enough so that the gasoline is level with the top of the tube, m, the float rises against the levers, g, g, and closes the needle valve, h. The outlet (not fully shown) of the little tank at *i* is regulated by an adjustable needle (not shown) so as to produce what tests may show to be the best mixture for usual speeds of travel. The jet, *j*, maintains operation of the engine during stops. Just below *j* is seen an adjustable needle valve to supply gasoline for sudden accelerations. Both of these inlets arise from the "accelerator well" which is fed from the tube, *m*, through the passage, *k*. An air inlet, shown just above the float tank at its left, communicates through fine openings (not shown) into the accelerator well when the throttle opens. A small supply of air is sucked into the passage, *m*, through the apertures, *l*, in order to help break up the gasoline spray to promote a better mixture. These little air jets also serve the important purpose of retarding undue acceleration of the gasoline supply at high speeds. Many other carburetors, varying in certain respects, have been devised, but this explanation covers the principles underlying most of them.

Even before automobiles were invented the radial internal-combustion engine had been constructed, though rarely. Stephen M. Balzer employed a three-cylinder radial gasoline engine in his automobile of 1894. He furnished to S. P. Langley, then Secretary of the Smithsonian Institution, a very small one and also a larger one, being respectively for the quarter-size model and the full-size airplane tested in 1903. The latter, however, required more power, and Charles M. Manly built for it a five-cylinder radial engine of 52 horsepower, following generally the Balzer model but with important changes. This Manly engine is the prototype of the present Wright radial engine and many others of similar form now commonly used in airplanes. It is shown in Plate 76, upper. Plate 58 represents a modern Packard radial airplane engine of the Diesel type.

Owing to the very high temperature of the explosions it is impossible to work internal-combustion engines at their full possibilities of thermal efficiency. The material of the cylinder walls and pistons would not bear such high temperatures nor could proper lubrication of the cylinders be accomplished. Hence they have to be cooled, and the temperature of the gases at maximum compression is not allowed to exceed about 2500° F. Yet this is so much above what is possible with steam that the internal-combustion engines have a great thermodynamic advantage. On the other hand, they suffer from complications of parts in their valving, compressors, pumps, fans, and other auxiliaries, which partly counteracts their natural advantage in high temperature. Good internal-combustion engines can turn from 35 to 40 per cent of the energy of their fuel into mechanical work. The best reciprocating engines seldom exceed 20 per cent. Steam turbines may reach a little above 30 per cent. Mercury and steam turbines in combination have reached 37 per cent in thermal efficiency.

CHAPTER VIII

MECHANICAL TRANSPORTATION[1]

EARLY in the nineteenth century one Brunton, a citizen of Derbyshire in England, built a mechanical horse. It ran upon a track like a railroad train, but its steam engine worked mechanical legs that kicked up the ground as it went. "The legs or propellers," says an account, "imitated the legs of a man or the forelegs of a horse, with joints, and when worked by the machine alternately lifted and pressed against the ground or road, propelling the engine forward, as a man shoves a boat ahead by pressing with a pole against the bottom of a river." Unfortunately, the mechanical beast blew up after a few miles, injuring some of the spectators.

THE STEAMBOAT

Much earlier, the unlucky John Fitch (1743–1798), of New Jersey, had tried a somewhat similar scheme on the water. After engaging unsuccessfully in watch making, in making potash, in button making, and in marriage, and after having been captured by Indians while surveying in Kentucky, he began at the age of 42, in 1785, to promote steamboats. The State of New Jersey in 1786 granted him a monopoly for 14 years to build and operate steamboats on its waters. Although he had tried both paddle wheels and the screw propeller, strangely enough he preferred a boat operated by steam-driven oars, with which he made a successful trial trip on August 22, 1787, on the

---

[1] Parts of this chapter are quoted or abridged from Carl W. Mitman's article, The beginning of the mechanical transport era in America, Ann. Rep. Smithsonian Inst. for 1929, p. 507, 1930.

Delaware River. Twelve large wooden paddles, six in tandem fashion along each side of the boat, alternately dipping into and drawing out of the water as an Indian paddles his canoe, propelled the boat at 3 miles per hour. Watt's engines not yet being available, the steam engine which actuated these clumsy devices through sprockets, chains, and cranks was on the Newcomen principle, in which the cylinder was cooled at every cycle by the injection of cold water. Plate 59, upper, shows a model of Fitch's steamboat now in the United States National Museum. The Federal Constitutional Convention, then in session at Philadelphia, adjourned on the afternoon of its trial so that its members might witness the demonstration. Some of them even rode on the boat.

Fitch was disappointed with the slow speed made by his boat, and immediately began a larger one, which he completed in 1788. It was 60 feet in length and was propelled by a stern paddle wheel driven by a steam engine with a 12-inch cylinder. In July, 1788, he made a trial trip of 20 miles from Philadelphia upstream to Burlington, N. J. After this he made many trips, in one of which he carried 30 passengers from Philadelphia to Burlington in three hours and ten minutes. He built a third boat, still larger, and advertised a regular schedule of sailings in the Philadelphia newspapers in 1790. The Federal Congress granted him a patent in 1791 for 14 years. It was signed by George Washington and the commissioners, Thomas Jefferson, Henry Knox, and John Randolph. The French Government also granted John Fitch a patent in 1791 protecting his invention for 15 years. The original French document is on exhibition at the United States National Museum. Despite these fair prospects, Fitch's unlucky star prevailed. His fourth boat was totally destroyed by a violent storm, his stockholders refused further support, no help was found in France, and Fitch died in poverty and disappointment in 1798. A principal cause of his poor success with steamboats was probably the lack of an efficient steam engine. Watt's improvements were not yet available in America.

John Stevens (1749–1838) became perhaps the most accomplished steam engineer of his time in this country. He ardently pursued the project of the steamboat for many years in association with his brother-in-law, the eminent diplomatist and statesman, Robert R. Livingston. The latter served in the Continental Congress. As Chancellor of the State of New York he administered the oath of office to President Washington. As Minister to France in Jefferson's administration he negotiated the purchase of the Louisiana Territory.

Among his various experiments Stevens designed and built a rotary steam engine to be used with a screw propeller. He placed this combination in a little 25-foot boat in the summer of 1802 and used it occasionally in crossing the Hudson between New York and Hoboken. About this boat Stevens wrote: "She occasionally kept going until cold weather stopped us. When the engine was in the best of order, her velocity was about 4 miles an hour." The engine, while very simple, was hard to keep steam-tight. That winter Stevens resorted again to the reciprocating engine.

Early in 1802 he designed, built, and sold to the Manhattan Company, proprietor of the waterworks of New York City, a Watt-type steam engine for operating the water pump, worked up to that time by horses. Engine and pump handled 500,000 gallons of water every 24 hours. Yet his studies and experiments with steam extending over a period of 20 years had not produced a really successful steamboat. The obstacle consisted undoubtedly in the lack of tools and metal-working equipment. His 1802 experiment showed great promise, however, and in 1804 with the help of his 17-year-old son, Robert, he launched and successfully navigated in New York Harbor the first twin-screw-propellered steamboat, operated by a high-pressure reciprocating steam engine and multitubular boiler, both of his own design. The boat was a small one, hardly more than 25 feet in length. In its trips back and forth across the Hudson it attracted much attention.

Dr. James Renwick, who was at that time professor of natural philosophy at Columbia University, in describing one of the trips of the boat, wrote:

We went to walk in the Battery. As we entered the gate from Broadway we saw what we in those days considered a crowd running toward the river. On inquiring the cause we were informed that Jack Stevens was going over to Hoboken in a queer sort of boat. On reaching the bulkhead we saw lying against it a vessel about the size of a Whitehall rowboat in which was a small engine, but there was no visible means of propulsion. The vessel was speedily under way, my late much-valued friend, Commodore Stevens, acting as cockswain; and I presume the smutty-looking personage who fulfilled the duties of engineer, fireman, and crew, was his more practical brother, Robert L. Stevens.

The engine, boiler, and propellers of this historic steamboat still exist. Stevens Institute at Hoboken, founded by Colonel Stevens' son, Edwin, took care of them until 1893, when they were presented to the United States National Museum, where they have been carefully preserved and exhibited ever since.

In 1806 John Stevens began the construction of a large boat 103 feet long, rigged with two masts and sails. It was equipped with a cross-head steam engine, with two condensing cylinders 16 inches in diameter and with 3-foot stroke. The boiler, set in brickwork in the bottom of the boat, consisted of a cylindrical shell with one return flue. The engine, in turn, operated a pair of side paddle wheels. Colonel Stevens had the *Phoenix*, as the boat was called, ready for trial in 1807, but no sooner was it afloat than it was debarred because of the monopoly granted by the State of New York to Livingston and Fulton for steamboat service on the waters of New York. Stevens decided to send the *Phoenix* to Philadelphia. In June, 1808, with his son Robert in command, the *Phoenix* made the trip by way of Sandy Hook and Cape May, the first

PLATE 59

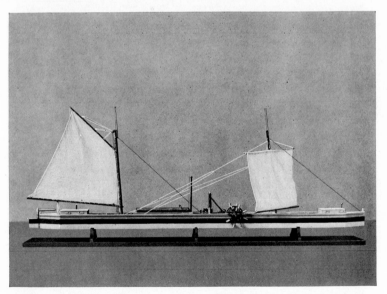

Upper: Fitch's steamboat of 1787. Lower: Fulton's *Clermont* of 1807.
From models in the National Museum

PLATE 60

Brazilian native balsa

sea voyage ever made by a steam vessel. On her passage
she encountered a storm which damaged her somewhat
and compelled her to seek shelter in Barnegat Bay. After
reaching Philadelphia, however, the boat ran as a packet
for six years on the Delaware River between Philadelphia
and Trenton, and was finally wrecked at Trenton.

The performance of the *Phoenix* ought certainly to have
brought to Colonel Stevens the greatest acclaim of his
career, but, unfortunately, the feat was accomplished too
late. As has often been the case before and since his time,
public fancy rested at the moment on another (Robert
Fulton), and so the accomplishments of the *Phoenix*
passed almost unnoticed.

Discouragement does not seem to have had a place in
Stevens' makeup, for he continued with his experiments,
although hampered somewhat by Fulton's monopoly.
His years prevented him from taking as active a part as
formerly, but he had in his son Robert an admirable
successor. Robert Stevens soon became the foremost
marine and railroad engineer in the United States.
Within three years, in 1811, father and son had built a
steam ferryboat and laid the foundation for the present
extensive ferry system between New York and New
Jersey. Thereafter and until his death at the age of 89
Colonel Stevens devoted the major part of his time and
energy in fighting for the establishment of railways as
against canals, in the attainment of which his influence
ranked high.

When Chancellor Livingston sailed for France to take
up his duties as United States minister, he no doubt
believed that he was leaving his interest in steamboats
behind him. As a matter of fact his new post was to see
that interest greatly increased, for shortly after his
arrival in France he met Robert Fulton. From that
meeting great results flowed.

Fulton was born in Little Britain, Lancaster County,
Pa., in 1765. He displayed no more than the normal

boy's interest in mechanics while in school but showed a marked aptitude in drawing. By the time he was 21 he had made quite a name for himself as a portrait painter. On the advice of a group of interested Philadelphians, in whose city he had lived and worked for a number of years, he went to England in 1786 to study under the patronage of Benjamin West, a noted Philadelphia artist then living in London. Through West, Fulton met many prominent people, among whom were the Duke of Bridgewater and the Earl of Stanhope. Their interest in and discussions of engineering problems of the day so influenced Fulton that before long he, too, began thinking, studying, and talking of inland navigation and canal systems and forgot about his portrait work.

Fourteen years passed, during which he was engrossed in experiments on submarine and torpedo inventions, in the hope of improving on the work begun in the United States during the Revolution by David Bushnell. Most of these 14 years were spent in Paris, where Fulton lived with another American, Joel Barlow. It was there that he met Robert Livingston, the new American minister. One can well imagine that before long the two were comparing notes on their several experiences with inland navigation problems, from which presumably came a revival of interest in steamboats. They became close friends and Fulton later on married Livingston's niece.

At all events, from his own personal knowledge of what English and French engineers as well as Rumsey had attempted in steam navigation, and after studying the drawings of Fitch's French patent, which he borrowed from Alfred Vail, the American consul, Fulton, with the help of Joel Barlow, who designed the boiler, built a steamboat in the spring of 1803. When he tried it out on the Seine, the hull unfortunately could not stand the weight of the machinery and it broke in two. Undaunted, Fulton immediately undertook the building of another boat, this time 66 feet long, and had it ready for trial in August of 1803, but it moved so slowly as to be altogether a failure. Having heard of William Symington's successful steamboat, *Charlotte Dundas*, which was put in operation in 1802 on the Forth and Clyde Canal, Fulton went to England in 1804, and obtained permission to make drawings of all of Symington's machinery. He proposed to go back to the United States to build a steamboat there and he wanted to have all possible data to take with him. In addition he began the movement to raise the ban then in force prohibiting the export of Boulton & Watt engines, for from his experiments he realized that his chances for success rested a great deal on the engine he should use, and Watt engines were then the best made. With the help of his influential friend he succeeded in having the embargo raised. In 1806 he returned to New York with an engine and late in that year began the construction of the *Clermont* (Plate 59, lower). Under his supervision the hull was built by Charles Brown, a shipbuilder of New York, the Boulton & Watt engine was put in place, and the whole made ready for its trial trip on August 7, 1807.

Fulton and a few friends, mechanics, and six passengers were on board. An incredulous and jeering crowd gathered on shore as the boat cast loose at 1 o'clock in the afternoon. "Bring us back a chip of the North Pole" and similar facetious remarks could be heard by those on board as the nose of the *Clermont* was pointed north and up the Hudson. But, as the boat kept right on her way the attitude of those on shore gradually changed and great was the scramble for hats thrown high in the air by the cheering and no longer jeering mass.

Fulton's skill in selecting and combining the best mechanical equipment developed from the ideas of the foremost inventors of England, France, and America gave to the world the first practical and commercially successful steamboat. The *Clermont's* trip to Albany and return completely changed public opinion of the possibilities of steam navigation, and those who a few years before clamored for the maintenance of the old order of things were wondering a few years after how in the world one got along without steamboats. Fulton is to be honored for this acheivement but not for the invention of the steamboat, a claim he personally never made.

Although the steamship became a practical device at the beginning of the nineteenth century, and steam was used for the first time in crossing the Atlantic by the *Savannah* in 1819, sails were the principal dependence in ocean transportation until more than a half century later. The height of the era of the beautiful clipper ships that made the China voyages and raced for honor's sake was indeed from 1850 to 1870. The *Witch of the Wave*, one of America's finest, made the voyage from Canton, China, to Dungeness, in the English Channel, in 90 days. Her best day's run was 338 knots in 24 hours. Plate 61 shows a model of a full-rigged ship in the United States National Museum. Such a ship, to make fast time, required a large crew to man the numerous unwieldy sails. In our day only the simpler-rigged schooners with their smaller crews are able to compete in ocean trade with the steamers. Plates 60 and 61 show the advance of sailing craft from the South American balsa to the clipper of 1850.

It was merely a coincidence that the decline of the sailing ships attended the advent of iron and steel ship construction. The real cause of the decline of sail power was the growing efficiency of the steam engine and the screw propeller. Although earlier inventors had proposed it, the first practical development of the propeller occurred in 1836, when F. P. Smith and Capt. John Ericsson (later of *Monitor* fame) each took out English patents for screw propellers for steamships. They each tested small vessels of this type in the Thames, and Capt. Robert H. Stockton, acting for the United States Navy, was so favorably impressed that he ordered two propeller

PLATE 61

Full-rigged merchant ship.   From model in the National Museum

PLATE 62

The *Leviathan* leaving New York.   Courtesy of the United States Lines

boats of the Messrs. Lairds of Birkenhead. Ericsson's invention was soon very largely adopted in the American Navy, but the British clung to paddle wheels until 1845. Then the Admiralty tested two ships identical in all respects otherwise, and found the propellered ship pulled the paddle-wheel ship stern backwards at the rate of 2½ knots an hour. By 1854 the entire British fleet in the Black Sea operating against Russia was equipped with screw propellers.

The triumph of steam over sails was assured, however, from the first. As early as 1822 a Parliamentary report on the two methods of propulsion showed that on 30 principal coasting trade routes steamships made from two to six times quicker passage than sailing ships. With the introduction of high-pressure steam engines and multiple expansion of steam about 1870, steamships forged rapidly ahead. About equal tonnage of steam and sailing ships was built in 1865, but by 1900 steam construction was more than 50 times the greater.

Since 1900 the use of oil fuel and steam turbines has greatly accentuated the advantage of steam over sailing ships. In size, too, steamships have proportionally as far excelled sailing vessels as in speed. Among the largest sailing vessels was the *Great Republic*, a clipper built in 1853. She was 305 feet long, could carry 40,000 square feet of canvas, and had a tonnage of 3,400. Her maximum speed was perhaps 14 knots an hour, but her average speed including storms and calms, probably did not exceed 4 knots. Compare her with such ships as the *Empress of Britain*, 733 feet long, of 42,348 tons, or the *Leviathan*, 908 feet long, of 59,957 tons shown in Plate 62. Both ships average well over 20 knots in speed. Much greater speed, even up to 40 knots, is attained by first-line naval vessels.

When iron and steel ships were first proposed some objected, saying that since the metal is heavier than water it must needs sink. The answer is, of course, that, concerning floating, the ship is not to be regarded as of iron or steel, but as composed of a small part iron and steel but almost wholly of the included air, which is much lighter than water. As a matter of fact steel ships are lighter than wooden ships of equal dimensions.

It was also objected, and this was a very real objection, that the magnetic compass would be unreliable in iron or steel ships. The Astronomer Royal, Sir G. B. Airy, was able to show how compensating magnets may be applied so as largely to correct this error. It is necessary to adjust the compensation slightly, however, from time to time. Naval vessels are sometimes seen at sea "swinging ship" as it is called—turning in all directions to determine the corrections to their compasses.

Recently, however, the gyroscopic compass has come into general use as the more important instrument on naval and large merchant vessels. American and British vessels mostly employ the gyrocompass invented by the late Elmer A. Sperry. In foreign marines, variations of the application of the gyroscopic principle, notably by the Anschutz Company in Germany, by Brown in England, and others, are in wide use. The mechanical principle of the gyroscopic compass is quite too difficult to explain here, but the effect is obtained by a heavy wheel driven at tremendous speed by an electric motor. The compass is free to turn in every way except as governed by the influence of gravitation. The gravitational control tends to make the instrument set itself so as to indicate the true north and south line. A large master gyroscopic compass is located in the center of the ship at a place as free from motion as any, and several smaller subordinate gyros located at convenient points are controlled by electric connection with it. By electric devices the rudder of the ship is governed by one of these controlled gyros. Once the course has been set by hand, the gyrostatic control is switched on, and thereafter the ship is steered

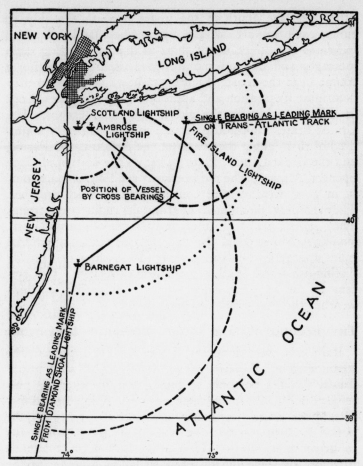

FIG. 37. Radiobeacons guiding the approach to New York. From "Radiobeacons," by George R. Putnam, Commissioner of United States Lighthouse Service

automatically to a straighter course than any helmsman could imitate.

Other ingenious technical devices are found on the bridge of a modern steamer. One automatically detects and locates a fire starting in any part of the ship. Another tells the depth of the water beneath the ship 10 times each minute as she approaches land. A third indicates the directions of ships in distress sending radio messages and of land radiobeacons useful for setting a course near the coast. Figure 37 shows how a ship may determine its position and approach the port of New York in thick weather by the aid of the radiobeacons. The United States Lighthouse Service maintains nearly a hundred of them along the coasts of the Atlantic, the Pacific, and the Great Lakes. Plate 39 shows the station at Cape Spencer, Alaska. The radiobeacons send out signals hourly in good weather and continuously in thick weather. They employ modulated continuous radio wave-trains. Their signals are of 21 different varieties of dot and dash, similar to Morse code. No two stations within a hundred miles apart use the same signal. Thus ships can readily distinguish which stations are being observed. This system is the greatest safeguard to navigation in thick weather that has ever been invented.

THE LOCOMOTIVE AND OTHER RAILROAD INVENTIONS

Railroads were invented before Watt improved the steam engine. Wooden railways were used with horse-drawn vehicles not only in mines, but for carrying passengers and goods in the open country. The first locomotives were merely ordinary stationary engines of the period mounted on flat cars and connected in some way to drive their wheels. It was a moot question among directors of some of the early railways whether steam would be a real improvement over horses for power.

Strange-looking to our eyes are the early locomotives. Plates 63 and 64 show the *Best Friend* and the *John Bull* engines which operated respectively on the Charleston and Hamburg Railroad and the Camden and Amboy Railroad in 1830 and 1831. The *Best Friend* was the first locomotive designed and built in America for actual service on a railroad. It was constructed by the West

PLATE 63

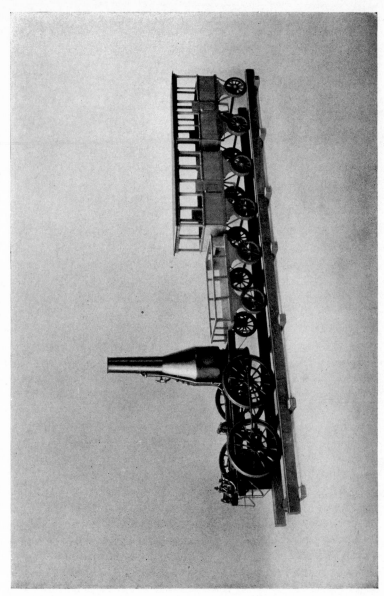

The locomotive *Best Friend*. First locomotive designed and built in America

PLATE 64

The locomotive *John Bull*. Still in good running order. In the National Museum

Point Foundry of New York City. The *John Bull* was built by Stephenson, England's pioneer locomotive builder. It is now in good running order and is exhibited in the United States National Museum. Much nearer the modern style was the *Old Ironsides*, designed and built by Matthias W. Baldwin (1795–1866) in 1832. Baldwin was the founder of the famous Baldwin Locomotive Works in Philadelphia. In his early manhood he was a jeweler and was extremely skillful in making jewelry. Later, with a partner, he engaged in the manufacture of roller machinery for stamping dress patterns on cotton goods used in making the calico dresses formerly so much worn. His entry into locomotive building was the result of a request that he prepare a model locomotive for exhibition in the Philadelphia museum. This he did so well that he was requested to build a full-size locomotive for the Philadelphia, Germantown and Norristown Railroad Company. Though his shop machinery was very inadequate he succeeded, and the *Old Ironsides* was the result. It continued in service for 10 years, although at first the company advertised that it would use the engine only in fine weather, reverting to horse traction when it rained.

Although so dissatisfied with his treatment by the officers of the railroad that he intended to do no more locomotive building, Baldwin was so fascinated by locomotive problems that he soon accepted an order from the Charleston and Hamburg Company. In the meanwhile he had examined English engines and spent much time and thought on design. A very great improvement, essential to high speeds, had been made meanwhile in the invention, in 1832, of the swiveling forward truck by John B. Jervis, chief engineer of the Mohawk and Hudson Railroad. In his second full-size locomotive Baldwin incorporated the Jervis truck with the best features of English practice. The result was the locomotive *E. L. Miller*, finished in February, 1834, which established the prevailing type for the American locomotive for many years. Plate 65 contrasts the prevailing type of locomotive of Baldwin's time with a modern fast passenger locomotive.

Baldwin was very hard hit by the bank suspensions and profound depression of the great financial crisis of 1836 to 1840. He offered to his creditors everything he possessed, but offered at the same time to pay every dollar if they would permit him to retain his business. They agreed, and in 1841 he cancelled every obligation. During the remainder of his life the Baldwin Locomotive Works prospered and had constructed over a thousand locomotives at the time of his death in 1866. Baldwin was a man of profound religious convictions and great liberality in support of religion and charity. He also took great pleasure in the jeweler's handicraft of his early years, and throughout his life continued to practice it at his home as a pastime.

In applying steam to railway traction several troublesome problems were encountered and solved by American engineers. First was the problem of flexibility necessary for rounding curves at high speed. From English practice had been inherited the flanged wheels holding the train between the rails, and Robert, son of John Stevens, had modified the English T rail into that American type of rail section which we still retain. But in rounding curves there was a tendency for the locomotive wheels to climb the rail, with much friction and loss of power at high speeds until the invention by John B. Jervis of the swiveled four-wheeled bogie truck.

In some railroads of very steep grades, as in Sumatra, cog-wheels upon the engine engage racks set between the rails in order to insure positive traction. The same practice was used to some extent in the early days of railroading for roads of moderate grade in England. It has been mentioned that the officers of the Philadelphia, Germantown and Norristown Railroad Company advertised horse traction on wet days, probably for fear of unsatisfactory tractive power on a slippery track from smooth engine wheels. Two expedients were resorted to and have proved sufficient to overcome the difficulty of traction. These are increased engine weight and distribution of the weight on numerous driving wheels placed under the heaviest parts of the engine. For a long time the American type of engine was that designated on the Whyte system as 4-4-0—that is, a bogie of four wheels, four drivers, and no rear or trailing wheels behind the drivers. Later, to meet the demands of heavier freight and even passenger traffic came various types of heavier engines. Of these, among the most common is the Atlantic type, 4-4-2, in which the driving wheels are moved forward to carry a larger proportion of the engine weight, thus necessitating a pair of trailers. Still later came the Pacific type, 4-6-2, still heavier and much longer, with six drivers. There are also in use for very heavy duty, engines of 8, 10 (for instance the Santa Fe type, 2-10-2), 12, and even 16 drive wheels. Plate 66 shows the ponderous heavy-duty engines of types 4-8-4 and 2-8-8-2.

About 1837 M. W. Baldwin invented an arrangement of driving wheel connection whereby the driving wheels were able to follow the curvature of the track, notwithstanding their linkage. But it was rather complex and has never come into general use. In the present-day long engines with many driving wheels, the fore and aft trucks are swiveled, and the center drivers of each group have no flanges, only the front and back pair of drivers of a group being flanged. This arrangement is found adequate to follow the curves of present trackage.

For many years a principal danger in railroad travel was from inadequate brakes. With lengthening trains there came times when the train required half a mile of braking to bring it to a stop. Then came the hand wheel and chain brake applied to each car, invented by Willard J. Nichols, shop foreman of the Hartford and New Haven Railroad. One brakeman could set the brakes on two cars, stepping from one platform to the other for this purpose. But with heavy trains it took a long run under such brakes to bring the train to rest.

The air brake was invented by George Westinghouse, whose electrical work we have already referred to, and was first tested on a train of the Pennsylvania Railroad, consisting of a locomotive and four cars, at Pittsburgh in September, 1868. This was a brake operated from the engine by air pressure working through hose upon pistons actuating brakes on the wheels of the engines and all the cars. The witnesses to the first test were thrown out of their seats by the first unexpected application of the brake. But it saved a man's life who had rashly crossed in front of the train, then running at 30 miles an hour. All the witnesses were convinced of the emergency efficiency of the air brake, and a little farther on, it was applied in a more gradual and entirely satisfactory manner.

Yet this form of air brake was not a complete success. It would not stop cars which might break away from the train, and indeed would be helpless if the air hose should break. Nor on a long train would the brake be simultaneously applied. It worked first, of course, nearest the engine. Westinghouse overcame this difficulty by the invention of the automatic air brake. For this device he invented the famous "triple valve," patented March 5, 1872.

The drawings and description of this famous invention are so complicated as to preclude a satisfactory explanation here. Two separate hose connections supplied air under several atmospheres pressure from the engine to the entire train. Besides these two connecting air supplies, each car was provided with a reservoir charged from them. Connecting the air pipes, the reservoirs, and the brake cylinders, a complicated set of passages was provided. These passages were equipped with double-ended piston valves which might seat at either end or at neither end, according to the relative pressures prevailing in the train pipes and in the reservoirs. The piston valves were provided not only with double-ending seats, but also in some instances with flap valves, through which air could pass in one direction only. By this rather complex series of devices, Westinghouse made it possible for the engineer to stop the train or release the brakes through either of the two air hose pipes, even if one of them should be broken. But if both pipes were broken, then the reservoir of air under each car came into play and set the brakes.

For passenger service, the automatic air brake of 1872 was very satisfactory. But with very long freight trains of 50 cars or more, the brakes would be set on the forward end before the change of air pressure could be effective at the rear. In an emergency stop this tended to telescope the rear cars, and serious damage sometimes resulted.

Freight cars must be shifted from line to line. About 1885 it was felt to be necessary that some uniform brake system should be adopted. Accordingly, in 1886, tests were conducted by a committee of the Master Car Builders' Association at Burlington, Iowa, in which all brake manufacturers were invited to compete. Only the devices employing air brakes or vacuum brakes were found to have any prospect of meeting the tests, but none submitted was satisfactory in emergency stops. Another trial was therefore held in the spring of the following year, at which six competitors appeared. In the interim electricity had been called to the service, either alone or in combination with air or vacuum devices. Of these mixed brake services, the Westinghouse combination appeared simplest and safest. Though the time lag on the rear car with automatic air brakes alone had been more than cut in half, none of the nonelectric brakes fully satisfied the judges. Dangerous shocks to rear cars, either to equipment or lading, still occurred with emergency stops unless the valves were electrically operated.

Despite fears for its certainty of action under all

circumstances, it seemed certain that electricity must be used to operate the valves, so that the domination of the Westinghouse air brake seemed over. Westinghouse, however, was not discouraged. He set about improving the automatic air brake and within three months introduced changes that met the situation without recourse to electricity. With his quick-acting improved air brake a train of 50 cars was brought to rest on down grade from a speed of 40 miles per hour within half its length, and without sensible shock. The delay of application on the rear car was little more than two seconds. The test, however, was unofficial, and its results could not influence the report of the judges, which had necessarily given preference to electrically operated devices. Westinghouse therefore provided a train of 50 cars with several engines and ran it over the important roads, holding demonstrations at all principal railway centers, to which local railroad men were invited. Several hundred thousand dollars were expended on this grand tour.

The result was a supplementary report printed in the Proceedings of the Master Car Builders' Association for 1888, in which, after reviewing their former finding for electrically operated valves, the committee cited the remarkable results achieved by air pressure alone, and proceeded to recommend that whatever brake should be adopted should meet conditions which Westinghouse's brake did already meet, and which no other up to that time had ever met. Consequently Westinghouse's quick-acting automatic air brake was adopted, although the committee had nowhere mentioned its name. Congress soon after required the use of power brakes on all cars of interstate carriers.

The coupling of cars in the first half century of railroading was done by means of heavy elongated iron loops or links fitting loosely into recesses at the ends of the cars and secured by heavy coupling pins dropped through holes in the platforms. To make a coupling it was necessary for a man to go between the cars as they were backed together, guide the link by his hand to enter the recess, and just at the right instant to let it go and to drop the coupling pin. Many men were killed or injured in this dangerous work.

Eli H. Janney (1831–1912), a native of Virginia and an officer during the Civil War on the staffs of Generals Lee and Longstreet, losing everything by the war, found employment as a dry goods clerk at Alexandria, Va. He had daily occasion to pass a freight yard where the coupling of cars was always going on and became much concerned over the frequent injuries of the brakemen. It is said that[2]:

Happening one day to hook the four fingers of each hand together it flashed into Janney's mind that this involuntary action might be the clue to the solution of the coupling problem. He began immediately to whittle out small wooden models, working at night most of the time. The deeper he got into the subject the more he learned of the host of conditions that had to be considered, such as simplicity, ease of operation, strength of parts, cheapness of manufacture, and the like. Eight years passed during which he converted the clutching fingers idea into a workable mechanism of cold steel and applied for a patent. It was granted April 29, 1873.

Janney was in no position to go into the manufacture of the coupler nor had he any market for it, but with the help of friends he succeeded in making several in a local foundry and having them tried out on the old Loudoun & Hampshire Railroad. They gave full satisfaction in this test, but as Janney soon realized, this was not sufficient to attract the attention of the great railroad companies. Car-coupler inventions and inventors then were the bane of the railroad officials' existence and Janney, after a few discouraging experiences with them struck out on another tack. For 10 years he went from one iron founder to another with his coupler, improved year by year, until he found one in Pittsburgh who had sufficient faith in it to undertake its manufacture at his own expense and try to introduce it, paying Janney a royalty. Because of his perseverence he finally induced the Pennsylvania Railroad to permit the equipping of 100 cars with the coupler. Again the test proved successful.

By this time, however, coupler patents were numbered by the thousands. The most likely ones were in trial use and each had its

[2] Ann. Rep. Smithsonian Inst. for 1929, pp. 544–546, 1930.

champions among railroad men. All realized that for the betterment of the service some one form of coupler should be adopted by all railroads, but no agreement could be reached as to which one. Then, too, various cliques had been organized on different railroads in the interest of some patent, and in such cases arguments addressed to them were generally wasted. Things went along in this chaotic way for a number of years and until public indignation and the stimulus of legislation in several States and in Congress compelled railroad officers to give serious attention to the subject. The burden of making a selection fell to the Master Car Builders' Association, composed of officers of railroad companies who were in charge of car construction. A special track was laid outside of Buffalo, N. Y., in 1887, having all conceivable sorts of curves, bumps, and hollows, and every coupler maker was invited to submit his device for test.

The Janney coupler came through with flying colors and was recommended for general adoption by the association. To insure the carrying out of this recommendation completely, Janney magnanimously relinquished his rights to that part of his patent bearing on the unique curvature of the coupler jaw, so that this essential part could be made by every manufacturer. From that time on, anyone desiring to make couplers simply applied to the Master Car Builders' Association for drawings and specifications and Janney's invention became known universally as the M. C. B. To-day every railroad car in the United States, Canada, and Mexico must be equipped with the M. C. B. or Janney coupler.

Until the time of his death, 1912, Janney was constantly experimenting and devising improvements for the coupler, particularly for passenger cars. For years, even after his royalties ceased, he had expert mechanics in his private employ, he visualizing his ideas in little wooden models carved with a pen knife and they converting them into finished models of wood and metal. Two of these form most interesting and valuable accessions in the railroad exhibits in the National Museum. With them is a third model of the coupler improvement devised and patented by Janney's son Robert. The latter grew up with couplers all about him and eventually became associated with one of the large coupler manufacturers, continuing in this special field until his death in 1923.

Two Great Railroad Pioneers

The 51st Congress was the first in the history of the United States to appropriate more than a billion dollars during its two years of existence. Naturally the opposition raised the cry of extravagance and dubbed it the Billion

PLATE 63

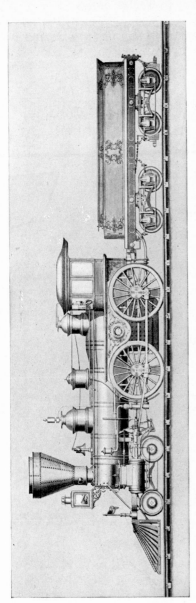

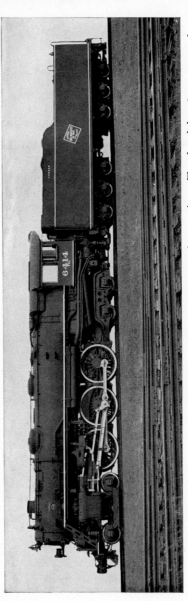

Upper: Early passenger locomotive. Lower: Modern passenger locomotive. Total weight 380,220 pounds. Diameter of drivers 72 inches. Wheel base 41 feet. Boiler pressure 225 pounds. Heating surface 4,200 square feet. Built 1931. Courtesy of the Baldwin Locomotive Works

PLATE 66

Upper: Heavy-duty passenger or freight engine. Total weight 408,000 pounds. Boiler pressure 250 pounds. Heating surface 5,422 square feet. Tractive force 66,400 pounds. Built 1931. Lower: Articulated locomotive for heavy freight duty. Total weight 665,100 pounds. Tractive force 137,000 pounds. Courtesy of the Baldwin Locomotive Works

Dollar Congress. Thomas B. Reed, of Maine, that doughty Republican war horse, retorted, "This is a billion dollar country." Building on their keen appreciation of the unprecedentedly rapid development of the United States, there arose such a group of giants of engineering and finance as we are not likely to see soon again. Already in this volume we have sketched George Westinghouse and Thomas A. Edison, and we shall have occasion in later chapters to speak of the careers of Henry Ford, Andrew Carnegie, and George Eastman. But the story of the rise of the great railway systems of the United States displays a group of extraordinary characters, none of whom is more picturesque than the two great rivals, James J. Hill of the Great Northern, and Edward H. Harriman of the Southern Pacific and Union Pacific systems.

James J. Hill (1838–1916) was called the Empire Builder. He had the tireless physique and rugged features of the pioneer. He was born of Scotch and Irish stock at Rockwood, Ontario, and after attending the district school until 11 years of age, spent four years at the Rockwood Academy under the tutelage of a remarkable man, the Quaker, William Wetherald, whom he ever after revered. As a boy, James J. Hill was fired by the story of the conquests of Alexander the Great, and he longed to go to India. Some of the boys at Rockwood Academy were from the Red River country near Winnipeg, and Hill thought a visit to them would take him on the way toward the Pacific and the Orient. In the summer of 1856 he reached St. Paul, then a little village, hoping to join the trappers who penetrated the Red River country, but he was a few days too late. No other party would go until the next spring. This apparently trifling mischance determined the life of James J. Hill.

Gradually he built himself into the business of St. Paul, trading in wood, acting as transportation agent, taking long trips, reading the best accounts of the resources of the country, and questioning those who had first-hand knowledge until he became thoroughly informed regarding the fur trade, the transportation conditions, the agricultural outlook, the mineral resources, and everything which might determine the future of the Northwest. Illustrating the hardihood of the man, it is related that on one of his journeys, returning from Fort Gary, he found the crossing of the Bois de Sioux River too deep to ford and no boat to be had. He dismissed his driver, made a little raft to sustain his clothing and valise, and swam the river in which ice cakes were floating. After dressing he reached a farm house, ate a warm supper, and pressed on through the night to Morris, a 55-mile drive. He reached there just before the departure of the train in the morning.

Hill availed himself of a United States law which required all goods passing through the United States for Canada to be bonded. It had been a dead letter as far as the Canadian Red River country was concerned, but Hill found means to have it enforced. He placed a steamer on the Red River, and by the requirements of that law took away the business from the agent of the Hudson Bay Company who had held a monopoly. Donald Smith, afterwards Lord Strathcona and Mount Royal, was governor of the Hudson Bay Company. Hearing of the matter, he said "Hill must be a very able man." The company's steamer was instantly transferred to their St. Paul agent, an American citizen, Commodore Kittson. Then the competition revived. But Hill proposed a partnership, and Kittson, finding it more profitable, agreed.

Hill, Kittson, Smith, and George Stephen, afterwards Lord Mount Stephen, president of the great Bank of Montreal, became firm friends. They formed a partnership and pledged their entire fortunes to purchase from the Dutch bondholders the bankrupt St. Paul and Pacific Railroad. This road had a few miles of disconnected tracks, a franchise, and a claim on a lot of public lands on condition that it finished certain trackage before a certain date. Hill for years urged the scheme of joining it to a proposed Canadian road from Winnipeg and so controlling the traffic of the rich country of the Red River of the North. He talked over all the other partners and at length succeeded in inducing the Dutch bond-holders, to whom the bankrupt road was worthless, to sell for $280,000 cash—all the partners could raise—and promises of several millions secured by the property. He was able to get the tangled court action decided just in time so that by almost superhuman efforts the required track was finished one day before the land grant would have been lost. Within a few years the St. Paul and Pacific was a prosperous money-maker. Settlers poured in on the rich lands it served, and its profits correspondingly increased. All this was greatly to the chagrin of the Northern Pacific Railroad, which had also an eye on the Red River country.

Then Hill and his partners turned westward, building the St. Paul, Minneapolis and Manitoba into North Dakota and giving an outlet to the province of Manitoba. Next they promoted the Canadian Pacific. But when the latter became a reality, Hill withdrew from its directorate, and Smith and Stephen withdrew from the directorate of the other two roads, to avoid criticism, though all remained close friends and mutual stockholders.

And now Hill, who had carefully informed himself of the resources of Montana, first promoted through local names the Montana Central Railroad, in order to preempt the territory and prevent its falling altogether to the Northern Pacific and Union Pacific systems. Meanwhile he was obtaining the permission of the Government to build through the Indian and military reservations that separated the termini of the Manitoba and Montana roads. When all was ready, he persuaded his directors to purchase the Montana Central, and in less than eight months constructed a first-class railroad connecting the two lines.

Meanwhile he had obtained a fine terminus in St. Paul, another at the head of Lake Superior, a friendly agreement over the Burlington to Chicago, a fleet of steamers on the Great Lakes to Buffalo, and elevators in Buffalo. The system took the name the Great Northern. Its road bed was well constructed, curves wide, grades a minimum, and finances of the strongest. When the Northern Pacific and the Union Pacific went into receiverships in the depression of 1893, the Great Northern stood firm.

But Hill was not content. He wished to build to the Pacific. Meticulous and exhaustive surveys were made. Building began in 1890. In January, 1893, the stretch of 834 miles from Pacific Junction, Mont., to Everett on Puget Sound was completed. The great Cascade tunnel, avoiding the switchback, was completed in 1900. The Great Northern had become transcontinental.

Hill was ever on the watch for economy in service. His roads were all built with minimum curves and grades. The Great Northern has but little track above 4,000 feet in crossing the divide. Hill gave frequent orders to diminish the number of empty or idle cars, and he also promoted such freight schedules as gave each engine maximum duty. He found that with the completion of the line to Puget Sound more cars were required for westbound than for eastbound traffic. To avoid pulling back empties he made so low a rate for Washington lumber that presently the tide was reversed. Then he sent agents to seek Japanese and Chinese markets for goods which Europe had been furnishing, and made such rates on steel and other commodities of the Eastern states as again balanced his east and west freight. He was continually taking measures to build up local traffic, by promoting emigration, by encouraging a diversification of farm products, by starting new local industries, and in other ways. He spent several hundred thousand dollars of his own money in buying choice cattle and swine in England and Scotland and distributing them in many counties of Minnesota to improve the local breeds for the production of milk, beef, and pork. He ran a model farm near St. Paul where he showed how prize winners were produced and how poor land could be made productive by able farming. He made many addresses on agricultural and business subjects, wherein he inculcated diversified farming and better methods of business in all lines. By all these activities Hill fostered the business of the Great Northern and added to its steady prosperity, as well as the prosperity of the settlers.

With his ally, J. Pierpont Morgan, Hill fought several gigantic railroad battles. The Northern Pacific system was in receivership in 1893. Its lines penetrated deep into the northern territory which was occupied by the Great Northern. To prevent the Northern Pacific from falling into unfriendly hands, whereby cut-throat competition and discriminatory rates might be established, the Hill and Morgan combination purchased a large minority holding of Northern Pacific stock, sufficient under the usual practices of those days to insure a friendly board of directors after the reorganization. Hill became virtually in control of the Northern Pacific, and installed those savings which had made the Great Northern prosperous.

Hill felt that these two transcontinental roads under his direction required a friendly eastern extension in order to be in position to give attractive through rates for Eastern freight to the Pacific Coast and the Orient. He and Morgan discussed it, and after an unsuccessful negotiation with the Northwestern, they purchased the Chicago, Burlington and Quincy system outright from its stockholders, at a price per share some 20 points above the prevailing market. The Burlington was then absorbed in equal parts by the Great Northern and Northern Pacific systems.

E. H. Harriman, however, with his Union Pacific

system, had no liking for these arrangements. Without exciting suspicion until the very last, the Union Pacific interest purchased in one month enough common and preferred stock in the Northern Pacific to give them a voting control in the election of its directors, and thereby in the half interest in the Burlington which it had just acquired. Some of this stock they procured from Hill's unsuspecting friends. When the coup was accomplished they broke the news to Hill and Morgan.

But even the astute Harriman overlooked one loophole— he did not control a majority of the common stock. There was a provision in the Northern Pacific charter whereby a majority vote of the common stock could retire any or all of the preferred stock on January 1 of any year. Hill and Morgan went into the market and bought common stock until their strong minority had become a majority. Outsiders, not realizing the inner meaning of this battle of the giants, sold short, and in attempts to cover, ran the price up to $1,000 a share on May 9, 1901. When Harriman knew that his scheme was beaten, he consented to a truce and compromise. But it is said that this affair was very profitable to him, as, indeed, were almost all of his security transactions.

In order to prevent such raids in future Hill and Morgan organized the Northern Securities Holding Corporation to hold the stocks of their railroads. But after several years of litigation this corporation was ordered to be dissolved by decision of the Supreme Court of the United States. The decision was based on the Sherman Antitrust Act of 1890 and was handed down by a vote of five judges against four. By that time, however, the Great Northern, the Northern Pacific, and the Burlington had become such a homogeneous loyal system that the danger of assaults upon it had passed away.

The character of James J. Hill as a strong, honest, shrewd, economical administrator, loyal to local interests, who rose by his own efforts from nothing to great power and who was ready to spend his resources for the good of his State and his friends, is on the whole very engaging.

E. H. Harriman (1848–1909), Hill's great rival, reached his eminence by quite another path. Harriman was the son of an Episcopal clergyman, and during his boyhood the family were in poverty, although toward the end of it they received a legacy. At 22 years of age he was a broker's clerk in Wall Street and was soon able to buy himself a seat on the New York Stock Exchange. He displayed great shrewdness, and made money on almost every deal, both on rising and falling markets. He took large profits from several panic situations.

At 40 years of age, Harriman was drawn by Stuyvesant Fish into the management of the Illinois Central Railroad, and became vice-president. Harriman became close in a business way with the Rockefeller interests and the international bankers, Kuhn, Loeb & Company, especially with Mr. Schiff of that firm. When the Union Pacific road went into receivership in the depression of 1893, Harriman and his friends bought it for $58,000,000. He immediately spent great sums to improve and extend the trackage and to add to the rolling stock and other facilities. On the death of Collis P. Huntington in 1899 a shrewd coup brought Harriman the control of the Southern Pacific also, and in addition he obtained control of the Oregon lines and many other extensions. Thus by 1903 Harriman controlled one of the greatest railroad systems in the world and used his powerful position to attempt to gather in several other great systems. His old patron, Fish, angered him by giving the 'Frisco road entry into New Orleans, and Harriman caused his expulsion from the Illinois Central.

These were the times of President Roosevelt's vigorous expressions. He did not hesitate to class Harriman among his "malefactors of great wealth" and called him "an undesirable citizen." The geologist, John Muir, and others, however, give a very much more pleasing impression of Harriman. At all events, three great constructive works of his will be long remembered, besides his building up of the great combined railroad system. I refer to the Lucin cut-off over the Great Salt Lake, the San Francisco relief, and the conquest of the Colorado River.

Formerly the Union Pacific line from Ogden skirted the north end of the Great Salt Lake and made a wide circuit before taking up its western course toward San Francisco. E. H. Harriman pushed to success the audacious project of building an embankment for the road 32 miles across the lake. A fill of gravel and great rocks was dumped into the lake from a temporary track. In some places the fill sank down and down in the soft bottom, forcing up great banks of mud on either side, sometimes above the surface of the lake. At first, trestle work was used in the deeper portions of the lake, but the trestle work was later replaced by fill, and rock was used more and more in place of gravel in the fill. Again and again, after the railroad embankment was in use, sinkings occurred, and the cut-off had to be temporarily abandoned while more filling was done, but finally the embankment became stable. It cuts off 44 miles from the old route, and avoids troublesome grades. At one point there was formerly a climb of 680 feet, whereas the cut-off is, of course, perfectly level and straight across the lake and has easy grades beyond.

The San Francisco earthquake of April 18, 1906, resulted in breaking the water mains, emptying the reservoirs, and setting the city on fire in numerous places. For three days the fire raged, destroying 28,000 buildings and making 200,000 people homeless. The fire was stopped only by dynamiting whole rows of the finest mansions on Van Ness Avenue. E. H. Harriman went immediately to the city and put his great railway system at its disposal. It is said that he evacuated 200,000 people over its lines without charge.

PLATE 67

James J. Hill. Photograph by Pach Bros., New York

PLATE 68

Edward H. Harriman.   Courtesy of Mrs. Harriman

Harriman's greatest single act of public service was the saving of the Imperial Valley and all the irrigation area that is or can ever be watered from the lower Colorado River by gravity flow. Ages ago the Gulf of California extended as far northwest as San Gorgonio Mountain. But the Colorado River, bringing down from its mountain sources enormous quantities of sediment, built a bar across the Gulf and turned its upper part into an inland salt sea, which eventually dried up. The bar of silt was but a feeble barrier to the Colorado, and in some of its great floods it crossed the bar and emptied itself into the Salton Sink, as the great depression is called. Thus a fresh-water lake was formed, and quantities of sediment deposited on top of the salt crust. Many times the fickle Colorado turned from the Gulf to the Sink and back again, and hundreds of feet of sediment were laid down in the Salton Sink.

About the year 1900, hundreds of years having elapsed since the Colorado had emptied into the Salton Sink, the California Development Company brought in an irrigating system. Their main canal left the Colorado near Yuma, followed through Mexican territory nearly parallel to the river for a long distance until it reached the old dry bed of the Colorado called the Alamo, and then, from about 40 miles west of the Colorado, struck northward into southern California. They advertised the irrigated country under the name of Imperial Valley, by which it is known to this day. The irrigated land, under cloudless skies and tropical heat, proved of the very highest fertility. By 1905, 12,000 inhabitants were living there, raising cotton, melons, grapes, asparagus, citrus fruits, olives, figs, dates, pomegranates, apricots, peaches, and pears. As many as six cuts of alfalfa could be made in a year.

But the river silted up the upper part of the canal, so that the irrigation supply grew short. The Company was unable to dredge the canal sufficiently and in season, and in October, 1904, it cut through a new water entrance from the Colorado about 4 miles below Yuma. They intended to close this before the floods came, when their original entrance would carry ample water. The Colorado itself is more or less trustworthy as to the times of its flooding, but its great southern branch, the Gila, is altogether capricious. Unexpectedly four floods occurred when the records of 27 years would have indicated expectation of none, and the new canal entrance became a large branch of the Colorado.

The California Development Company had not the means to cope with this great peril, and appealed to the Southern Pacific Railroad. Epes Randolph, acting president of the Harriman Lines in Arizona and Mexico, telegraphed that the expense "might easily run into three quarters of a million dollars." Harriman replied: "Are you certain you can put the river back into the old channel?" Mr. Randolph replied: "I am certain that it can be done." Harriman replied, "Go ahead and do it." Several promising plans were tried in 1905 at the recommendation of able engineers, but December, 1905, came with the river still uncontrolled. By that time a lake of 150 square miles surface had been created, and the Southern Pacific main line was threatened to be submerged.

It was proposed to dredge out the original canal so as to save the settlers' farms, and then to build a barrier across the new entrance. A powerful dredge was ordered from San Francisco, but owing to the great fire there it was not ready. Nor could the barrier be built until the summer floods of 1906 had so far advanced as to prevent its satisfactory completion. Already $200,000 had been expended and little accomplished. Mr. Harriman was in the midst of the rescue of San Francisco from its great disaster. But he authorized $250,000 more for the fight against the Colorado. The Southern Pacific Railroad assumed full control of the situation, and their engineers replaced those of the California Development Company. The Salton Sea was rising 7 inches a day over an area of 400 square miles. Cataracts on the river were cutting back toward Yuma sometimes nearly a mile a day. The river had carried into the Sink in 9 months a yardage of silt four times as great as the whole Panama Canal. Eminent engineers of America and foreign lands who visited the ground felt that the chance of saving Imperial Valley was practically negligible.

Epes Randolph, acting on his own judgment in opposition to expert advice, proposed to line the bottom of the crevasse with a brush mattress, and thereon to build a rock fill till the break was closed. Huge preparations were made during the summer flood. They borrowed 300 of the side dumping cars called "battleships" which had been used for the Lucin cut-off in Utah. They brought in 10 complete Southern Pacific work trains. They levied on all the rock quarries within 400 miles and opened an immense new one. They hauled tremendous quantities of gravel from near the Mexican boundary. From Los Angeles they brought 1,100 piles each 90 feet in length, and 19,000 feet of heavy timber for trestles. All the Indian tribes in the United States and Mexico within easy reach were mobilized, and many Mexicans and stray Americans were added. The Mexican Government put the district under martial law.

In August, 1906, the great push began. In 20 days they blanketed the bed of the river with a mattress woven of brush, baling wire, and steel cable. A railway trestle was built across the crevasse, a rock fill was rapidly made, and by October 10 only a small stream was flowing by the dam. But now the pressure broke through in a new place, and the river carried away a 200-foot head gate that had cost over $100,000.

Disappointed but not disheartened, they dredged out the main canal, and began preparations to close the breach again. Operations were pushed night and day, and after half a mile of dam had been built by November 4, 1906, all the water was turned down the proper Colorado channel.

But it was still the furious Colorado. On December 7, 1906, a great flood came down the Gila River, and an earthen levee south of the rock dam went out. The fight was on again. Already the Southern Pacific had spent about $1,500,000. It had removed its main-line tracks out of all danger and had no pecuniary interest of importance to defend. Mr. Harriman asked President Roosevelt if the Government would share the cost of a new battle against the river. The President replied to the effect that Congress had adjourned for Christmas, that he held the railroad as responsible for the state of affairs, and that he regarded it as their imperative duty to close the break at once. He held out some hope that the Government might do something later.

If Harriman withheld further action the Imperial Valley would be lost in the Salton Sea, its inhabitants would be forced to flee through a terrible desert, the river would eat a canyon back to Yuma and beyond, the Laguna dam on which the Government had already expended millions would be carried away, and the whole region of 2,000,000 acres, then a garden of irrigation, would thereafter be a lost wilderness. President Roosevelt was then calling Harriman a "malefactor" and "an undesirable citizen." The statement was unwarranted that the Southern Pacific had been responsible for the disaster: it had acted only the part of a generous friend.

Harriman explained these points to the President and said: "I am giving authority to the Southern Pacific officers in the West to proceed at once with efforts to repair the break, trusting that the Government, as soon as you procure the necessary Congressional action, will assist us with the burden." Roosevelt replied: "Am delighted to receive your telegram. . . . As soon as Congress reassembles I can recommend legislation which will provide against a repetition of the disaster and make provision for the equitable distribution of the burden."

On December 20, 1906, Harriman ordered the break to be closed. At that time 160,000,000 cubic feet of water were discharging into the Salton Sea every hour. The engineers determined to build two trestles on 90-foot piles across the crevasse and make a fill with rock from 1,000 flat cars without waiting to make a mattress. Three times in a month the river washed away their trestles. The fourth time they held. On January 27, 1907, the rock fill began. The rocks brought from the quarries were often too large to be pushed off the cars. They were cracked with pop shots of dynamite on their waiting trains while men swarmed upon the trains stopping over the crevasse and dumped carload after carload of rocks into the stream. It sounded like a great battle with artillery in action. On February 10 the crevasse was closed and the Colorado was forced back into its old channel. Chief Engineer Cory testified before a committee of the House of Representatives:

For three weeks, two divisions of the Southern Pacific system, embracing about 1,200 miles of main line, were practically tied up because of our demands for equipment and facilities. We had a thousand flat cars exclusively in our service, and shipping from Los Angeles' seaport—San Pedro—was practically abandoned for two weeks until we returned a considerable portion of the equipment. It was simply a case of putting rock into that break faster than the river could take it away . . . In 15 days after we got the trestle across and dumped the first carload of rock we had the river stopped. In that time I suppose we handled rock faster than it was ever handled before. . . . We hauled it from Patagonia, Ariz., 480 miles, over two mountain passes; from Tacna, 60 miles to the east; from three other quarries— one on the Santa Fe, one on the Salt Lake road, and one on the Southern Pacific—all near Colton, 200 miles to the west, and over the San Gorgonio Pass. . . . We brought in about 3,000 flat cars loaded with rock from these immense distances, and we put in, all together about 80,000 cubic yards of rock in 15 days.

Then, in order to prevent the river from ever breaking through again, the Southern Pacific reinforced and doubled the levees all up and down its banks for miles. Many years have elapsed and that sound work still stands.

Although President Roosevelt and after him President Taft repeatedly recommended Congress to reimburse at least a part of the $3,000,000 spent by the Southern Pacific in conquering the Colorado River, it was never done. At one time a majority of the Committee recommended a reimbursement of $733,000, but a strong minority described it as a raid on the Federal Treasury, a gift of the people's money to a soulless corporation. The bill never passed. When Mr. Harriman visited the spot shortly before his death, a reporter asked him if he regretted the large expenditure. "No," said Harriman. "This valley was worth saving, wasn't it? We have the satisfaction of knowing that we saved it, haven't we?"

THE AUTOMOBILE

Prior to the beginning of World War II the country passed through a depression quite as severe as that of 1836 to 1840, which temporarily ruined Matthias W. Baldwin, the locomotive builder. Unemployment was rife. For many years the invention of labor-saving devices had been making idle many of the hands necessary in olden times to produce article after article of public demand. But on the other hand invention had been creating new industry after new industry, in which all the labor thrown out of employment by invention had been reemployed. However, the balance of production and consumption became deranged, and the outbreak of World War II threw the world back into a chaos of misery, just as it was recovering from the depression. One cannot pierce the fog to see clearly what social state will follow it.

No new industry in recent times has had a larger share in preventing unemployment than the rise of the automobile. It has been said that 21,000,000 motor cars were in use in the United States in 1930, and that they were renewed on the average of once in seven years. The production, upkeep, sales, fuel supply, driving, road maintenance, and other requirements of this enormous business entailed the payment of billions of dollars a year to employees. And yet this business did not exist in 1900.

No one man has had as great a share in the spread of the automobile as Henry Ford. His wholesale production methods penetrated widely throughout industry. They became our salvation when World War II forced America to become the arsenal of democracy. They were adopted for building tanks and planes and engines. The great automobile manufactories ceased making cars and built far greater plants for war purposes in which new processes were applied and the wholesale methods of production and interchangeability of parts were pushed far beyond anything known before. Industry rose inspiringly to the emergency, but the waste of rare and precious resources was tragic.

The automobile as we know it became a possibility with the invention in 1876 by Dr. N. A. Otto of Cologne, Germany, of the four-cycle gas engine. For some years engineers considered it necessary to build heavy gas and oil engines to run at no more than 200 revolutions per minute. In 1883, however, Dr. Gottlieb Daimler, greatly lightening the four-cycle engine, adapted it to run at 800 to 1,000 revolutions per minute, and soon applied one to a motor bicycle. In 1887 he ran a gasoline motor car. French builders obtained the right to use the Daimler engine, and by 1895 Levassor, of Panhard and Levassor, had devised the arrangement of parts which prevails in the modern automobile.

In Levassor's automobile, as at present, the engine was placed under a hood in front, parallel to the wheel base. Back of the engine was the flywheel, clutch, and variable-speed gearing connecting to a transmission shaft parallel to the wheels. Levassor considered the loosening of the clutch and shifting of gears as merely an awkward temporary expedient, but it was over 30 years before "free wheeling" began to improve it. As in the modern automobile, Levassor employed a differential gearing to permit the rear wheels of the machine to go at unequal speeds on curves, but he employed an auxiliary axle and chain drive which have since been discarded. All these parts formed with their frame and wheels the chassis, on which, as in present practice, Levassor supported the separate body. Although great improvements in detail have been made in the engine, frame, and body, in braking, and in other features, the modern automobile is still based on the Levassor type.

In America, George B. Selden, of Rochester, N. Y., applied in 1879 for a patent on a horseless carriage with gasoline engine of the Brayton type which approximated the Diesel. Selden, though he manufactured no machines, kept this application alive in the Patent Office for 16 years, and obtained in 1895 a patent under which he claimed royalty on all motor cars driven by internal combustion engines. His claim was admitted, and in 1910, 71 manufacturers forming the Association of Licensed Automobile Manufacturers were paying to Selden's patent license fees of 1½ per cent on their machines.

Charles E. Duryea[3], an American pioneer automobile builder, was born on his father's farm near Canton, Ill., December 15, 1861. His boyhood came just at the time when machinery was being rapidly adopted for farm use, so that he became quite familiar with a wide variety of mechanical devices. Transportation had always fascinated him, however, and almost as soon as he learned to read he obtained what books and magazines he could on the subject. When in his teens, velocipedes came into vogue and from descriptions in some magazines he built one out of old carriage wheels. A short while after that he went to what was known as a seminary, and for his graduation

[3] The accounts of Duryea and Haynes are taken from Ann. Rep. Smithsonian Inst. for 1929, pp. 553–558, 1930.

PLATE 69

First Duryea automobile.   In the National Museum

PLATE 70

First Haynes automobile.   In the National Museum

thesis in 1882 he chose the subject "Rapid transit," discussing transportation on land, on water, and in the air.

Duryea taught school for a year and then tried his hand at the carpenter and millwright trades for a while. Later he went to St. Louis and got a job in a bicycle-repair shop. Three years later he was selling bicycles of his own design and made by several manufacturers. He continued in the bicycle business for over 10 years, both in St. Louis and in Washington, D. C., and as a side line, was a licensed steam engineer. At the Ohio State Fair at Columbus in 1886 he had an exhibit of his bicycles. Next to his stand a gasoline engine had been exhibited, the first he had ever seen. It was a clumsy affair weighing about a ton, although only developing 2 horsepower. The carburetor consisted of a tin tank larger than a wash boiler stuffed with excelsior. Duryea felt that in time this engine would be refined into a more portable unit. Nor did he have long to wait, for that same year he read of Daimler's newly patented light-weight engine. By 1891 he concluded that the public would be ready to buy horseless carriages as soon as he could make them.

That summer he went to Springfield, Mass., where the Ames Manufacturing Company was making bicycles for him, and while the plant was shut down in August began some gasoline engine experiments. Daimler engines were then available in the United States but they seemed too big and heavy for Duryea's purpose. While his brother Franklin, a toolmaker for the Ames Company, conducted the experiments, Charles, with a pencil figured and sketched and sketched and figured for the rest of the year on a design for a gasoline buggy.

Duryea set out to raise money to build the machine. Luckily he found a man in Springfield willing to risk some of his, so Duryea set to work early in 1892. First he hired a draftsman to make detailed drawings of the various parts. Then he let contracts to make the parts. He rented the second floor of a machine shop in March.

He purchased and brought to the shop a lady's phaeton, with top, regulation oil lamps, whip socket, and so on. Assembling began as soon as the parts started to come in. With the completion of each unit for the buggy it was tested and any changes thought desirable were made, but by September 12, 1892, it was so nearly completed that the engine was cranked up and the machine operated on the shop floor to find out "how powerfully it pulled." When fully assembled the next month, test runs were made in an empty lot adjoining the shop and also on the streets of Springfield at night when there were less horses to scare.

While the carriage did not stall, the engine proved disappointingly low in power, so that shortly after these October trials the machine was taken back into the shop, the engine torn out, and a new one started. Duryea felt, too, that heavier parts were needed about the rest of the vehicle so he dismantled the whole during the winter and started a second one immediately. Following the same design as the first, the second carriage was finished late in the summer of 1893 and successfully tried out on the road in September of that year. Thirty years later this same machine came to light in a barn in Springfield, Mass., covered with dirt, its metal parts thick with rust, and its leather dashboard stiff and hard. The National Museum was immediately notified and, disheveled as it is, it now proudly heads the line of historic automobiles there (Plate 69).

Duryea realized after seeing a Daimler car and an electric vehicle at the World's Fair in Chicago, that he had aimed too low in putting out a machine to sell for $500, so he and his brother began immediately on a third, this time a "quality" car.

As with the earlier carriages, this one went through much preliminary experimenting with engines, transmissions, electric ignition, and the like, but eventually, in March, 1895, a 2-cylinder, pneumatic-tired buggy was on the road. It had some of the features of the modern automobile such as a water-cooled engine with water pump, a bevel-gear transmission with three speeds forward and reverse, electric ignition, and, like the preceding cars, it had a rigid front axle with steering knuckles at the ends. It was steered by a tiller handle, the up-and-down motion of which changed the speeds—"one hand control."

On Thanksgiving Day, 1895, America's first automobile race took place, the run being over snowy roads from Chicago to Waukegan, a distance of 52 miles. Duryea entered this same machine and won the race and the money prize. It was the only car in the race (the others were foreign makes or electrics) to cover the distance without being pushed and to return to its garage the same day.

In the meantime the Duryea Motor Wagon Company had been organized in Springfield, Mass., and, during the winter of 1895–96, 13 motor carriages were built and sold—the first automobiles to be regularly made for sale in the United States. Thus the great ambition of America's pioneer automobile manufacturer, Charles E. Duryea, became an accomplished fact.

If an automobile could have been purchased anywhere in the United States in 1890, it is more than likely that Elwood G. Haynes (1857–1926) would never have had the notion of building one. He was engaged in the production of oil and gas and his duties obliged him to travel constantly with a horse and buggy. He wanted a faster conveyance and could not find one, so he undertook to make one for himself.

Haynes prepared for college and entered Worcester Polytechnic Institute at Worcester, Mass., in 1877. His thesis on graduation dealt with "The Effect of Tungsten on Iron and Steel." He returned home, but three years later he enlisted in a postgraduate course in chemistry and metallurgy at Johns Hopkins University. A year later he became the science teacher in the Eastern Indiana

Normal School at his home in Portland and taught for three years. Just about that time the natural gas and oil business began to boom around Portland. Haynes joined the new industry and from 1889 to 1892 he served as manager of the Portland Natural Gas & Oil Company. Visiting the company's wells by horse and buggy proved too slow for him and led him to seek a speedier substitute.

In 1892 he moved to Kokomo, Ind., and soon afterward made some rough sketches of a self-propelled vehicle. In the fall of 1893 Haynes bought a single-cylinder, 1-horsepower gasoline engine, made by the Sintz Gas Engine Company of Grand Rapids, Mich. Next, after much deliberation and examination of various styles of carriages, he purchased a single buggy body as being best suited for his proposed vehicle. He had considered the problem of putting together the two units which he had already purchased into a workable whole, and had his plans rather completely worked out before deciding in which of the machine shops of Kokomo he would have the work done. But late in the autumn he made financial arrangements with Elmer Apperson, proprietor of the Riverside Machine Works, to do the work. Haynes stood alone in having faith in the successful development of his idea, and it was only upon his assuming full responsibility for the success or failure of the machine that Apperson would take on the job.

His first disappointment came when he realized that the heavy vibration of the engine was far more than the buggy he had bought could stand and that a special framework would have to be constructed. Accordingly a hollow square of steel tubing was made and the buggy seat, floor, and dash secured to it. The rear cross member of the square constituted the rear axle and the engine was swung within the square and just in front of the axle. By means of sprocket chains the engine power was transmitted to a countershaft forward beneath the seat

PLATE 71

Balzer motor wagon. In the National Museum

PLATE 72

Henry Ford. Photograph by Harris and Ewing, Washington, D. C.

and from there back to the rear wheels by another set of chains. As the work progressed, Apperson and his brother Edgar, a bicycle-repair man, became more and more interested in the machine and numerous suggestions made by them pertaining to the mechanical arrangement as well as the mode of construction were incorporated. A flat rectangular gasoline tank was installed under the floorboards, while the water tank for cooling found a place under the seat cushion with a small rubber hose connecting it to the engine. The machine had no radiator. The engine was started by cranking from the side, the crank being poked between spokes of the right rear wheel.

By the 1st of July, 1894, the machine stood ready for the finishing touches. It had solid rubber-tired wire wheels and a tiller handle steering mechanism. On July 4 Haynes decided to give it a road test. A horse-drawn carriage pulled the machine 3 or 4 miles out into the country. For safety's sake the faithful horse was first driven some distance to the rear. Then they cranked the engine, Haynes and Apperson got aboard, Haynes threw in the friction clutch, and the horseless buggy moved forward out Pumpkinvine Pike. For a mile and a half two delighted men "flew" at an estimated speed of 6 or 7 miles an hour, then turned the machine around and drove all the way into town and to Haynes' house without a stop.

Haynes now had the horseless carriage he had been looking for since 1890. He abandoned the gas business and busied himself about the commercial possibilities of this new transportation agent. Haynes entered his car in the Chicago auto race of 1895 and drove it there for the meet. Though he did not win the race he did get a prize of $150 for having the best-balanced motor of any of the machines there. In 1898 he organized the Haynes-Apperson Automobile Company, and built 50 cars that year in spite of the warnings of advisors that the horseless carriage was only a plaything for the wealthy. After four years as president of this company he became president of the Haynes Automobile Company, serving in this capacity for a number of years but eventually retiring to resume his work in metallurgy. In this field he continued actively until his death in 1926. Even when president of the automobile company, Haynes gave his main attention to the metallurgical side of the industry. He was a pioneer in the introduction of nickel, steel, and aluminum in engine construction and also was much interested in the improvement of the carburetor.

For upwards of 16 years Haynes cherished his first horseless carriage, but in 1910 he reluctantly parted with it to the National Museum, where it now stands second in the line of America's pioneer automobiles (Plate 70).

We have referred already in Chapter VII to Stephen M. Balzer's pioneer motor wagon of 1894, with its rotating radial cylinders and fixed crank shaft, as in some ways the pioneer of the radial airplane engine development of the present day. This machine is also in the National Museum collection (Plate 71).

By far the most outstanding and astounding thing in the automobile business, or perhaps in any other, was the rise of Henry Ford and the Ford automobile. He was born on his father's farm near Dearborn, Mich., in the year 1863, of English and Dutch ancestry. As a boy at school, and working out of school hours, and in vacations on the farm, he showed a strong taste for mechanics. With homemade small tools he took to repairing watches and clocks. At 16 years of age he left the farm and got a job in a machinist's shop, where he worked 10 hours a day. But in addition he got a night job as a jeweler between the hours of 7 and 11 p.m. After a year in the machine shop he left it to enter an engine shop, where he worked two years, and then spent several years at installing and repairing farm engines.

When Ford was 21 years of age, his father gave him 40 acres of land to lure him away from mechanics, and he cleared the land, sold lumber, removed his shop to his new home, and married in the year 1887. But not long after, he secured a job with the Detroit Edison Company and removed to Detroit, setting up his shop in his back yard. There Henry Ford began to build with his own hands his first gasoline motor car. It was completed in 1892, and after he had run it 1,000 miles he sold it for $200 in order to build a better one.

Ford's first connection with an automobile company was in 1899, when he became the Detroit Automobile Company's chief engineer. But whereas the directors wished only to turn out cars on order, Ford had already conceived the idea of making automobiles to standard pattern for the multitude. In 1902 he resigned from the company and went into business for himself. To obtain prestige he built two highly powered racing cars, the "999," named after the New York Central's famous flyer, and the "Arrow." The "999" won every race it ever entered, and on its reputation the Ford Motor Company was formed in 1903, capitalized at $100,000. Actually but $28,000 was paid in, but within 25 years the company's assets exceeded $1,000,000,000. The company has never sold bonds or borrowed money, for it has been built up entirely by turning back profits into the business. Henry Ford and his son Edsel are now its sole owners, for they bought out the minority stockholders in 1919.

For several years the Ford Motor Company built various types of small cars, but in 1909 it concentrated on the famous "Model T." Mr. Ford expressed humorously his determination to keep to an unvarying construction by the remark: "Any customer can have a car painted any color that he wants, so long as it is black." In the beginning the Ford touring car was sold for $850, but when production of it ended, in 1928, it sold for $310. Meanwhile the machine had been much improved, Ford had raised wages over threefold, and materials cost fully double what they did in 1908. Toward the end Model T machines were being turned out at the rate of 2,000,000 annually.

The secret of this extraordinary development was in novel methods of mass production. Subdivision of labor was pushed very far, and the work was carried to the workmen by automatic carriers in such positions that each man's contribution was made with a minimum of time and labor. No man used more than one tool, and the various lines of assembly all converged in steady movement till the car left the shop under its own power. As for raw material, the Fords own their own forests, saw their logs to the right shapes without intermediate products, and the waste is distilled. Transportation is done by Ford railways and Ford steamships. From the Ford furnace the iron or steel is poured directly into shapes without reheating. As it proved too expensive to ship cars in complete form, subsidiary plants for assembly were erected at many strategic points over the world to which parts only were shipped. At first all parts were made in Detroit, but with the establishment of many assembly branches, the different parts were assigned to small branch factories, where one part only is made in each.

Henry Ford has many original ideas on social and economic problems which he has worked out from time to time. His writings on mass production, on labor problems, on the responsibilities of the manufacturers, and on the duties of citizens and officials have had wide circulation. With Thomas A. Edison and Harvey Firestone he had a close friendship, the three forming, till Edison's death, a famous triumvirate of successful inventors with congenial tastes.

Starting from practically nothing in 1900, the automobile business of the United States grew until its annual output was by 1930 over 2,900,000 cars for passengers, and 600,000 automobile trucks. The wholesale value of motor vehicles, parts, and tires produced was $3,330,000,000.

PLATE 73

Left: Wilbur Wright.   Right: Orville Wright.   Courtesy of the National Advisory Committee for Aeronautics

PLATE 74

Samuel P. Langley

MECHANICAL TRANSPORTATION

Including all types of motor vehicles of United States design, 560,000 were exported from the United States and Canada in 1930. They were valued at $350,000,000. American automobiles are found predominating over foreign makes in most foreign countries, often specially made with right-hand drive to suit the custom of the country. The American motor output in 1930 was 87 per cent of that of the whole world.

THE AIRPLANE

Prior to the work of the Wrights, numerous experiments in gliding were made, notably by Otto Lilienthal in Germany, Percy S. Pilcher in England, and by Octave Chanute and his assistant, Augustus M. Herring, in America. These men were keenly alive to the scientific aspects of the problem. They took up gliding, not merely as a sport, but as a necessary school for obtaining knowledge of the aerodynamic factors involved in soaring flight and skill in its actual practice, before venturing to add motors to their machines. Lilienthal and Pilcher both fell martyrs to the cause of flying. Herring died in poverty after many discouragements.

The work of Lilienthal had great influence in attracting the attention of Wilbur and Orville Wright to this field. They also had close and helpful relations with Dr. Chanute.

Some very significant contributions were made three quarters of a century earlier by Sir George Cayley. He was a physicist, mathematician, and engineer of great ability. He worked out theoretically, and to some extent in practice, the problems of wing loads, bending moments, and the best constructions to combine lightness and strength. He it was who conceived the idea of the biplane with its bridge bracing. He foresaw the great importance of streamline construction to avoid head resistance, saying "every pound of direct resistance that is done away with, will support 30 pounds of additional weight without any additional power." He prescribed the identity of the position of the center of pressure on the wings with the center of gravity of the loaded plane. In a glider of 300 square feet wing area which he built, he employed both horizontal and vertical rudders, thus anticipating in part modern methods of control. His glider, which would lift a man from the ground when he ran with it, was cracked up, though not until, according to contemporary accounts, it had made gliding flights of 900 feet.

That curvature of the wing surfaces was required for gliding flight was known to F. H. Wenham of England about 1860, and practiced by Prof. J. J. Montgomery, Otto Lilienthal, and by Chanute and Herring. Lilienthal expressed the matter thus clearly: "For a long time I have assumed that the thickening which all birds' wings have at the front edge produces a favorable effect in soaring flight . . . By means of free sailing models I have now learned that . . . the thickened front edge is not only harmless, but . . . helpful." Herring also in applying for a patent, December 11, 1898, described and claimed curved wing sections of unequal curvature above and below.

Before taking up the Wright brothers' persevering campaign which led to their world-renowned flights at Kitty Hawk on December 17, 1903, let us now consider the work of two men who approached the problem by the application of motors to flying machines without preliminary practice in gliding flight. These were Sir Hiram S. Maxim of England and Dr. Samuel P. Langley, third Secretary of the Smithsonian Institution.

Maxim made experiments on models in a wind tunnel 3 feet square and 12 feet long to determine best wing sections and to measure parasitic resistances. He also used a whirling arm, whereon he whirled models of wings and propellers in a circle of 200 feet diameter at speeds up to 90 miles per hour. With data thus obtained, Sir

PLATE 75

Upper: Langley model No. 5. Lower: Langley model No. 5 in flight,
May 6, 1896

PLATE 76

Upper: Manly 52-h.p. radial gasoline engine, built for Langley's full
scale airplane. Weight 120 pounds. Lower: Langley's full-scale airplane poised for flight

Hiram constructed an enormous machine with total wing area of over 5,500 square feet and 4 tons weight, and provided it with a steam engine of 300 horsepower. To it he added running gear adapted for experiments on an 1,800 foot track. He did not wish the machine to actually fly, and therefore provided restraining tracks 2 feet above the level of appropriate outrigger wheels as a precaution against actual flight. However, in one test, made in 1894, during a run with 320 pounds steam pressure, the outrigger wheels were all engaged after a run of 600 feet, and after a further run a breakage set the machine free for a sort of hopping flight. Steam was then cut off, just missing perhaps a free flight.

Langley also made many experiments on the lift and drift of surfaces by use of a whirling arm. These he published in 1891 in "Experiments in Aerodynamics." He then constructed large four-wing models automatically stabilized on the dihedral-angle principle, powered by extremely light steam engines. He had gratifying success. On May 6, 1896, his 13-foot model made a flight of approximately half a mile at Quantico on the Potomac River, landing softly and unharmed when steam was exhausted. On November 28, 1896, another 13-foot model made a flight of three-fourths of a mile at the same place.

Of these experiments Langley said:

I have brought to a close the portion of the work which seemed to be specially mine—the demonstration of the practicability of mechanical flight—and for the next stage, which is the commerical and practical development of the idea, it is probable that the world may look to others. The world, indeed, will be supine if it do not realize that a new possibility has come to it, and that the great universal highway overhead is now soon to be opened.

Plate 75 shows Langley's model No. 5 at rest and in the flight of May 6, 1896.

Langley was persuaded to rescind his determination and in 1898 began the construction of a man-carrying machine for the War Department. A total allotment of $50,000 was made to him from War Department funds. No direct appropriation by Congress was ever made for that object.

By that time the development in gasoline engines led him to hope that steam power might be advantageously displaced. A contract was made with Stephen M. Balzer of New York City for a 12-horsepower light radial gasoline engine. It was intended to order a second similar one after the successful completion of the first. Mr. Balzer, however, though very cooperative, after exceeding his contract time on the large engine by many months, did not succeed in producing more than 8 horsepower. His engine was fully paid for by Langley and removed to Washington. There Charles M. Manly, Langley's engineer, made certain alterations in it, whereby he raised its output to 21 horsepower. Calculations indicating that this was insufficient, Manly designed and constructed an engine on similar lines to Balzer's, but with some features from European engine practice, some of his own invention. This Manly engine delivered 52 horsepower continuously in long tests, weighed 120 pounds without water for cooling, and was a highly efficient and creditable pioneer airplane engine. It is now on exhibition in the United States National Museum and is shown in Plate 76, which also shows the great Langley airplane for which it was built.

Langley had flown the models from a houseboat on the Potomac, catapulting them into the air by strong springs. By this method, in August 1903 a successful trial was made of an exact quarter size model of the large machine. It was powered with a small gasoline engine similar to the large one of Manly. Langley decided on the same method of launching for the large machine, though it is said that Manly advised flying on land from bicycle wheels. A large, costly houseboat was built for the purpose, with a machine shop and storage for the great

PLATE 77

Wilbur Wright at Rome, 1908

PLATE 78

Wright machine of 1908. First airplane bought by any government. In the National Museum

airplane below. Two trials were made on October 7 and December 8, 1903, with Charles M. Manly as pilot on both occasions. In the first of these trials a projecting lug caught the front wing guy post as the machine was being catapulted, wrecking the guying of the front wings, and the machine plunged into the river 150 feet from the start. In the second trial the guying of the rear wings collapsed. The machine then soared upwards, turned a complete somersault, and plunged into the river.

In 1914 Glenn Curtiss repaired the machine, placed pontoons under it, and made some flights above Lake Keuka in New York. These flights, however, being made long after flying had become a common art, and with certain changes of the machine, many of them necessary in using pontoons, can not be said to prove definitely that the great Langley machine was capable of sustained flight, though many experts are convinced that it was so because of the success attained with the similar powered model.

A very regrettable controversy [1] arose between partisans of the Wright brothers and those who admitted the airworthiness of Langley's large machine. Very harsh things were said of the Smithsonian Institution and of Secretary Walcott for having allowed Curtiss to make the tests of 1914 and for claims made in exhibiting the restored Langley machine. The present writer, upon succeeding Doctor Walcott as Secretary, published "The Relations between the Smithsonian Institution and the Wright Brothers," [2] and he altered the label on the great Langley machine to read simply as follows:

LANGLEY AERODROME
The Original Samuel Pierpont Langley Flying Machine
of 1903, Restored.
Deposited by the Smithsonian Institution. 301,613

[1] In 1941 the Wright-Smithsonian controversy came to an end through the publication of withdrawal of unwarranted claims based on the 1914 tests of the Langley plane (see Smithsonian Misc. Coll., vol. 103, No. 8, 1941). The case as stated in that publication was acceptable to Mr. Orville Wright.
[2] Smithsonian Misc. Coll., vol. 81, No. 5, 1928.

The following extracts from the account by Orville and Wilbur Wright of their experiments and their historic flights of December 17, 1903 at Kitty Hawk is taken from The Century of September 1908, by permission of the Appleton-Century Company.

In the field of aviation there were two schools. The first, . . . gave chief attention to power flight; the second, . . . to soaring flight. Our sympathies were with the latter school . . . .

After considering the practical effect of the dihedral principle [the scheme of inclined wing and tail surfaces used by Langley and others to promote automatic balance], we reached the conclusion that a flyer founded upon it . . . could be of no value in a practical way. We therefore resolved to try a fundamentally different principle. We would arrange the machine so that it would not tend to right itself. We would make it as inert as possible to the effects of change of direction or speed, and thus reduce the effects of wind-gusts to a minimum . . . . Then by some suitable contrivance, actuated by the operator, forces should be brought into play to regulate the balance.

. . . In order to meet the needs of large machines, we wished to employ some system whereby the operator could vary at will the inclination of different parts of the wings, and thus obtain from the wind forces to restore the balance which the wind itself had disturbed. . . . A happy device was discovered whereby the apparently rigid system of superposed surfaces, invented by Wenham, and improved by Stringfellow and Chanute, could be warped in a most unexpected way, so that the aeroplanes could be presented on the right and left sides at different angles to the wind. This, with an adjustable, horizontal front rudder, formed the main feature of our first glider.

. . . . . .

We began our active experiments [kite-fashion] . . . in October, 1900, at Kitty Hawk, North Carolina. . . .

We then [in 1901] turned to gliding . . . and in a few days were safely operating in twenty-seven-mile winds. . . . We found [unexpectedly] that, contrary to the teachings of the books, the center of pressure on a curved surface traveled backward when the surface was inclined, at small angles, more and more edgewise to the wind. We also discovered that in free flight, when the wing on one side of the machine was presented to the wind at a greater angle than the one on the other side, the wing with the greater angle descended, and the machine turned in a direction just the reverse of what we were led to expect when flying the machine as a kite. . . .

The experiments of 1901 were far from encouraging. . . . We saw that

PLATE 79

The Langley gold medal for aerodromics. Founded by the Smithsonian
Institution to honor the Wright brothers. Presented to them in 1910;
to Eiffel and Curtiss, 1914; to Lindbergh, 1927; and to Byrd and Manly,
1930

PLATE 80

NATIONAL ADVISORY COMMITTEE FOR AERONAUTICS

Meeting, October 19, 1939

Left to right: Brig. Gen. George H. Brett, Army Air Corps; Clinton M. Hester, Administrator, Civil Aeronautics Authority; Rear Admiral John H. Towers, Chief, Bureau of Aeronautics, Navy Department; Dr. L. J. Briggs, Director, Bureau of Standards; Col. Charles A. Lindbergh; Dr. Orville Wright; Dr. J. C. Hunsaker; Dr. George W. Lewis, Director of Aeronautical Research; Dr. Vannevar Bush, Chairman; Dr. George J. Mead, Vice Chairman, John F. Victory, Secretary; Dr. Charles G. Abbot, Secretary,

the calculations upon which all flying-machines had been based were unreliable. . . .

We had taken up aeronautics merely as a sport. We reluctantly entered upon the scientific side of it. . . . We began systematic measurements of standard surfaces, so varied in design as to bring out the underlying causes of differences noted in their pressures. Measurements were tabulated on nearly fifty of these at all angles from zero to 45 degrees, at intervals of 2½ degrees. Measurements were also secured showing the effects on each other when surfaces are superposed, or when they follow one another.

[The authors describe also the original researches they made on propeller design before employing power.]

In September and October, 1902, nearly one thousand gliding flights were made, several of which covered distances of over 600 feet. Some, made against a wind of thirty-six miles an hour, gave proof of the effectiveness of the devices for control. . . .

With accurate data for making calculations, and a system of balance effective in winds as well as in calms, we were now in a position, we thought, to build a successful power-flyer. . . .

The first flights with a power-machine were made on the 17th of December, 1903. . . . The first flight lasted only twelve seconds, a flight very modest compared with that of birds, but it was, nevertheless, the first in the history of the world in which a machine carrying a man had raised itself by its own power into the air in free flight, had sailed forward on a level course without reduction of speed, and had finally landed without being wrecked. The second and third flights were a little longer, and the fourth lasted fifty-nine seconds, covering a distance of 852 feet over the ground against a twenty-mile wind.

. . . . . .

We had not been flying long in 1904 before we found that the problem of equilibrium had not as yet been entirely solved. . . .

. . . These troubles . . . were not entirely overcome till the end of September, 1905. . . .

A practical flyer having been finally realized, we spent the years 1906 and 1907 in constructing new machines and in business negotiations. . . .

The year 1908 was a great year for the Wright brothers. They built for the United States Government the first airplane ever purchased by any government for military purposes. It was tested before great crowds at Fort Myer by Orville Wright in September. Wilbur Wright was at the same time making world records in France. The following paragraphs are from a paper by Chanute reprinted in the Smithsonian Report for 1910 from the Journal of the Western Society of Engineers, April, 1910.

The more remarkable performances which he made I have undertaken to tabulate, but I will not inflict those statistics upon you this evening. Mr. Wright established great records, however. On the 18th of December, 1908, he flew 62 miles in 1 hour and 54 minutes, this being at that time the world's record, and he beat this directly afterwards, on the 31st of December, by flying 77 miles in 2 hours 20 minutes and 23 seconds, thus winning the Michelin prize and establishing a world record, which was only beaten in the tournament at Rheims three weeks ago. In Rome he took up a great many passengers, and on one occasion he started without the use of starting weights, simply facing a wind of sufficient intensity and going up straight from the ground. Plate [77] shows one of these flights. On the 25th of September, after returning to America and after he had been universally acclaimed in this country and overwhelmed (modest man that he is) with public dinners, receptions, and medals, he encircled in flight the Statue of Liberty in New York Harbor and made a magnificent flight of 21 miles, from Governors Island to Grant's Tomb and return.

· · · · · ·

Orville Wright made a number of unofficial tests in 1908. On the 8th of September he rose to a height of 100 feet and flew 40 miles; on the 12th he made a little higher ascension, estimated by the Army officers at 200 feet, and flew 50 miles in 1 hour and 15 minutes. Altogether that year he made 14 flights. On the morning of the 17th of September he made several short flights. In the afternoon of that same day he met with a terrible accident; his propeller broke while he and Lieut. Selfridge were in mid-air, the machine falling to the earth, when Orville was seriously injured and Lieut. Selfridge was killed. This ended the tests of that year. The Government granted an extension of time and the trials were not resumed until July of this year (1909). The results this year, as you know, have been very successful. The official time test shows that on the 27th of July the machine remained in the air for 1 hour and 13 minutes, with two persons on board.

On the 30th of July the machine traveled 5 miles and back cross-country in 14 minutes, with two persons on board, at a speed which averaged over 42 miles an hour. Therefore, the machine was accepted by the Government and a premium was given the Wrights of $5,000 for the extra 2 miles of speed.

The first Wright machine accepted by our Government is now on exhibition in the United States National Museum. It is shown in Plate 78.

N.A.C.A. 8-FOOT HIGH-SPEED WIND TUNNEL

Langley Field, Va.

This tunnel is used for research on large-scale models and full-size airplane parts at air speeds from 85 mph to more than 500 mph.

Official Photograph, National Advisory Committee for Aeronautics

PLATE 82

N.A.C.A. FULL-SCALE WIND TUNNEL
Langley Field, Va.

The Brewster XF2A-1 airplane mounted for test in the full-scale tunnel, the largest wind tunnel in the world.

Official photograph, National Advisory Committee for Aeronautics

N.A.C.A. 12-FOOT FREE-FLIGHT WIND TUNNEL

Langley Field, Va.

View of test section of 12-foot free-flight wind tunnel showing dynamic scale model of modern fighting airplane in free flight.

PLATE 84

MODEL HULL UNDER TEST IN N.A.C.A. TANK

Long-range flying boats depend on improved hull shapes to take off with the heavy fuel loads necessary for transoceanic flights. Improvements worked out here have made transoceanic service possible

MECHANICAL TRANSPORTATION

On motion of Alexander Graham Bell the Regents of the Smithsonian Institution established in December, 1908, the Langley Gold Medal for Aerodromics for the primary purpose of doing honor to the Wright brothers for their great achievements. It was presented to them on Februay 10, 1910, by Senator Henry Cabot Lodge, acting for the Regents. Plate 79 shows the obverse and reverse of the medal presented. Later on it was presented to Gustave Eiffel, of Paris, for advancing the science of aerodromics by his researches relating to the resistance of the air in connection with aviation; to Glenn Curtiss for advancing the art of aerodromics by his successful development of a hydroaerodrome whereby the safety of the aviator has been greatly enhanced; to Colonel Lindbergh for his daring nonstop flight from New York to Paris on May 20 and 21, 1927; to Admiral Byrd for his remarkable employment of the airplane for North and South Polar flights, and the nonstop flight of the Atlantic Ocean, and for the scientific achievements associated therewith; and to Charles M. Manly (posthumously) for his pioneering work in the development of the airplane engine. Plate 79 also shows the reverse of the Lindbergh and Byrd medals.

THE NATIONAL ADVISORY COMMITTEE
FOR AERONAUTICS

Appreciating that the advance of the art of aviation depended on scientific research and careful experimentation, and that more and more the airplane would take its place in military and commercial affairs, Secretary Charles D. Walcott of the Smithsonian Institution exerted his powerful influence to set up the needed research establishment. In his first venture he secured authorization by the Board of Regents of the Institution in 1912 to create an advisory committee for aeronautics. But it became apparent that to enlist the cooperation of the military services, legislation was needed. This legislation was enacted under date of March 3, 1915, establishing the present National Advisory Committee for Aeronautics.

The Committee, under the terms of the law, is charged with the supervision and direction of the scientific study of the problems of flight, and is authorized to direct and conduct research and experiment in aeronautics in such laboratories as may be placed under its direction.

The Committee comprises the following fifteen members, appointed by the President and serving as such without compensation: From the War and Navy Departments, two high ranking officers each; from the Civil Aeronautics Authority, two eminent representatives; the Secretary of the Smithsonian Institution, the Chief of the United States Weather Bureau, the Director of the National Bureau of Standards, and six persons from private life, outstanding for accomplishments in aeronautics, but preferably not associated with airplane corporations.

Among the noted men who have served on the Committee are Dr. Orville Wright, General Henry H. Arnold, Admiral David W. Taylor, Dr. William F. Durand, Dr. Joseph S. Ames, Dr. Edward Warner, and Colonel Charles Lindbergh. These are but a sample of the galaxy of eminent practical and theoretical students of aeronautics who have given distinction and thoroughness to the ever-expanding and fundamental investigations promoted by the N.A.C.A.

An indispensable element which has contributed to the outstanding success of the operations of the Committee is the fact that though a Government bureau it is not a part of any of the great executive departments, but is an independent office. Thus the widely representative organization meets on a platform of independent equality for all the members. Jealousies and factions have always been absent. Other elements contributing to the success of the N.A.C.A. are its close associations with the aeronautic

PLATE 85

Official photograph, National Advisory Committee for Aeronautics

N.A.C.A. 20-FOOT FREE-SPINNING WIND TUNNEL
Langley Field, Va.

The large structure shown to the left of the photograph is the free-spinning wind tunnel in which dynamic scale models of modern airplanes are tested to determine their spinning characteristics and ability to recover from spins from movement of the control surfaces.

PLATE 86

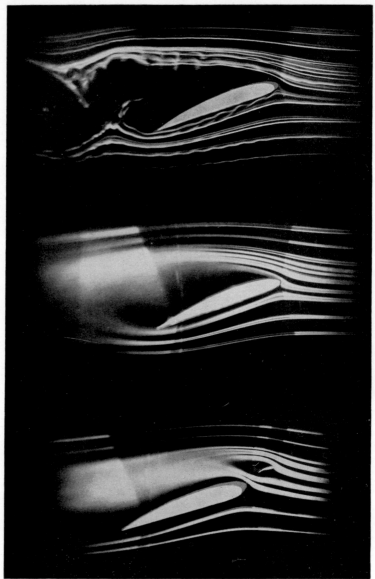

Official photograph, National Advisory Committee for Aeronautics

N.A.C.A. SMOKE-FLOW TUNNEL
Langley Field, Va.

Flow of smoke streamers over model of airplane wing. Lower figure shows improved character of flow by use of auxiliary airfoil.

industry in the United States, with the universities and technical schools, and its well-maintained touch with the development of aviation in foreign countries, through visits and correspondence by its officers and members, and by the maintenance in time of peace of a foreign observer stationed at Paris, but widely traveled.

The Committee has three experimental laboratory establishments: The Langley laboratory at Langley Field near Norfolk, Va., the Ames laboratory at Moffett Field, near San Francisco, Calif., and the Power Plants laboratory at Cleveland, Ohio. In these three experimental research institutions and the small home office in Washington the N.A.C.A. has approximately 4,000 employees. But the experiments are not confined to these three laboratories. Funds from the Committee's appropriations are assigned to the National Bureau of Standards and to numerous universities and technical schools to promote special investigations.

The N.A.C.A. has principal committees covering the following fields: aerodynamics, power plants, aircraft materials, aircraft structures, and operating problems. But under these broad headings the Committee has set up numerous technical subcommittees which deal with specific problems. A roster of the names of the many scores of specialists who serve on these subcommittees for the N.A.C.A. would include the cream of the chemists, physicists, metallurgists, meteorologists, and technicians of the United States, and of the aviation engineers from the manufacturing establishments.

The committees hold frequent meetings and recommend investigations, whereby the fundamental problems of aviation are continually being carried toward solution in the N.A.C.A. laboratories and cooperating institutions. But by far the major part of the research work comes from specific questions by the army and the navy as to the flying characteristics of airplanes of new designs. There was never a new type of military airplane that has not been bettered by the laboratory testing done at the Committee's laboratories.

Especial praise is due the energetic direction of leading officers of the Committee, and particularly to Dr. Charles D. Walcott, Dr. Joseph S. Ames, Dr. Vannevar Bush, and Dr. Jerome C. Hunsaker, who have served as Chairmen, and to Dr. George W. Lewis, Director of Aeronautical Research, and John F. Victory, Secretary, both of whom have served through almost the entire life of the organization.

The organizations at the N.A.C.A. laboratories are models of enthusiastic zeal in their fascinating researches, tempered by the most thorough knowledge and long experience of the leaders. In times of peace masterly yearly exhibitions of progress were given each May at Langley Laboratory, to which several hundred guests were invited. The arrangements were always superb, and the interest of the demonstrations and proceedings was so great that the technical men of the manufactories came from great distances to attend. The number increased every year until a second day had to be devoted for the hundreds of guests. This feature had to be given up as war approached, and the publications of original researches by the Committee also had to be sharply restricted.

The N.A.C.A. has developed at its research laboratories special instruments and techniques for investigating the important scientific factors involved in the design of airplanes. N.A.C.A wind tunnels of new and unusual types have been copied by leading foreign nations and have been the means of providing information of the utmost importance in the advancement of aeronautics.

Nearly every type of military and naval aircraft which is put into production has been investigated by the N.A.C.A. either at the Langley Memorial Aeronautical Laboratory, at Langley Field, Va., or at the Ames Aeronau-

PLATE 87

Official photograph, National Advisory Committee for Aeronautics

ENGINE PROPELLER TEST HOUSE

PLATE 88

Official photograph, National Advisory Committee for Aeronautics

N.A.C.A. 16-FOOT WIND TUNNEL
AMES AERONAUTICAL LABORATORY
Moffett Field, Calif.

tical Laboratory, Moffett Field, Calif., and improvements effected leading to better performance as regards speed, controllability, or some other characteristic. Greatly increased speed has resulted from investigations of drag reduction conducted in the Committee's full-scale wind tunnel, as well as from the development of the N.A.C.A. cowling and of the N.A.C.A. wing-nacelle location.

More efficient wing forms have been developed by the Committee with the aid of its special variable-density wind tunnel and its more recent two-dimensional tunnel. Compressibility effects, that is, the effects of the shock or compression waves of air resulting from the high speeds at which airplanes now operate, have been studied with the result that changes in design necessary to avoid these shocks could be made.

By means of the N.A.C.A. free-spinning wind tunnels, study is made of the spinning characteristics of an airplane with a small dynamic model before the full-size airplane is constructed so that it is possible to modify the design to avoid undesirable spinning characteristics. Improvements in stability and control of many airplane types have resulted from research conducted in the free-flight wind tunnel.

Contributions of outstanding importance in the design of large flying boats have been made as a result of research in the N.A.C.A. tanks, in which hull models are towed on the surface of the water and their resistance and stability determined. By means of a newly constructed impact basin, information is being obtained on the forces on seaplane hulls in landing on the water. With the aid of an instrument known as a N.A.C.A. V-G recorder and other special instruments, information on the air loads acting on airplanes in flight under various conditions has been obtained with the result that it has been possible to design airplanes so as to provide strength where most needed and to avoid unnecessary weight in the structure.

Data on the strength of structural elements used in aircraft are being obtained in the new structures laboratory leading to improvements in structural design.

Important developments in de-icing of airplane surfaces by means of heat from the engine exhaust have resulted from N.A.C.A. flight research.

At the new Aircraft Engine Research Laboratory at Cleveland, the N.A.C.A. is constructing an altitude wind tunnel in which conditions of temperature and density at 40,000 feet will be reproduced. From this equipment, information of the utmost importance on problems of aircraft-engine design will be obtained, including data on the design of superchargers, intercoolers, etc. At this laboratory, also, research on fuels, lubricants and lubrication, piston design, ignition, flame damping, and other engine problems will be conducted.

So original and powerful have been the research and experimentation of the National Advisory Committee for Aeronautics, that despite the relatively very small sums expended until war conditions supervened about 1940, other countries followed its leadership, for the most part, and appropriated its results, rather than forging ahead with their own. The world at war forced aviation into a tremendously accelerated pace of development. As speeds approaching the speed of sound became a commonplace in the use of airplanes, new problems suddenly were thrust forward, which could not be solved without far more powerful apparatus. This led to the extraordinary types of wind tunnels shown in the illustrations, and to an imperative demand for new researches which hitherto had never been necessary. So the N.A.C.A. facilities were tremendously enlarged, but even so the Committee could not hope to keep its fundamental research, as previously, far ahead of the demands of the industry. The outlook for the future ever widens.

THE COMPRESSIBILITY BURBLE

N.A.C.A. 4412 airfoil
−2° angle of attack

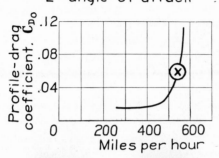

Sketch made from a photograph of
Shock waves at point ⓧ above

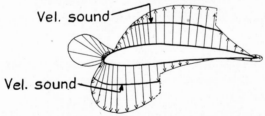

Unusual character of pressure distribution on
airfoil after compressibility shock waves
have formed at air speed of about 550 miles
per hour.

Fig. 38

PLATE 89

Autogiro invented by Juan de la Cierva. Photograph by Aero Service Corporation. Courtesy of the Autogiro Company of America, American makers

CHAPTER IX

HOUSEHOLD AND FARM INVENTIONS

MECHANICAL REFRIGERATION

FORMERLY, on long voyages, salt beef, salt pork, salt fish, and sea biscuit were the main staples. Live poultry, cattle, and hogs were sometimes carried as luxuries. For lack of fresh vegetables, scurvy often decimated the crew. Refrigeration has changed all that. Fresh provisions of all sorts are expected at sea quite as much as on land, and the cities of cold countries receive sea-borne tropical fruits of many kinds at all seasons of the year. Eggs are preserved from summer to fill the demands of winter. Long trains of refrigerator cars carry the beef slaughtered in Chicago to all parts of the country.

The paradox about all this is that the cold is almost all produced more or less directly by heat. Either heat is used in engines to produce the power which is used in refrigeration, or hot steam or flame is used to heat the cooling medium in the refrigerating apparatus. Thus, in the hottest weather, amusement halls are cooled by heat. Not only has the mechanical refrigerator largely superseded the iceman, but some residences are already made comfortable in summer by artificial cooling. Perhaps it would not be too rash to prophesy that the next century will see the sun's heat utilized to cool homes in summer as well as to heat them in winter.

The action of refrigerating machinery depends on the effects of temperature and pressure on the physical state, the expansion, and the solubility of gases. Taking ammonia for illustration, the following table shows the pressures in pounds per square inch required to condense ammonia gas into liquid form at the given temperatures. We are speaking here of water-free ammonia.

Temperature, °F.	−30	−20	−10	0	10	20	30	40	50	60	70	80	90	100
Pressure, lbs. per sq. in.	14	18	24	30	39	48	60	73	89	108	129	153	181	212

At the atmospheric pressure of about 15 pounds per square inch, we see from the table that ammonia would remain gaseous unless the temperature were lowered to about −30° F. On the other hand, if ammonia gas is heated to 100° F., it requires 212 pounds pressure per square inch, or about 14 atmospheres pressure to make it liquid. Gaseous ammonia, if kept at constant pressure, expands in volume about 2 per cent for 10° rise of temperature at temperatures between 0° and 100° F.

A large quantity of heat, called the latent heat, must always be expended to convert a liquid into its gas at the same temperature. Conversely, when a gas condenses to liquid, it gives out to the surroundings this large quantity of latent heat. In the case of ammonia, the latent heat of evaporation is exceptionally large. A pound of liquid ammonia to be evaporated at atmospheric pressure requires as much heat as it requires to warm 590 pounds of water 1° F. In ammonia refrigeration the supplying of this enormous quantity of latent heat is used to chill the surroundings. Other gases may be employed, but ammonia has exceptionally good refrigerating properties.

Water dissolves ammonia gas, and it is in the form of aqua ammonia that druggists sell it. The following table shows how many pounds of ammonia gas 100 pounds of water will dissolve at different temperatures. The figures are given for one, six, and twelve atmospheres of pressure.

POUNDS OF AMMONIA GAS DISSOLVED BY 100 POUNDS OF WATER

Temperature, °F.		27	54	77	103	126	154	175	199	222	247
Pressure, lbs. per sq. in.	15	100	66	71	32	22	11	5	—	—	—
	90	—	—	—	—	85	61	47	35	25	16
	180	—	—	—	—	—	104	82	61	47	35

From this table we see that 200 pounds of a concentrated solution of ammonia at 27° F., containing 100 pounds of ammonia gas in 100 pounds of water, if raised to a temperature of 247° F. must lose 65 pounds of ammonia gas if kept at a pressure of 12 atmospheres, 84 pounds if kept at a pressure of 6 atmospheres, and the entire 100 pounds if kept at atmospheric pressure. From the next preceding table we see further that if the gas expelled from the water at 247° F. should be forced into pipes bathed with cool water at 80° F., liquefied water-free ammonia must be produced, because at 80° F. ammonia gas is liquefied by all pressures over 153 pounds per square inch. If this liquid ammonia gas were then permitted to expand through a valve against atmospheric pressure, the energy required to supply the latent heat of evaporation, and the work of the expansion could only be gained from the heat of the liquid ammonia, which must therefore be greatly cooled on becoming a gas and would extract heat from all of its surroundings. If, finally, the cold ammonia gas after expansion is bubbled into the ammonia solution which has been much weakened by boiling off its ammonia gas, then strong ammonia water will be made ready again for new heating.

Such is the cycle of the ammonia-absorption refrigerating machine. First, the heated generator; second, the cooled condenser; third, the expansion chamber; and, fourth, the recharging of the weakened ammonia solution. A pump is needed only to circulate the solution. In order to save heat and to dry the ammonia gas, devices called the exchanger and the rectifier are included, but these are only aids to efficiency, not indispensable elements of refrigerating machines.

Instead of using heat to compress the gas, it is more common to use a pump. The gas is then employed without water. If compressed entirely without loss of heat, beginning at atmospheric pressure and continuing to a pressure of 12 atmospheres, the ammonia gas, if originally at 80° F., is warmed to a temperature of about 500° F. by the work done upon it. If then cooled again by water or air circulation to 80° F., the gas must be liquefied as shown by the table above. It can then be allowed to expand, and cool air, or, if the gas is enclosed in coils of pipe immersed in strong brine, the cooled brine will act as a reservoir of cooling for a long time. The cycle of operations of the compression refrigerating machine is similar, therefore, to the absorption ammonia machine, except that power for compression is substituted for heating, and water to dissolve the ammonia gas is unnecessary.

Commercial refrigeration for the preservation of foods and the making of ice has attained immense proportions. Every city has its refrigerating plants, and the railroads run great numbers of refrigerator cars for perishable goods, chiefly meats and fruits. Several precautions must be observed in preserving foods, and differences of treatment are necessary for different commodities.

Citrus fruits must be kept dry while the skins are drying out, but later the air must be humidified to prevent excessive drying and shriveling. Grapefruits are preferably kept at 33° to 36° F., lemons about 5° warmer, and oranges 10° warmer. Most fruits, including cantaloupes, strawberries, and peaches, are kept between 35° and 40° F., apples, pears, and plums preferably about 3° cooler. Ventilation is necessary to prevent the carbonic acid gas given off by fruits from producing a brown outer burning or rotting appearance. This effect may be diminished by wrapping each piece of fruit in tissue paper. Ventilation, of course, adds to the expense of cold storage, because new volumes of air must be brought to the temperature desired.

Dairy products present difficulty because of the fact that they take up odors and tastes from their surroundings. They must, therefore, be stored in separate cool rooms of which the walls themselves and all accessories are clean and odorless. Butter is usually stored in frozen condition to prevent contamination, but milk requires a temperature of 34° to 36° F. Eggs are stored both in whole and canned form. The annual storage in the United States amounts to fully 50,000,000 dozen, and they are shipped in refrigerator cars from the western States to the eastern market. The period of storage lasts from early summer to the following spring, and the temperature preferred is from 33° to 35° F. For the use of bakers and confectioners, eggs to be canned are first candled to detect and eliminate the bad ones, then broken, poured into cans and hard frozen to −5° F. for two days, and afterwards kept at 15° to 20° F. until sold to local bakers and confectioners or shipped in cold storage to distant cities.

Vegetables are shipped in carload lots in cold storage at temperatures between 32° and 40° F. and may be kept for some time in cold storage warehouses. Evaporation leads to withering. Careful control of the humidity is essential because too moist an atmosphere is even more prejudicial than one too dry. Different vegetables require different treatment in respect to both temperature and humidity.

Fish are stored at very low temperatures of 15° to 20° F. and sometimes are frozen solidly with cakes of ice. Poultry is preserved at a little below freezing, pork at 32° to 36° F., and beef at 36° to 40° F.

Certain substances are now made commercially at much lower temperatures than those obtained by ordinary refrigeration. These include frozen carbonic acid, often called dry ice, liquid air, and liquid oxygen. In laboratory experiments all gases have been liquefied and solidified, though for helium the temperature of melting of the solid form under atmospheric pressure is but 1°.1 C., or 2°.0 F., above the absolute zero. Liquid helium boils at 4°.2 Abs. C. or 7°.6 Abs. F. These very low temperatures are reached with much difficulty. To freeze carbonic acid gas, however, is very easy. The gas as ordinarily prepared for commerce is compressed in iron cylinders to a pressure of about 60 atmospheres. If allowed to escape from the iron cylinder through a suitable nozzle, the flakes of solid carbonic acid form at the nozzle and may be collected in a bag. Carbonic acid snow is now very cheaply produced. As it leaves no residue on evaporating, it is a popular means for keeping ice cream and for other purposes. The temperature of evaporation of carbonic acid snow at atmospheric pressure is $-70°$ C., or $-110°$ F.

Domestic mechanical refrigerators must be so made as to require no expert attention. Both absorption and compression machines have been adapted to this field. A very interesting type of absorption machine, which adds a new principle to those we have discussed, is the so-called Platen-Munters, shown in diagram in Plate 90, as made by the Electrolux Company. The ammonia solution in the generator, *a*, being heated by a lamp, gives off ammonia gas and steam which pass together to the rectifier, *b*. This is cooled just sufficiently to condense the steam into water, which trickles back to the generator. The ammonia gas goes over to the condenser, *c*, where it is cooled to liquid form. Thence it runs down into the siphon within the rectifier, and produces on the left leg of that siphon the moderate cooling mentioned above as being employed to condense the undesired steam.

From the siphon, the liquid ammonia runs through the tube shown, to emerge at slightly lower level in the evaporator, *d*. In this evaporator, *d*, in the space above the liquid ammonia, in the right hand leg of the rectifier siphon, and in other parts of the apparatus shortly to be mentioned, a supply of hydrogen gas is permanently charged to a considerable pressure. Hydrogen has no chemical action on ammonia and is only slightly soluble in water. According to the principle announced by John Dalton in the year 1800, each of two different gases, chemically indifferent to each other, can simultaneously fill a chamber just as fully as if the other were absent.

They diffuse together into a uniform mixture which occupies no more space in total than each does separately. The mixed gas exerts the sum of their two pressures. In the case we have before us, the presence of the hydrogen at a considerable pressure does not prevent the ammonia from evaporating and cooling as it expands until it reaches the same gaseous pressure in the chamber, *d*, that it would have reached if, when it entered, the chamber were a vacuum. Many plates covered with wire netting are included within the chamber, *d*, to promote uniform diffusion of the two gases through each other. The result is to make a very cold gas mixture, much heavier than hydrogen, which (after the machine is in regular operation) runs down by no other force than gravity through the gas exchanger, *e*, into the bottom of the absorber, *f*. This absorbing chamber, *f*, is bathed by a flow of water around the coil, *g, g*. The same water current also flows through the condenser, *c*.

The ammonia is absorbed in the receptacle, *f*. Weak ammonia solution runs down by gravity from the top of the generator, *a*, through the pipe, *h*, and drips down over the baffle plates, *i, i*, within the absorber, *f*, through the mixed gases. The hydrogen gas, thus freed from its load of heavier ammonia, rises from the absorber, *f*, through the siphon passage shown above, and through the gas exchanger, *e*, at length rising into the higher level of the evaporator, *d*.

Meanwhile the strong recharged ammonia solution, falling to the bottom of the absorber, *f*, runs back into the bottom of the generator, *a*, being warmed on the way as it passes through the hot weak ammonia solution at *j*. The generator, *a*, works like a coffee percolator. By reason of its separator, *l*, and tube, *m*, it throws hot strong ammonia solution to the top, where it loses its gas, and so the process goes on automatically.

The General Electric compression machine employs sulphur dioxide in place of ammonia as the refrigerant gas. The arrangement of the operative parts is indicated in Plate 91.

The electric motor, *a*, *b*, is mounted with a vertical shaft, *c*, carrying near its lower end a crank and pin, *d*, which drives directly without any intervening linkage the piston, *e*. In order to allow the piston to follow the rotary motion of the crank-pin, the compression cylinder, *f*, is pivoted to oscillate about a vertical axis. An auxiliary lubricating piston, *m*, forces oil from a pool at the bottom of the closed cylinder *h*, *h*, to lubricate all the moving parts. The use of the cylinder and piston, *g*, in this connection will be explained below.

As the piston, *e*, moves about in its stroke, it sucks gaseous sulphur dioxide from the valved receptacle, *i*, compresses it and forces it into the chamber, *h*, which contains the compressed gas. Cooling to the temperature of liquefication is produced by the air of the room bathing the coil, *j*, which is wound on a divided sheet-steel cylinder. The liquefied refrigerant drips into the float chamber, *k*. When deep enough it raises the float, opening a float valve, so that a little of the liquid may run down to replenish the charge in the superfreezer, *l*, *l*.

This chamber, in which ice blocks are frozen, is enclosed by a hollow tubular wall filled with the liquid refrigerant. As the liquid evaporates by boiling from the superfreezer, the gas forms in the communicating header above it, and is piped by the passage shown back to the vessel, *i*. The motor works intermittently, governed by a thermostat at the superfreezer comprising a metallic bellows filled with compressed gas. When the gas warms, the bellows expands and starts the motor.

The oiling is forced by a secondary small piston, *m*, parallel with the gas compressor. When the motor is running, the oil is forced around the piston into the cylinder above, where it raises the piston, *g*, so as to close the float valve and cut off the connection, *o*. When the machine stops, the oil recedes and the float valve opens and allows the high-pressure gas from the cylinder, h, h, to close the valve in the valve chamber, i, and thus prevent a back flow of gas from the cylinder, h, h, to the superfreezer, l, l.

The cycle of cooling consists, as will be seen, in starting the motor to cause the pump, e, f, to compress the gas into the cylinder, h, h. Air circulation removes the heat of compression and allows the liquefied gas to collect in the float chamber, k. When a certain amount has collected there, it flows to the superfreezer, l, l, where the cooling is done by boiling the liquid into the reduced pressure created by the suction of the pump. When the temperature is sufficiently lowered in the superfreezer, the electric current is automatically cut off by the thermostatic bellows. These two machines have been described as typical of absorption and compression machines for domestic use. Variations of each type are marketed, both here and abroad, by other manufacturers. Users are loud in their praises of the comforts of the mechanical refrigerator with its low temperature and its freedom from the daily care of ice supply and cleaning.

The Sewing Machine [1]

The idea of a machine that would use a needle and thread for the purpose of sewing together two or more pieces of cloth or leather after the manner in which this had been done by human hands for thousands of years appears to have been first thought out by an Englishman, Thomas Saint, who in 1790 received a patent for a machine for sewing leather. His drawings show certain features which are essential to the sewing machines used today, but so far as known Saint's idea was not put to any practical use by him.

Thiry-five years later, Barthelemy Thimonnier, a poor French tailor, entirely ignorant of the principles of

[1] The historical part of this account is abridged from an article by F. L. Lewton, Curator of Textiles, United States National Museum. See Ann. Rep. Smithsonian Inst. for 1929, pp. 559-584, 1930.

mechanics, became so absorbed with the idea of producing a machine to sew the seams of garments, that he spent four years endeavoring to make it sew, only working at his trade enough to obtain for his family the barest necessities of life. By 1829 he had mastered the mechanical difficulties and had produced a sewing machine which made the chain stitch by means of a hooked needle like a crochet needle. The next year he was given a patent on his machine and soon attracted the attention of a skillful engineer who took Thimonnier and his machine to Paris. By 1831 he had made so much progress that he was made a member of a prominent clothing firm and had 80 of his sewing machines at work upon uniforms for the French troops. But the tailors looked upon the new invention as a dangerous competition, and an infuriated mob smashed every machine they could find, forcing the inventor to flee for his life. We see poor Thimonnier trudging homeward from Paris with his sewing machine on his back and exhibiting it as a curiosity for a living.

Thimonnier sent his machine to the Universal Exhibition in London in 1851, but through a mistake it was not seen by the judges and no attention was paid to it. This greatly discouraged him and although he continued to work with his machine for a few years his lifelong struggle had exhausted him and he died in poverty in 1857, aged 64 years.

About the time that Thimonnier had so developed his invention that 80 of his machines were sewing for the French Army, an inventive Quaker genius in New York City was turning his attention to a sewing machine. This man, Walter Hunt, was then 39 years old and already had to his credit a number of useful inventions such as a flax-spinning machine, a knife sharpener, gong bells, a yarn twister, the first stove to burn hard coal, etc. From 1835 to the year 1859, when he died, Hunt had a greater number and a greater diversity of inventions

PLATE 90

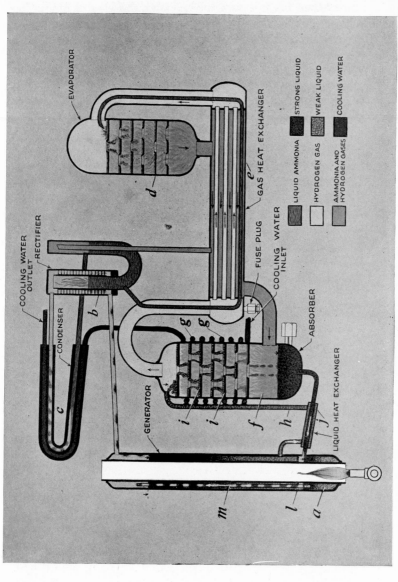

Domestic absorption refrigerator. Operates by transfer of ammonia gas by heat from strong water solution, cooling and expanding. Courtesy of the Electrolux Refrigerator Sales, Inc.

PLATE 91

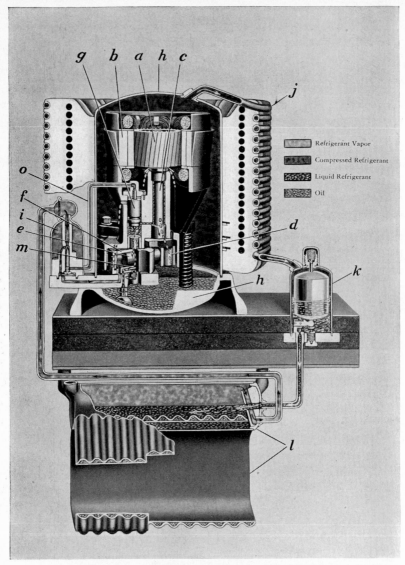

Refrigerant Vapor

Compressed Refrigerant

Liquid Refrigerant

Oil

Domestic compression refrigerator. Operates by highly compressing sulphur dioxide gas, cooling and expanding. Courtesy of the General Electric Company

based on fundamental original ideas than any known man of his time, which in their original or some modified form are in use today. Among his inventions of this period were the following: Machinery for making nails and rivets, ice plows, velocipedes, a revolver, a repeating rifle, metallic cartridges, conical bullets, paraffin candles, a street-sweeping machine, a student lamp, paper collars, and the safety pins which mothers find so indispensable in the nursery. His friend J. R. Chapin, a draughtsman, who prepared many drawings to accompany Hunt's applications for patents, says of the safety pin, that it was thought out, a model made of an old piece of wire, and the idea sold for $400, all within the space of three hours, in order to pay a debt of $15 which Hunt owed him.

At some time between the years 1832 and 1834, Walter Hunt made in his shop on Amos Street, New York City, a machine "for sewing, stitching, and seaming cloth." This first machine was quite successful, so that others like it were built by the inventor, assisted by his brother Adoniram.

Many samples of cloth were sewn by these machines, and friends and neighbors of the inventor came to see them work. While Hunt's machine could not be made to do curved or angular work, nor sew a continuous seam for more than a few inches without removing and readjusting the cloth, it was capable of doing certain classes of work with speed and accuracy and to that extent must be regarded as a practical success, even though it was still incapable of the general adaptation which sewing machines afterwards attained. Walter Hunt's invention, however, contained nearly all the essential parts of the best modern machines. He has an eye-pointed needle, moved by a vibrating arm, working in combination with a shuttle carrying a second thread so as to make an interlocked stitch fully as well as it is done by our present improved machines. The cloth feed was no doubt imperfect, which thus made the machine of little practical value, but for all that it was a step in the right direction, and was undoubtedly the pioneer of the present sewing machine, and far in advance of anything which had been done before it.

The invention appears to have dropped completely out of sight until the successful introduction of sewing machines drew attention to it some 15 years later, when a search for the old machines resulted in the discovery of essential parts of both of the Hunt machines in a garret in Gold Street, New York City, where they had been thrown among a lot of rubbish recovered from a fire.

Hunt himself, like most inventors, was then working on other ideas and was satisfied that he had invented, built, and put into practical operation, a machine capable of doing mechanical sewing with speed and precision, and having sold the invention—as he had many others—for a mere trifle, felt at that time no further urge to manufacture it.

Elias Howe, Jr., who was born on his father's farm at Spencer, Mass., in 1819, had his attention directed at an early age to mechanics. There were a grist mill, a saw mill, and a shingle-cutting machine on the home place, but all of these and the farm together barely sufficed for the needs of the family of eight children.

When but 6 years old, Elias Howe worked with his brothers and sisters at sticking wire teeth into strips of leather to make cards used in the spinning of cotton. After "living out" for a year with a farmer in the neighborhood, he returned home to work in the mills there until he was 16. Then he obtained a learner's place in a factory in Lowell, Mass., making cotton machinery, until the financial panic of 1837 closed the shop and forced him to look for work again. Finally he found work in the shop of Ari Davis, an ingenious mechanic, where he one day heard a man say that the invention of a sewing machine would insure an independent fortune.

When Howe was 21, and still a journeyman machinist

earning $9 a week, he married and before long there were three children to be fed and clothed out of his weekly wage. About the year 1843 the pressure of poverty and the fatiguing nature of his work forced him to make earnest attempts to invent the machine which he had heard four years before would bring an independent fortune to the inventor. He wasted many precious months in endeavoring to copy the motions of his wife's arm when sewing, using a double-pointed needle with the eye in the middle. One day the idea came to him of using two threads and forming a stitch with the aid of a shuttle. By October, 1844, he had constructed a model which convinced him that he had a machine which would really sew. At this time he set up a lathe and a few tools in the garret of his father's house at Cambridge, Mass., and brought his family to the house, giving up his job as journeyman mechanic.

The money needed to purchase the raw materials for a working model that would put into concrete form his mental picture of a wonderful machine seemed beyond his reach. His earnestness, however, convinced a friend and former schoolmate, George Fisher, then a coal and wood dealer in Cambridge, of the feasibility of his project, and a partnership was drawn up for bringing Howe's invention into use.

By its terms George Fisher was to board Elias Howe and his family while Elias was making the model of his machine in Fisher's garret as a workshop, was to provide money for material and tools to the extent of $500, and in return was to be the owner of one-half of the patent if the machine proved patentable. In December, 1844, the Howe family moved into Fisher's house and the shop was set up in the small, low garret. With the idea of his machine clearly in his mind and undisturbed by the need of daily laboring elsewhere to feed his family, Howe worked steadily on during the winter and by April, 1845, had sewed a seam on his machine. In July of that year he sewed on his model machine all the seams of two suits of wool clothes, one suit for George Fisher and one for himself.

This pioneer of the millions of sewing machines made since July, 1845, after crossing the ocean many times, and having been used as an irrefutable witness in many courts, can now be seen in the United States National Museum, at Washington, D. C., where it has been deposited by the grandson of Elias Howe, jr. (Plate 92, left.)

When Howe had finished his machine he found that his next problem was to convince others that it could sew and do the work as well as that performed by hand. Accordingly, he took his little machine to the Quincy Hall Clothing Manufactory in Boston and offered to sew up any seam that might be brought to him. For two weeks he sat daily in one of the rooms demonstrating his invention and finally challenged five of the swiftest seamstresses in the establishment to sew a race with the machine. Ten seams of equal length were prepared for sewing, one each was given to the five girls and the other five to be laid by the machine. The umpire testified that the five girls were the fastest sewers that could be found and that they sewed as fast as they could; Howe's machine, however, finished the five seams a little sooner than the five girls finished their five, and the work done by the machine was declared to be the neatest and strongest. In spite of this and similar demonstrations no one gave Howe an order for a sewing machine. When pressed for reasons some said they were afraid it would ruin all the hand sewers by throwing them out of work, some objected because the machine would not make the whole garment, others said the cost of the machine was too high as a large shirt maker would have to have 30 or 40 of them. Howe was not discouraged by these objections and set about to get his invention patented. He again shut himself up in George Fisher's garret for three or four months to make another machine for deposit in the United States Patent Office, as the patent laws then required. Late in the summer of 1846, a beautiful model and the required papers were ready for the Patent Office, and Elias and George took them to Washington. This model, Howe's second machine, is also exhibited in the National Museum, alongside of his original machine. It is a better made machine and shows several changes in unimportant parts. As soon as the patent was issued on September 10, 1846, Howe and his partner returned to Cambridge.

Since no orders had been received from either garment makers or tailors for machines, Fisher did not see the slightest probability of the machine becoming profitable and regarded his advances of cash as a dead loss. But the inventor did not lose faith and decided to try to induce manufacturers in England to take up his invention. With a loan from his father, a third machine was made which Elias' brother, Amasa B. Howe, took with him to London in the steerage of a sailing packet. After a number of discouragements he made the acquaintance of William Thomas in his shop in Cheapside. This man claimed to employ 5,000 persons in the manufacture of corsets, umbrellas, valises, and shoes, and after studying the machine agreed to buy it. According to terms of this very one-sided bargain, Amasa Howe sold to William Thomas for £250 the machine he had brought with him from America (the third machine built by Elias Howe), and the right to use as many more in his own business as he wished. William Thomas proposed further to engage the inventor to adapt his machine to the making of corsets at a salary of £3 a week, and agreed to furnish workshop, tools, and materials. There was also an understanding that Thomas was to patent the invention in England and was to pay Howe £3 for every machine sold under the English patent. Thomas did patent Howe's invention but instead of paying him the promised royalty he collected for himself a tribute on all the sewing machines made in England, or imported into England, during the life of his patent. Elias Howe later estimated that the investment of £250 yielded Thomas a profit of a million dollars.

The brothers set sail for London, February 5, 1847, cooking their own provisions in the steerage. Elias took with him his precious first machine and his patent papers. William Thomas provided, as agreed, a shop and tools and advanced the passage money for the wife and three children of Elias Howe to join him in England.

After eight months of hard work the inventor succeeded in adapting his machine to the requirements of Thomas' business, but the latter began to make working conditions intolerable for Howe. The American resented his treatment which resulted in William Thomas discharging Elias Howe from his employment. A stranger in London, with a sick wife and three small children to support and no employment in sight was the disheartening predicament in which Howe now found himself. Through a chance acquaintance, a coach maker named Charles Inglis, he hired a small room for a workshop and with a few borrowed tools began to build his fourth sewing machine.

He was so poor that he had to pledge some of his clothing to obtain a few shillings necessary to hire a cab to take his sick wife to the ship on the stormy night of her departure. After three or four months of hard labor his machine was finished and he looked for a customer. Finally a man was found who offered £5 for the machine if he could have time in paying for it. Howe was obliged to accept the offer and took the man's note for £5. His friend Inglis found a purchaser for the note at £4. In order to pay up his debts and pay his expenses back to America, Howe pawned his precious first machine and the patent papers from the United States Patent Office. To save cartage he took his baggage to the ship in a handcart and again took passage in the steerage along with his friend Charles Inglis.

Elias Howe landed in New York in April, 1849, after an absence from America of two years, with but half a crown in his pocket. Nearly four years had passed since the finishing of his first sewing machine and the small piece of silver was all he had to show for his work on that invention. He and his friend went to a cheap emigrant boarding house and looked for work in the machine shops, which he fortunately soon found. When news reached him that his wife was dying of consumption he did not have the money for the journey to Cambridge, but with the help of $10 from his father he was able to reach his wife's bedside before she passed away.

Howe found to his surprise upon returning home from his experiences in London, that the sewing machine had become celebrated, though his part in its invention appeared to have been forgotten. Several ingenious mechanics who had seen the Howe machine, or who had read of a machine for sewing, had turned their attention to inventing in the same field and sewing machines were being carried around the country and exhibited as a curiosity. Several machines made in Boston had been sold to manufacturers and were daily in operation. Howe found that these machines all infringed his patent rights by using devices which he had combined and patented.

In February, 1851, George S. Jackson, Daniel C. Johnson, and William E. Whiting became joint owners with Howe of his patent rights, and helped him to procure witnesses in the furtherance of numerous suits. The next year a Massachusetts man named George W. Bliss was persuaded to advance the money needed to carry on the suits for infringement. Lerow & Blodgett had patented a sewing machine on October 2, 1849, the peculiar feature of which was that the shuttle was driven entirely around a circle at each stitch. It was in some ways an improvement on the Howe machine, but the circular movement of the shuttle took a twist out of the thread at every revolution and the machine was hard to keep in running order. Several of these machines had been brought for repairs to the shop of Orson C. Phelps in Boston, where in August, 1850, their operation was watched by Isaac M. Singer who had shortly before patented a wood-carving machine. With the experience of a practical machinist, Singer criticized the clumsy working of the sewing machine. The next day Singer showed Phelps and George B. Zieber, a machinist working in the shop, a rough sketch of the machine he proposed to build. It contained a table to support the cloth horizontally, instead of a feed bar from which it was suspended vertically as in the Blodgett machine, a vertical presser foot to hold the cloth down against the upward stroke of the needle, and an arm to hold the presser foot and vertical needle-holding bar in position over the table. The story continues as told by Mr. Singer himself in a statement made during the progress of some litigation in which he was at one time engaged.

I explained to them how the work was to be fed over the table and under the presser foot by a wheel having short pins on its periphery projecting through a slot in the table, so that the work would be automatically caught, fed, and freed from the pins, in place of attaching and detaching the work to and from the baster plate by hand as was necessary in the Blodgett machine.

Phelps and Zieber were satisfied that it would work. I had no money. Zieber offered $40 to build a model machine. Phelps offered his best endeavors to carry out my plan and make the model in his shop; if successful we were to share equally. I worked at it day and night, sleeping but 3 or 4 hours a day out of the 24, and eating generally but once a day, as I knew I must make it for the $40 or not get it at all.

The machine was completed in 11 days. About 9 o'clock in the evening we got the parts together and tried it; it did not sew; the workmen exhausted with almost unremitting work, pronounced it a failure and left me one by one.

Zieber held the lamp, and I continued to try the machine, but anxiety and incessant work had made me nervous and I could not get

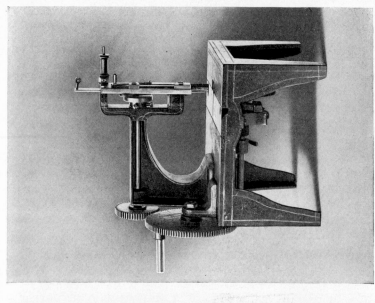

Left: Original Howe sewing machine. Right: Original Singer sewing machine. Both in the National Museum

PLATE 93

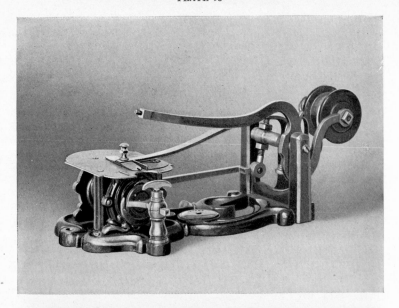

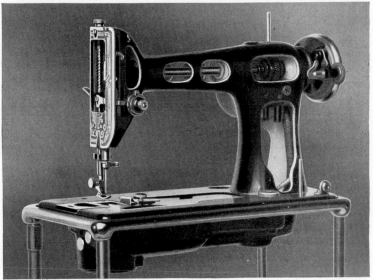

Upper: Original Wilson sewing machine. Lower: Modern Singer sewing machine, electrically driven. Both in the National Museum

tight stitches. Sick at heart, about midnight, we started for our hotel. On the way we sat down on a pile of boards, and Zieber mentioned that the loose loops of thread were on the upper side of the cloth. It flashed upon me that we had forgot to adjust the tension on the needle thread. We went back, adjusted the tension, tried the machine, sewed five stitches perfectly and the thread snapped, but that was enough. At 3 o'clock the next day the machine was finished. I took it to New York and employed Mr. Charles M. Keller to patent it. It was used as a model in the application for the patent, the extension of which is now asked.

Singer found to his sorrow that whoever attempted to bring out a sewing machine was confronted with all the consequences of previous failures. He borrowed a few hundred dollars from friends to enable him to manufacture machines in Boston, where, with Phelps and Zieber, he began work under the firm name of I. M. Singer & Company. The firm was gaining the attention of the public, when a new and formidable obstacle appeared. The news that Singer had made a machine that would actually do *continuous* stitching, the most conspicuous defect in the Howe machine, soon brought Elias Howe, jr., to his door with a demand that he pay $25,000 for infringement of the Howe patent, or quit the sewing-machine business. He soon found himself burdened with litigation which threatened to ruin him. About this time Singer secured the help of an acute legal mind in the person of Edward Clark, of New York, whose ability as a financier was hardly less marked. Although he contributed no money, Clark became an equal partner in the firm of I. M. Singer & Company, Phelps having been bought out some time before. Later Singer and Clark bought out Zieber.

Howe's patent of 1846, for the time being, made him a complete master of the situation and for several years he sued infringers right and left. The sewing-machine manufacturers, with the exception of the Singer Company, yielded to Howe and were carrying on their business under his licenses without interruption. I. M. Singer & Company had resisted him single-handed from the very beginning, setting up in justification of their right to manufacture sewing machines, the claims of Walter Hunt, the New York inventor, that he had made a sewing machine, using an eye-pointed needle and a shuttle to form the lock stitch, previous to the year 1834. As Walter Hunt was unable to produce a complete machine made at that time and admitted that he had failed to apply for a patent on his invention, the courts decided that it was never completed in the sense of the patent law and therefore did not anticipate the patent granted to Howe. I. M. Singer & Company submitted to the order of the court, for much damage was being done to their business by the competition of manufacturers who were working uninterruptedly under licenses from Howe, and in July, 1854, took out a license under the Howe patent, paying him $15,000 in settlement for royalties on machines made and sold prior to that time.

The copartnership of Singer and Clark was continued until 1863, when a corporation was formed to continue the business. Singer withdrew from active work, receiving 40 per cent of the stock of the new company, and left America to make his home in Europe. Upon his death, 12 years later, his estate was appraised at $13,000,000.

Singer's original patent model is preserved in the National Museum. This type of machine, in use for many years, required less modification than any one of the earlier makes of sewing machines. (Plate 92, right.)

Isaac Singer was the first to furnish the people with a successfully operating and practical sewing machine. After the introduction of the Singer machine other inventors, with patents of earlier date, were forced to alter their machines to meet the approval of the public.

One of the ablest of the early inventors in the field of mechanical sewing, and by far the most original, was Allen B. Wilson. This ingenious young man completed a practical sewing machine early in the year 1849 without ever having seen one and without having any knowledge of the work of Elias Howe, who was then in London.

Wilson had first begun the development of a needle and shuttle machine, but instead of using a shuttle pointed at one end and moving back and forth in a straight line, as had both Howe and Singer, he made a shuttle pointed at both ends and which moved in a curved path, forming a stitch at each forward and backward stroke. About this time Allen Wilson made the acquaintance of Nathaniel Wheeler, a manufacturer of buckles and other small metal wares at Watertown, Conn. In the meantime, Allen Wilson had thought out the plan of a substitute for the shuttle, the rotary hook, a marvelous piece of ingenuity. He showed his model to Mr. Wheeler, who became so convinced of its merits that he determined to develop the new machine and leave Wilson's first shuttle machine to those who, by fraud, had become the owners of it. This last firm possessed neither the mechanical nor business ability to put it properly on the market, and in a few years the original patent was purchased by the Wheeler & Wilson Manufacturing Company.

Wilson now bent all his efforts to improving his rotary hook which was a new departure from all previous ideas of sewing, and was described in his second patent, issued on August 12, 1851. It is a remarkable coincidence that on the same date a patent was granted to Isaac M. Singer for his first machine, which, with its improvements, was for many years the most formidable competitor of the Wheeler & Wilson machine.

Wilson's fourth patent, the universally used 4-motion feed, was issued on December 19, 1854. This, with the rotary hook and the stationary circular disk bobbin, the subjects of his second and third patents in 1851 and 1852, completed the essential features of Wilson's machine, original and fundamentally different from all other machines known at that time.

The first crude models, whittled out of mahogany by

Allen B. Wilson between 1847 and 1849, which clearly show the development of his ideas, and the original models deposited in the Patent Office establishing the claims made in his first three patents, are now preserved in the National Museum. The model representing the third patent, that of June 15, 1852, is a beautifully made, compact little machine, weighing but 6½ pounds, and contrasting greatly with the clumsy, heavy Singer models of that time which weigh over 55 pounds. (Plate 93, upper.)

The invention of the first practical single chain-stitch sewing machine came about through the curiosity of a young native Virginian having a mechanical turn of mind. James Gibbs had been helping his father build wool-carding machines, but the burning of his father's mill and the competition of large factories led him to turn to carpentering to provide for his family. It was in 1855 that his attention was first attracted to sewing machines by seeing a plain woodcut of a Grover and Baker machine in a newspaper advertisement. This picture showed only the upper part of the machine which left the course of the needle and the manipulation of the thread under the cloth a mystery. There was nothing in the cut to show that more than one thread was used and it at once excited his curiosity to know how the thing could possibly sew. His effort to solve the puzzle is thus described by him:

> I set to work to see what I could learn from the woodcut, which was not accompanied by any description. I first discovered that the needle was attached to a needle arm, and consequently could not pass entirely through the material, but must retreat through the same hole by which it entered. From this I saw that I could not make a stitch similar to handwork, but must have some other mode of fastening the thread on the underside, and among other possible methods of doing this, the chain stitch occurred to me as a likely means of accomplishing the end. I next endeavored to discover how this stitch was or could be made, and from the woodcut I saw that the driving shaft which had the driving wheel on the outer end, passed along under the cloth plate of the machine. I knew that the mechanism which made the stitch must be connected with and actuated by this driving shaft.

After studying the position and relations of the needle and shaft with each other, I conceived the idea of the revolving hook on the end of the shaft, which might take hold of the thread and manipulate it into a chain stitch.

While on a visit to his father in Rockbridge County, Va., he happened to go into a tailor's shop where there was a Singer sewing machine working on the shuttle principle. He was much impressed with the ability of that machine, but thought it entirely too heavy, complicated, and cumbersome, and also that the price was exorbitant. He then set to work in earnest to produce a more simple, cheap, and useful machine. By the end of April, 1856, he had so far completed his model as to interest his employers in his invention and induce them to furnish the money necessary to patent it and develop the machine. He took his machine to Philadelphia and showed it to James Wilcox, who was then engaged in building models of new inventions. After taking out some minor patents he obtained his most important one on June 2, 1857. The original models of these early efforts are preserved in the National Museum. This association with James Wilcox led to the formation of the Wilcox & Gibbs Sewing Machine Company, which has certainly done its share in the development of the sewing machine art.

The double-locked chain-stitch machine was invented by William O. Grover, a Boston tailor. Though the machines which he had seen were not very practical he came to the conclusion that the sewing machine was going to revolutionize the tailoring trade, and in 1849 began to experiment with the idea of making an improved stitch. One plan was to invent a machine which would take its thread directly from the spools and do away with the need of rewinding the under thread upon bobbins. After a great deal of experimenting he finally discovered that two pieces of cloth could be united by two threads interlocking with each other in a succession of slip knots, but the building of a machine to do this proved to be a very difficult task. It is remarkable that during his experiments he did not discover the single thread chain stitch, later worked out by Gibbs, as up to this time this stitch had not been heard of by any sewing-machine inventors in America. It is probable that, working on the assumption that it was absolutely necessary to use two threads, the idea of using one thread could not find room to develop in his brain.

Grover's patent was issued February 11, 1851, and the original model is shown in the collection of sewing machines in the National Museum. Mr. Grover associated with himself in the development of the business another Boston tailor, William E. Baker, and upon a reorganization of the company soon after under the name of the Grover & Baker Sewing Machine Company, took into the firm Jacob Weatherill, mechanic, and Orlando B. Potter, lawyer. This company built in Boston a most complete factory for the production of the machines. Mr. Potter, the president of the company, had, through his ability as an attorney, secured a one-third interest in the business without an investment at the start, and now obtained patents for Grover's inventions and managed all the lawsuits brought against the company. He was the promoter of the first trust of any prominence formed anywhere. It was known as the "sewing-machine trust," or more popularly, the "combination."

The celebrated suit between Elias Howe, Jr., and I. M. Singer & Company, was decided by Judge Sprague of Massachusetts in the year 1854, a verdict being rendered in favor of Howe. This verdict was of the greatest importance, for it covered the use of an eye-pointed needle in a sewing machine. Howe's success in the suit against Singer was followed soon after by a verdict against the Wheeler & Wilson Company, Grover & Baker Company, and other infringers of Howe's patent. These decisions put Howe in absolute control of the sewing-machine business and he made arrangements with the various companies to pay him $25 for every machine sold. From this enormous royalty he derived a large revenue for some time. However, Howe did not have entirely easy sailing, and more legal battles took place. While none of the other inventors' machines could sew without using the eye-pointed needle, patented by Howe, the latter's machines were in many ways so badly handicapped, especially by his slow and clumsy method of feeding the cloth, that they were of no practical use. When he attempted to improve his machine so as to overcome these defects, Howe got into further litigation with I. M. Singer & Company, the Wheeler & Wilson Company, and the Grover & Baker Company, for infringing mechanical patents which were owned by them. The quarrels over patent rights were by no means confined to Howe, as each individual company was suing all of the others on one claim or another. Finally, Orlando B. Potter, president of the Grover & Baker Company, conceived the idea of combining the various interests and pooling all the patents covering the essential features, which would enable them to control the sewing-machine industry, instead of continually fighting and trying to devour one another. He pointed out that while Howe and the three large companies then suing one another controlled all the basic patents, the pending lawsuits if carried to a conclusion, might be disastrous to all of them. His argument was convincing and thus was formed the "combination" which for several years was the terror of all unlicensed manufacturers. Besides Howe, the three companies which were parties to the combination, I. M. Singer & Company, the Wheeler & Wilson Company, and the Grover & Baker Company, had all begun business about the same time, and the main patents under which they were working had been granted between November 12, 1850, and August 12, 1851.

It is estimated that Howe received in the form of royalties as the result of this agreement not less than $2,000,000 from the business of the combination.

The most important patents contributed to the combination were the following:

1. The combination of the grooved, eye-pointed needle and a shuttle, by Elias Howe, jr.

2. The 4-motion feeding mechanism, by Allen B. Wilson.

3. The continuous wheel feed, the yielding presser foot, and the heart-shaped cam as applied to moving the needle bar, by Isaac M. Singer.

4. The basic patent covering a needle moving vertically above a horizontal work plate, a yielding presser resting on the work, and a "perpetual" or continuous feeding device, which had been issued to John Bachelder on May 8, 1849, and afterwards purchased by Singer and his partner Clark.

The Grover & Baker Company controlled several patents of importance which were contributed to the combination, but its most important claim for admission was the fact that Mr. Potter had promoted the scheme.

The essential features of the sewing machine (of which a modern specimen by the Singer Company is shown in Plate 93, lower) are: 1, A driving mechanism, now often electrical; 2, means to convert the rotary motion of the drive into a reciprocating vertical vibration of the needle; 3, the eye-pointed needle invented by Hunt; 4, the thread-feed with its adjustable tension, whereby the needle, as it intermittently pierces the cloth in its vibrations, carries through a loop of thread to the under side of the cloth on each downward stroke of the needle; 5, the cloth feed, which moves the work along by the length of one stitch after each upward stroke of the needle; 6, the pressure foot, an adjunct to the cloth feed; 7, the rotating hook, invented by Wilson, which catches the thread at the needle's eye after it has passed through the cloth on the down stroke and carries the loop entirely round the bobbin wound with the lower thread, thereby interlocking two loops formed by the upper and the lower threads; 8, the vibrating lever, with spring support, through which the top thread passes, and which allows a slack of the top thread sufficient to permit the rotating hook to carry the loop around the bobbin. With proper tension, the return strokes of the needle and the vibrating lever draw the crossing of the upper and lower threads into the middle of the cloth, and make the lock stitch.

SPINNING AND WEAVING [2]

I. PRIMITIVE LOOMS: PREHISTORIC, ANCIENT, AND MODERN

The spindle and the loom, the one for twisting fiber into thread and the other for weaving the thread itself into cloth, are prehistoric and almost universal tools. If the essential principles of the most modern spinning and weaving machinery be investigated, it will be seen that they are identical with those used in the most ancient times. The complicated textile machinery of today is, therefore, simply a natural development from that used by primitive weavers of all time.

Prehistoric examples of the weaver's art are extremely rare. This is owing, of course, to the perishable nature of the materials of which they are composed. Few as they are, however, and consisting, as they do, of the merest shreds of textile fabrics, they show unmistakably that the art of the loom, as well as that of the spindle and needle, was understood and successfully practiced in what has been poetically called by an eloquent French writer "the night of time." It is generally agreed that most of the lake dwellings of Switzerland, which were discovered and eagerly investigated during the last century, belong to the neolithic, or later stone period. It was among the remains of one of the earliest of these villages, discovered in the bed of the lake at Robenhausen, that bundles of raw flax fiber, fine and coarse linen threads, twisted string of various sizes, and thick ropes, as well as netted and knitted fabrics and fragments of loom-woven linen cloth, sometimes rudely embellished with needlework, were

---

[2] Abstracted by permission from a paper by Luther Hooper, published in Journ. Roy. Soc. Arts, September, 1912. The full paper may be found also in Ann. Rep. Smithsonian Inst. for 1914, pp. 629–678, 1915.

found. There were also spindle whorls and loom weights of stone and earthenware, one or two fragments of wooden wheels, which might have formed parts of thread-twisting machines, as well as rude frames which were possibly the remains of simple looms.

We should not imagine how quickly and easily things might have been made, but how simply, even though with infinite pains, the work could have been done.

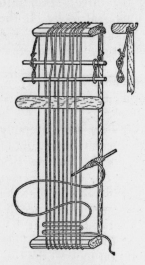

Bearing this in mind let us examine an interesting relic of the handiwork of a prehistoric weaver. It is not, like so many of the fragments, netted or knitted from a single thread. This is proved by the regular and flat interlacement of its strands, which cross each other at right angles. However small the original webs may have been, a set of threads—the warp—must in each case have been stretched on some kind of frame. The intersecting threads—the weft— must also have been passed before and behind alternate warp threads in regular sequence. This

FIG. 40. The simplest of looms. Courtesy of the Royal Society of Arts

could only have been done on a loom, however simple, and how simply a loom may be constructed let me exemplify.

Here is an oblong board, two sticks, and a piece of string. If I wind the string onto the board (Fig. 40) and insert the two sticks between alternate cords at one end, I have made the board and sticks into a simple loom, which is typical of the loom of every country and of all time. It is typical because it has the essential characteristic of all looms, which is the crossing of the threads between the sticks. This cross transforms a collection of any number of separate strings into a well-ordered weavable warp, which can easily be kept free from entanglement. In fact, without it no weaving could begin, much less be carried on to any length.

There is a roll of East African weaving in the ethnographical gallery of the British Museum. This beautiful strip of cloth is four inches wide and is a fine specimen of modern primitive weaving. The pretty web, with its delicate pattern of checkers, could quite easily be woven on such a board as this, no other appliances being necessary than the two or three sticks and a long thin spindle or needle for inserting the weft thread. Here is a tiny board loom, on which I have had woven a copy of one of the border stripes of the African native web (Plate 94, left). You will notice a number of loops hanging loosely to the unwoven threads. I need not refer to them just now, except to say that they are for the purpose of economizing time and facilitating the work. Without them the weaving would take longer and require a little more attention, but otherwise could be as well done.

There is no natural continuous thread except silk, all others being artificial. Silk is unwound from the cocoon of the silkworm in lengths of from 500 to 1,000 yards. Of this thread primitive man is unaware. But he seems to have an instinct which teaches him that various vegetable and animal fibers, however short they may be, can be twisted together and joined up into threads of any required length and thickness, as well as of great strength. Weaving is well nigh universal, but even in the few places where it is unknown the art of making very perfect thread and netting it into useful fabrics is commonly practiced.

The process of making thread may be stated very briefly. It consists of (1) stripping and cleaning the fibers, which is called skutching or ginning; (2) loosening and straightening out the cleansed fibers, which is termed carding; (3) drawing the carded filaments out in an even rove and twisting them together into fine or coarse continuous thread. This final process is called spinning.

There can be no good weaving without good spinning, for good cloth can not be made of bad thread. Spinning can be done slowly, of course, without any mechanical aid whatever. Here is a bundle of fiber ready for spinning.

It has been simply cleaned and carded. If I draw out a few fibers and, after slightly damping them with clear water, twist them together with my fingers, you will see that they have been converted, simply by the twisting, into a strong thread. Thread thus casually made is naturally coarse and rough, but an expert spinner would make in the same way a fine, strong, even thread with very few fibers.

If a small stick, having a hook at one end and a weight at the other, be suspended to the spinning thread, the further even twisting of the yarn will become much easier, because regulated by the continuous revolution of the weighted stick or spindle, as such an appliance is called. The spindle is also useful for winding the twisted or spun thread upon. Figure 41 shows the usual method of carrying the distaff, which, it will be seen, leaves both hands of the spinner free for drawing out the fiber and twisting the spindle.

FIG. 41. Spinning with distaff and plummet. Courtesy of the Royal Society of Arts

A primitive improvement comprises the attachment of the spindle to a small wheel actuated by a large one. With this wheel, as with the weighted spindle, twisting and winding on are alternate operations. The manner of using the wheel is as follows: The thread is first tied to the spindle, a convenient length of fiber being drawn out. The spinner turns the large wheel, which causes the spindle to revolve and twist the length of fiber, the latter being held in a line with the spindle. When sufficient twist has been given to the thread, the spinner adroitly moves the hand holding it so that the thread is brought at right angles with the spindle. The rotation of the wheel being continued in the same direction, the length of spun thread will be quickly wound upon the spindle. These alternate movements are repeated until the spindle is conveniently filled up with spun thread.

The well-known ordinary spinning wheel shown in Plate 95, left, sometimes called the Saxony or German wheel, has been in use since the sixteenth century. It has an ingenious arrangement by means of which the two operations of twisting the thread and winding it are done simultaneously. We shall revert to it later.

The presence among the textile relics of the lake dwellers of a few circular and conical-shaped objects of stone and earthen ware gives a clue to the form of loom on which the prehistoric webs were woven. Such objects, pierced with holes and sometimes elaborately ornamented, are found in excavations all over Europe. These objects are precisely like the weights which the Greeks and Romans and other ancient European peoples used for the purpose of stretching the threads of warp in their peculiarly constructed upright looms.

Figure 42 is copied from a beautiful Greek vase painting. Its date is about 500 B.C. The loom is of the same simple construction, but all the parts are carefully drawn and the pattern of the web—a highly ornamental one—is distinctly shown. There are also pegs on the top crosspiece of the loom on which spare balls of different-colored weft are kept handy for use. Spare warp was also probably hung from them at the back of the loom.

[269]

The weights at the bottom of the loom in this case are of a conical shape, very much like those found in Switzerland. There is also at the back of the loom another stick or beam, which is, I believe, for the purpose of holding the length of unwoven warp before it passes through the holes in the weights at the bottom of the loom. The loose

FIG. 42. Penelope's web. From a painting on an ancient Greek vase. Courtesy of the Royal Society of Arts

back threads are not shown in the painting, but the roll of cloth upon the beam indicates that more than a loom's length of warp is being manipulated. Probably the artist shirked the difficulty of representing these back threads, and so made the front ones appear to terminate at the weights. This painting is particularly interesting, because it shows unmistakably that the elaborate pattern webs, which the classic poets so often referred to, were woven on the simplest of looms by skillful handicraft, not by means of complicated machinery, as some have supposed.

Owing, no doubt, to the dryness of the climate of Egypt,

and the peculiar funeral customs of the Egyptians, many specimens of ancient Egyptian textiles have been preserved. Linen cloth, which was woven four or five thousand years ago or even more, may still be seen and handled, being as perfect as when it was newly cut out of the loom by the industrious Egyptian weaver. In the British and other museums many examples of such Egyptian linen textiles may be seen. These linen cloths were unwrapped from the mummies whose funerals took place under the various dynasties. As to the looms on which these textiles were woven, the few representations of them which exist show that they were constructed on a different plan from those of Europe, and bear out the statement of Herodotus that the Egyptians beat the weft downward instead of upward when weaving.

Fastening the warp at both ends to rollers and weaving upward are without doubt great advances on the ancient European methods of procedure. A further advance is the invention of what is now called the heddle rod. There is no direct evidence of this valuable addition to the loom either in ancient Europe or in Egypt, but it is difficult to believe that the extremely fine wide linen of Egypt could have been woven to the extent it was, without this simple and obvious appliance. Some of the finest Egyptian webs have as many as 150 threads of warp to every inch of their width, and it seems incredible that this multitude of fine threads could have been profitably manipulated with the fingers only.

Returning for a moment to Plate 94, left, let me call your attention to the loose loops which I pointed out as time economizers, but did not further describe. These loose loops are attached one to each thread of the warp, which is at the back of the lower cross stick. The cross stick makes one shed or opening for the weft. The loops, on being pulled forward, bring the back threads to the front, and so make the second or alternate opening. You will see this at once if I add loops to my simple loom and insert a rod, the heddle rod, to enable me to raise them altogether (Fig. 43).

Figure 44 is a design for a small tapestry loom from Mrs. Christie's "Handbook of Embroidery and Tapestry Weaving." This loom, simple as it is, can not be improved in its mechanism, except perhaps in some unimportant details, for the use of the artist weaver to work out his free designs upon. All the gorgeous and more or less elaborately ornamented carpets of the East, as well as the exquisitely wrought tapestries of the West, from the most ancient times to our own, have been woven on looms of no more complicated construction than this. Added mechanical contrivances limit the scope of the craftsman. Freedom of design is trammeled in proportion to the facilities invented for the automatic repetition of pattern in the loom.

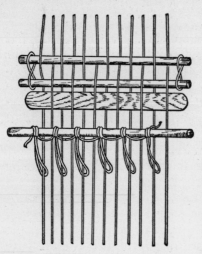

Fig. 43. Illustrating the heddle rod. Courtesy of the Royal Society of Arts

II. SPINNING MECHANISM AND THE LOOM FOR
AUTOMATIC WEAVING, PLAIN AND ORNAMENTAL

On the primitive spinning wheel, you will remember, I pointed out that the spinning of the thread and winding it on to the spindle were separate alternate operations. On the more modern spinning wheels the spinning and winding are made simultaneous by means of a little contrivance called a flier and bobbin attachment to the spindle. The first historic hint we have of this invention is from a

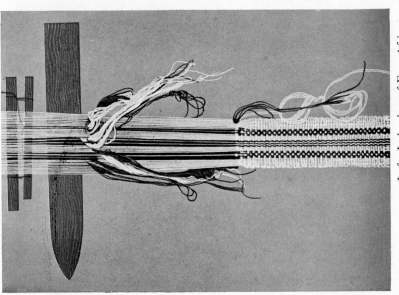

Left: Imitation of East African weaving.   Right: A Jacquard loom

PLATE 95

Left: Ordinary spinning wheel.   Right: Paddleford's ring spinner

drawing in one of the sketchbooks of the great artist craftsman, Leonardo da Vinci. But it was not until nearly a century after his death, which took place in 1519, that the spinning wheel with this clever attachment came into general use. Plate 95, left, shows the perfected device.

The piece, *a*, is called the flier. It is firmly fixed on the end of a shaft or spindle. A small pulley, *b*, is also firmly fixed to the spindle between the bearings. When this pulley is made to revolve very rapidly, by means of a cord or belt from the large wheel, the flier revolves with it and twists the thread which is passed through the hole in the spindle at *c* and thence out through a side hole of the spindle to the arm of the flier.

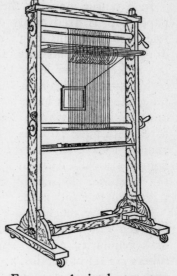

FIG. 44. A simple tapestry loom. Courtesy of the Royal Society of Arts

Another pulley, *d*, rather smaller than *b* is fixed on a hollow shaft, which extends from the pulley to *f*. In the hollow of this shaft the spindle can freely revolve, and on it the bobbin, *e*, tightly fits.

Now, if the different-sized pulleys, *b* and *c*, be actuated by cords from the same large wheel, the flier will revolve at a lesser speed than the bobbin, the difference in speed being, of course, in proportion to the difference in size of the pulleys, *b* and *d*.

The result of this arrangement will be that, if the thread, twisted by the revolution of the spindle, be passed through the eyes in the flier and fastened to the bobbin, two operations will take place: (1) The thread will be twisted by the flier; (2) because the bobbin revolves at greater speed than the flier the thread will be gradually wound upon the bobbin. A row of small hooks is placed along the arm of the flier, by means of which the thread can be guided onto the bobbin at any part of its barrel. This is the twisting and winding arrangement with which the improved spinning wheels of the seventeenth century in Europe were fitted up.

In a power machine the ring spinner, the bobbin, or paper cop, is fixed firmly on the spindle and the flier is free. The flier runs on a ring which encircles the cop and drags upon it. This acts in the same way, as to winding, but makes it possible for the spindle to revolve at a much higher speed. Although thus adopted for machine spinning, the idea of a loose bobbin was not, I believe, a new one. Spinning wheels had probably been previously fitted with loose bobbins. The loose bobbin, if not heavy enough to act as its own brake, has a string which is lightly attached to some fixed part of the framework of the machine. This being passed over, the bobbin brake pulley can be easily made to regulate its drag to a nicety.

In a power machine are found many pairs of rollers, between which the fibers to be spun are drawn out with such regularity as few spinners could boast of. Such rollers are set in a series, at very accurate distances apart, and revolved in a chosen direction. The front pair of rollers revolve more quickly than the second pair; the second pair than the third, and so on. Consequently, as the fibers pass between the series, they are gradually drawn out into a fine fleecy rove which, between the front rollers and the spindle, becomes twisted into fine even thread. Plate 95, right, shows this principle clearly from the patent model of Peter Paddleford, May 18, 1816. This system of drawing out fibers by means of rollers was invented by Paul in 1735 and made practical by Arkwright in 1775, when he patented it. His right, however, was disputed, and on trial the patent was annulled, but his adaptation of the system was soon generally adopted. Plate 96 shows a ring cotton-spinning room in a great modern factory.

When describing the primitive spinning wheel and the distaff and spindle, where the spinning and winding on were done alternately, I should perhaps have remarked that the finest threads were always produced in this manner. It is not surprising, therefore, that very early in the history of machine spinning it was found that very fine, delicate threads could not be spun on the simultaneous principle. To overcome this difficulty Crompton invented the mule machine, which imitates exactly the alternate twisting and winding of the primitive method of spinning. It was interesting to see at the Anglo-Japanese exhibition of 1909 the huge English machine of 250 spindles imitating with perfect precision the actions of a pretty girl in the Japanese handicraft section who was spinning gossamer thread on a primitive wheel, the same kind of wheel which had been in use in her country for a couple of thousand years or so, and which, we may hope, will be used for an indefinite number of thousands of years more by such charming little spinsters.

In conclusion, as regards the spindle, although we may congratulate ourselves on the performances of these wonderful thread-making machines and admire the inventive genius which has brought them to such perfection, it is interesting, though perhaps chastening and humiliating, to note that the untutored Hindoo spinner, squatting on the ground with a simple toylike spindle, can draw out and spin thread as fine, but infinitely stronger, than the most perfect machine of them all.

Four thousand years ago, more or less, probably at the time when the people of the stone age in Europe were cultivating flax and spinning and weaving its fiber into coarse cloth, the Chinese were inventing improvements in their primitive weaving appliances in order to adapt them to the weaving of an infinitely finer fiber than that of flax. This fiber was obtained by unwinding the case of the chrysalis of the mulberry-feeding moth, the caterpillar of which is familiarly known as the silkworm.

The silk fiber, on being unwound from the cocoon, is found to be a continuous, double thread of about the

Fig. 45. A primitive Indian or African loom. Courtesy of the Royal Society of Arts

four-thousandth part of an inch in diameter. It takes from eighty to a hundred threads of natural silk to make up one thread of the size of the finest spun flax. It may be well understood, therefore, that special preparation of silk thread and specially delicate appliances are necessary for weaving it. This necessity proved to be, as is proverbially the case, the mother of many inventions, and there can be no doubt it is from the original Chinese weaving appliances that almost all succeeding improvements in looms and loom fittings have been derived.

Figure 45 shows a very convenient form of Indian loom with the heddle rods suspended from the branch of a tree and having the heddle loops connected with another pair of rods beneath the warp. The lower rods have strings hanging from them, each terminating in a ring. By placing one of his great toes in each ring the weaver can pull down either set of loops at will and make alternate openings for the shuttle carrying the weft. His hands are thus left free to manipulate the shuttle.

The addition of a long comb, equal in length to the width of the warp, was an immense improvement to the

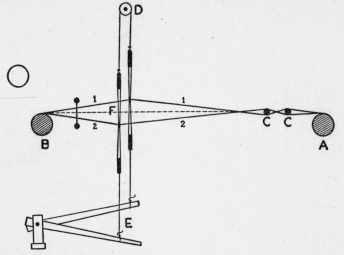

FIG. 46. Diagram of the essentials of a plain loom. Courtesy of the Royal Society of Arts

loom. The divisions in it were originally made of split reeds, hence it was called the reed, and is still so called, although the divisions are now always made of steel. The effect of the long comb, with the warp threads entered in it, swinging in its heavy frame, (Fig. 47, *I*), was not only that the weft was beaten together more evenly and with less individual strain on the threads, but the width of the woven web was kept automatically the same.

Figure 46 is a longitudinal section of the essential parts of a loom at the point of development now arrived at.

It is lettered for reference. *A* is the roller on which the warp is wound in the first instance. *B* is the roller onto which the woven cloth passes. *C C* are the sticks preserving the cross which keeps the warp in order. *D* is one of two pulleys suspended from the top of the loom frame, over which cords pass after being attached to the ends of the top laths of the two heddles. At *E* are two treadles which are tied to the lower laths of the heddles. Between the heddles and *B* the reed is shown suspended.

One treadle is represented depressed. This has pulled down one heddle and raised the other in consequence of the cord which passes over the pulley *D*. This movement has effected an opening in the warp at *F*, which between the roller, *B*, and the reed is wide enough for passing the weft through.

The successful weaving of plain silk necessitates a development of the loom to this point. It is therefore reasonable to credit the Chinese, who until the third century A.D. were the monopolists of silk and silk weaving, with all these essential contrivances. Subsequently to the third century these inventions spread through the East generally and finally to Europe, first to Spain and Italy, then to France, Germany, and England. It is remarkable that the loom of today, on which the very best silk fabrics are woven, should in all essential points be the same as the looms of ancient China.

The first impression given by Figure 47, which is a diagram of an English loom, is one of sturdy strength. Strength and the perfect adjustment of the various parts of the loom are prime requisites where rapid and accurate weaving are desired. Figure 47 is lettered similarly to Figure 46, so that its parts may be understood.

When the warp threads are very coarse and few in number, two heddles are sufficient for threading the warp, but when fine silk fabrics are to be woven, having three or four hundred threads to an inch, it is necessary to have several pairs of heddles in order to prevent the leashes, through which the silk is threaded, from being too crowded. In a Chinese silk loom the front harness, as a collection of heddles is called, consists of 10 separate heddles. In all looms the threads of the warp are passed through the eyes in the leashes of the heddles in regular order.

The first thread is passed through the first leash of the first heddle, the second thread through the first leash of

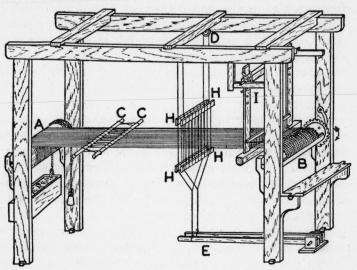

FIG. 47. Sketch of the plain English loom. Courtesy of the Royal Society of Arts

the second heddle, then through the first of the third, and so on until all are filled.

To manage this set of 10, or any even number of heddles, only 2 treadles are necessary for plain or tabby weaving. The heddles are first joined together in pairs at the top, each pair having its two separate pulleys, as in the typical English loom. (Figure 47.) The bottom laths of the first, third, fifth, seventh, and ninth heddles are then all connected with one treadle, and those of the second, fourth, sixth, eighth, and tenth heddles are joined to the other treadle. Now, it is manifest that if the first treadle be depressed half the warp, consisting of the first and all the odd-numbered threads, will be drawn down and the second and all the even-numbered threads will be drawn up. This will make the same opening for the weft as if there were only 2 instead of 10 heddles. This arrangement being at first made for plain tabby weaving of a close warp of fine threads, it would soon be discovered that by increasing the number of treadles and tying them to the heddles in different ways the interlacements of warp and weft might be varied to an astonishing extent and result in the production of an infinite variety of small patterns.

Patterns woven of single threads require the thread itself to be coarse in size in order to show as designs. But such designs, woven in fine silk, although indistinguishable as ornament, have a marked effect on the appearance of the texture of the web. The Chinese early discovered this fact, and it was for their various beautiful and rich textures that the woven silks of China were so much prized in classic times.

Figure 48 represents the back and front surfaces of a square of silk textile, which might have been woven in ancient China on a loom fitted up as I have described. It would require 16 heddles and 16 treadles to weave it, and the threads are so fine and lie so closely that the whole piece shown would be only the one-thousandth part of a square inch in size.

Looking at the lower square, which is the front of the material, it will be seen that the surface is nearly all warp, and that the intersections of the weft only occur at intervals of 16 spaces each way. In cloth of this pattern the intersections of the weft are invisible; therefore its whole surface has the rich texture and glossy appearance known as satin. In the same proportion as the front of the satin web is nearly all warp, the back, of course,

PLATE 96

Ring spinning room. Amoskeag Manufacturing Company, Manchester, N. H.

displays the weft. In pattern weaving these effects are called, respectively, warp satins and weft satins. Satins may be made on different numbers of heddles, from 5 up to 24.

The next step in the evolution of the loom was to adapt it for distinct pattern weaving. This was effected by adding a second set of heddles to the harness, making it what is called a com-pound harness. For double-harness weaving the leashes of the heddles of the front harness have an important peculiarity which must be described; for, though simple, it plays a most essential part in all pattern weav-ing with compound har-ness.

In this class of weaving each warp thread passes first through the eyes of the figure harness and then through those of the front harness, which makes the ground. Now, if both harnesses are alike fitted with leashes having

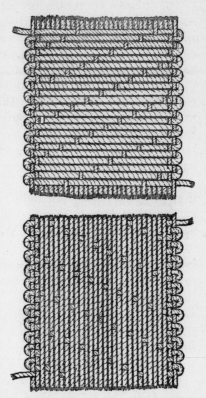

Fig. 48. Front and back designs of satin cloth. Courtesy of the Royal Society of Arts

the ordinary short eyes, only the front one can affect the shed. This is because any threads raised by the back harness are prevented from effectually rising in the reed by the leashes of the front harness. If, however, the front harness eyes are made long enough to allow the

[281]

warp threads to be lifted, the back harness will be free to affect the shed at the same time as the front harness, or to affect it alternately as may be required.

The points to notice are: (1) Two extra wefts are required for weaving in the design [shown by the lecturer] which has two separate colors of its own; (2) the figure is formed by allowing the colored weft in certain places to pass over two threads of the warp instead of one; (3) the necessity for five heddles in the figure harness is to be gathered from the fact that five different combinations of pairs of rising threads are required to complete the design; (4) as the figure throughout is made by two threads rising together, two threads together may be entered in each eye of the figure harness.

If this explanation is clear, it is only necessary to add that in silk weaving not only 2, but sometimes as many as 20, warp threads are entered in each leash eye of the figure harness. Therefore, it is evident that the possible scale of ornamentation and scope for the designer are immensely increased. For instance, this figure woven on two threads, as explained, on a fine silk warp of 400 threads to an inch, would only occupy the sixteenth of an inch in width and height, but if 20 threads were entered together in each leash eye of the figure harness the size of the ornament would be increased 10 diameters and would occupy nearly a square inch of surface.

In Figure 49 at No. 1, I have represented in diagrammatic form the simple draw loom and at No. 2 a design on ruled paper suited to its capacity, which is purposely kept very limited for the sake of clearness. The whole mechanism of the draw loom centers in the comber board and leashes which hang in the loom in place of the ordinary harness of few or many heddles. The advantage of the comber board monture over the ordinary heddle harness is that whatever width a design may be, even to the whole extent of the warp, the monture takes up no more longitudinal space in the loom than a harness of a few heddles.

The comber board, No. 3, is simply a board pierced with a number of holes equal to the number of threads of the warp which it is to govern. In each of these holes a

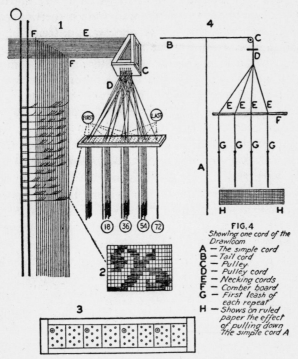

FIG. 4
Showing one cord of the
Drawloom
A — The simple cord
B — Tail cord
C — Pulley
D — Pulley cord
E — Necking cords
F — Comber board
G — First leash of
each repeat
H — Shows on ruled
paper the effect
of pulling down
the simple cord A

FIG. 49.   Diagram of a simple draw loom. Courtesy
of the Royal Society of Arts

separate leash is hung. Each leash has a long, thin lead weight at its bottom end; and in its center, instead of a string loop, a glass eye called a mail, through which a warp thread is entered.

The comber board in the diagram is only pierced with 72 holes; consequently it is only for a warp of 72 threads.

If it were for 72,000 threads of fine silk, it would not take appreciably more space in the loom. The drafted design at No. 2 is made on 18 lateral squares, so that it would repeat four times in the width of the web to be woven. In this comber board there are holes for four repeats of 18 leashes, but only six leashes of each repeat are shown in position, as more would confuse the drawing.

The bottom board of the triangular box, C (Fig. 49, 1), is pierced with 18 holes, the same number as that of the threads in each repeat of the design. Let us suppose the comber board to be filled with leashes, one suspended in each hole; also that 18 cords are hanging through the holes in the triangular box at D. The monture builder now connects, with fine cord, the first, nineteenth, thirty-seventh, and fifty-fifth leashes, which are the first in every repeat, with the first hanging cord at D. He next takes the second leash in each repeat, and connects it in like manner with the second cord at D. He proceeds thus in regular order to connect leashes and top cords until he reaches the last of the repeats, leashes 18, 36, 54, and 72.

When this work is done it is apparent that if any one cord at D is drawn up into the triangular box the corresponding leashes in every repeat will be drawn up through the comber board to a corresponding height. Moreover, if 72 threads of warp are entered in the leash eyes, the selected leashes as they rise will raise the threads necessary for the formation of the pattern shed. This is the essential portion of the draw loom, and so far is it from being obsolete that all the pattern-weaving looms of today, whether worked by hand or power, are identical with it. Thus the immense textile industry of modern times is indebted to and linked with the invention and industry of ancient China.

I resume the explanation of the diagram of the draw loom, Figure 49, at the point, D, where the 18 cords are seen to enter the triangular box, C. This box is fitted up with pulleys, 18 in number. Each cord passes over a pulley and is seen again at *E*. The collection of 18 cords, called the tail of the monture, is then securely fastened to the wall of the workshop, or some convenient strong post.

Between *F* and *F* another series of 18 cords, called the simple, is tied to the tail series and fastened to the ground. A simplified diagram, showing one cord in all its parts, is given in No. 4.

Now, it will at once be seen that if the cord, *A*, be pulled down by an assistant standing at the side of the loom, the eyes of the leashes, *G*, through which the warp threads pass, will be pulled up. It is necessary, then, in the simple, to have as many cords as there are threads or groups of threads in each repeat of the comber board. And it is possible to weave on the loom any design, of whatever length, that can be drawn on the number of threads arranged for in each repeat.

If we turn to the design No. 2 we shall see that it is drawn on 18 squares, and if we compare the design with the loops tied from the large guiding cords to the separate cords of the simple, we shall see that they agree. The black squares in the design represent a tie. Take the first line, beginning at the left-hand side. Here are six black squares. If we follow the dotted line to the first cord of the simple, a group of six ties will be found. Then passing over six cords, a group of four ties are found which correspond with the four black squares in the third division of the sketch. •

By means of these loops the drawboy, as he was called, selected the cords for pulling down, and, having gathered them together on the prong of a large fork, to which a lever was attached, he pulled the lever and drew the leashes up, thus opening the shed for the weaver's shuttle. The design had to be tied up on the simple cords line by line before weaving could commence; but when this was once done the drawboy had only to pull the cords, in regular sequence, in order to repeat the design continuously in the length of the web.

On this mounting of the loom entered with single threads of warp any possible interlacements of warp and weft can be worked out. It may well be called, therefore, the most perfect loom. Its only limitation is in the size of the design. It would require a simple of 400 cords to tie up a design one inch wide for a silk web 400 threads to an inch.

III. THE JACQUARD MACHINE; POWER-DRIVEN LOOM

In the early part of the eighteenth century, weaving, as a handicraft, reached in Europe its point of highest perfection. France, England, and Italy were the chief countries in which it was practiced. At that time, in England particularly, the condition of the textile craftsman, of whatever grade, seems to have been better than at any other period of which we have record. The weaver of the eighteenth century was a prosperous and respectable tradesman, whether working in the secluded country village, in the suburbs of the great towns of the north and east, or near the metropolis in the pleasant district of Spitalfields, notable as the silk-weaving quarter of London. This happy condition of the weaver in the eighteenth century declined to one of misery in the nineteenth. The economic causes of this change are not far to seek, but form not part of my subject. I only refer to this period of prosperity, as it marks an important stage and change of direction in the development of the loom.

Hitherto the motive of inventors was to increase the scope and perfection of the loom as a pattern-weaving tool. The perfection attained and the care bestowed on loom construction are shown in the beautiful illustrations of Diderot's Dictionary and other technical works of the period. During the latter portion of the eighteenth century, and since, the chief purpose of invention has

[286]

been, not excellence of work and extended capacity of the loom, but economy of time and cheapening of production.

The first indication of the coming change in the broad-weaving trade was given as early as 1687, when Joseph Mason patented a machine which he described as "an engine by the help of which a weaver may performe the whole work of weaving such stuffe as the greate weaving trade of Norwich doth now depend on, without the help of a draught-boy, which engine hath been tryed and found out to be of greate use to the said weaving trade." It is necessary to the understanding of the mechanism of the important machine which superseded it, to have a general idea of this drawboy machine. In order to give this idea, however, I must first describe the work of the human drawboy.

In a rich silk loom there were often as many as two or three thousand lead weights, called lingoes, hanging three to each leash of the monture. These weighed altogether a couple of hundredweight. On an average half of them had to be drawn up at every line of the design. Moreover, their dead weight would be so increased by the friction of the multitude of cords and pulleys that the boy would have to raise and hold for several seconds a weight equal to a hundredweight and a half. This would, of course, be impossible but for some mechanical help. The implement devised for the boy's assistance was called the "drawboy's fork." This is shown in Figure 50. The vertical lines in this diagram represent the cords of the simple.

To the left is a solid stand having two broad uprights joined together at the top by two parallel bars. *A* is a block of hard wood, which fits between the bars, and is held in position by four pairs of small wheels. These not only support it but allow it to run freely from end to end of the stand. This block with the fork and lever attached, is shown separately at *E*. The fork and lever are hinged to the block at its top and can be moved from the vertical to a horizontal position. When about to be used the block is moved till the points of the fork are just beyond the backmost cord of the simple, the lever being in an upright position. By means of loops tied to the simple, the required cords are drawn forward and the upper prong of the fork inserted in the opening thus made, as shown

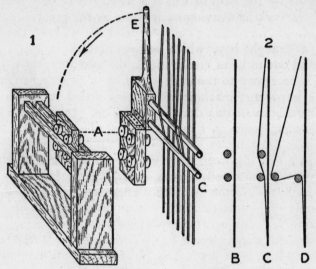

FIG. 50. The drawboy's fork. Courtesy of the Royal Society of Arts

in Figure 50. Then, grasping the lever, the boy draws it down and holds it. The result of this is that the selected lingoes and leashes are drawn and held up. At No. 2 three sections of the simple are shown lettered *B*, *C*, and *D*. At *B* the cords are at rest. At *C* some cords have been selected and the fork inserted. At *D* the lever has been pulled over and the cords drawn over with it.

Figure 51 shows the mechanical drawboy, a machine invented in the seventeenth century and improved during the eighteenth. It was attached to the pulley cords of the loom, on which, when the machine was used, the tie-up

PLATE 97

Worsted weaving machine.   Amoskeag Manufacturing Company, Manchester, N. H.

of the design was made, instead of on the simple. The active part of this machine is the pecker, which by means of two treadles and some little mechanical arrangements had two movements: (1) It rocked from side to side; (2) it moved, as it rocked, along the machine from one end to the other. Through holes in the side cross-pieces of the frame strong cords terminating in heavy weights were hung. To the tops of these cords the loops of each row of

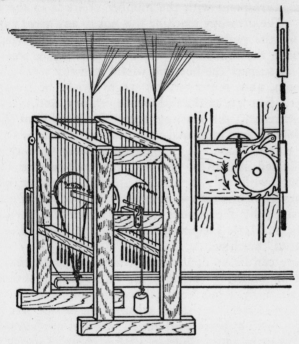

FIG. 51. The mechanical drawboy. Courtesy of the Royal Society of Arts

tie-ups were attached in regular succession. Only two rows are shown connected in the diagram to prevent confusion of lines. The pecker had a deep notch cut in its points and was of such a size that as it rocked the cord toward which it inclined caught in the notch. At the center of the cord a large bead was fixed. When the rocking pecker came in contact with this bead it pushed it and its cord down and held it until the second treadle moved the pecker in the opposite direction. As the pecker traveled along the shaft each cord was drawn down in its turn, thus opening the shed, line by line, for the working out of the pattern.

The number of lines in the length of a design, of course, had to correspond with the number of cords in the machine. The drawboy machine was not to any great extent used for the purpose for which it was intended, viz., to supersede the drawboy of the compound figure weaving loom. I suspect the boy was useful in many ways about the loom, and, moreover, his wages would be no great matter. But late in the eighteenth century, and well into the nineteenth, the machine received a good deal of attention and was improved and adapted for use with the treadle hand loom. It enabled the weaver to work any complicated system of heddles, for small-pattern fancy weaving, with only 2 treadles instead of 20 or more. Further improvements were made later, but it was finally superseded by the famous machine which was perfected by Joseph Marie Jacquard, and known in England as the "Jackard" machine.

There can be no doubt that it is to Jacquard that the credit of rendering this machine thoroughly practical is due, although it has been proved that the fundamental idea of it, which consists in substituting for the weaver's tie-up a band of perforated paper, was first applied to the draw loom in 1725, while in 1728 a chain of cards was substituted for the paper and a perforated cylinder also added. But it was reserved for Jacquard to carry the machine to such perfection that, although many slight improvements have since been made in it, it remains to-day practically the same as he introduced it in 1801, notwithstanding the astonishing development of textile machinery during the nineteenth century and the universal adoption of the machine both for hand and power weaving.

May I here repeat and emphasize that the invention of the Jacquard machine did not alter in the least the draw-loom method of pattern weaving? It only took the place of the drawboy and the pulley box, and substituted the endless band of perforated cards for the weaver's tie-up. The designs, too, drafted on ruled paper, would be worked out in precisely the same manner, whether for tying up on the cords of a simple or for punching in a set of Jacquard cards. Each card, in fact, takes the place of one row of loops of the tie-up.

The term Jacquard weaving, then, which one so often hears used, is a misnomer. It should be draw-loom weaving with a Jacquard machine, the machine being only an ingenious substitute for a less compact and manageable adjunct of the draw loom, an adjunct, moreover, which, as we have seen, has continually varied from the time of the invention of this form of loom. After the draw loom itself I should class the Jacquard machine as the most important invention in textile mechanism. It therefore claims a careful description.

Figure 52 is a drawing of the front elevation of a 400 Jacquard machine. The number 400 refers to the number of needles and hooks with which the machine is fitted up. These needles and hooks answer to the number of the simple cords of the draw loom. A design is still technically spoken of as being drafted for so many cords.

The position of the machine in the loom is at the top, where it is fixed on a solid frame just over the comber board, usually with its end to the front of the loom, so that the elevation shown in the figure is parallel with the side of the loom frame. The machine frame is oblong in shape. It is made of hardwood for hand looms and of iron for power looms. But in either case it needs to be of great strength. To the principal frame a smaller one is hinged at the top, so that it can be raised like a flap.

In this drawing 50 wire hooks are seen standing upright

on the bottom board of the machine. The bottom board is perforated with as many holes as there are hooks in the machine, in this case 400. The hooks represented are only one rank out of eight, which the machine contains. Each hole in the bottom board has a dent or groove cut across the top, in which the bent end of the wire hook rests. This

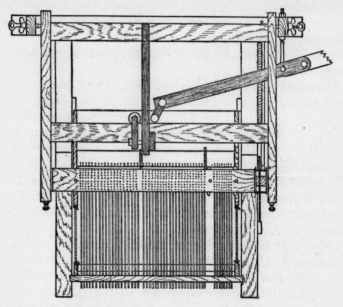

FIG. 52. Front elevation of a Jacquard machine. Courtesy of the Royal Society of Arts

keeps the hook firmly in position, especially when the necking cords of the harness are brought up through the holes and looped on to the wire.

Figure 53 gives two sections of the machine, one showing it at rest and the other showing it in action. In both sections 8 hooks are drawn, 1 from each rank of 50. The hooks have the necking cords attached at the lower ends, and just below the small hook at the top may be seen a set of eight wires crossing them at right angles. Each of these wires, called needles, is bent into a loop or eye, where it crosses one of the hooks, and it is because the hook is passed through this eye that it is retained in an upright position. Figure 54 will show this arrangement quite clearly. Each hook thus resting on the bottom board, and held down by the weight of the leashes of the harness,

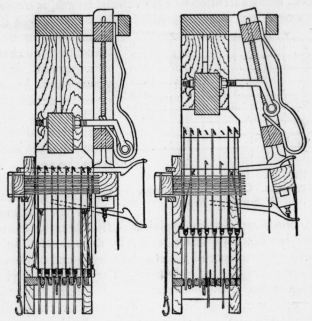

FIG. 53. Sectional views of a Jacquard machine.
Courtesy of the Royal Society of Arts

though supported at the top by the eye of the needle, through which it passes, is still free to rise and raise with it the leash or leashes to which it is attached.

Leaving the hooks thus standing, let us consider the arrangement for lifting them. Above the hooks the section of a solid block of heavy wood or iron is shown. This block runs from end to end of the machine, and has projections at its ends which fit into the narrow spaces between the two pairs of uprights of the machine frame in such a manner that the block can be caused to slide up and down steadily but freely.

Now, let us look at the block in the drawing of the front elevation (Fig. 52) and then at a drawing showing the block in detail, separately. The lever for raising the block, being extended to a convenient length, is connected by a rope to a treadle worked by the weaver's foot in the hand loom, or by any ordinary mechanical arrangement in the power loom. Figure 55 gives us details of the block (1) as seen in front elevation; (2) from above; and (3) from the end.

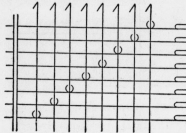

FIG. 54. Detail of a Jacquard machine. Courtesy of the Royal Society of Arts

The block, the lever, and the arrangements for sliding up and down are already explained. But hanging from the block is a kind of gridiron, called by the weaver a "griffe," which requires careful notice. Near each end of the block a flat plate of iron is firmly fixed. The shape of the plate is shown at No. 3, and between the plates, eight bars of hoop iron are fitted, as at No. 2. These bars are placed diagonally (see No. 3) and their top edges are sharpened so as to fit under the carefully made small hooks at the top ends of the upright wires as they stand in their several rows.

The first section of Figure 53 shows the block at its lowest position, with the hooks caught on the bars of the griffe. Should the block now be raised the whole of the 400 hooks will be drawn up and the whole warp will rise with them. When released, of course, all will fall together, pulled down by the lead weights. Again, if the projecting ends of the needles are pushed inward, the needle eyes will deflect the hooks and remove them from the griffe, which will then, if the block be raised, rise by itself, leaving the hooks, leashes, and warp all down, as in section 2.

In section 2 the points of the needles are seen to pass through and project beyond the surface of an accurately

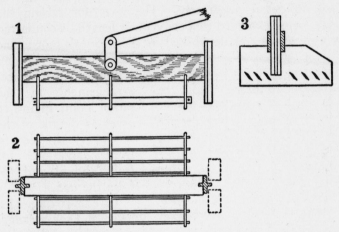

FIG. 55. Further details of a Jacquard machine. Courtesy of the Royal Society of Arts

perforated board fixed to the front of the machine frame opposite the needles. Hung in the frame, hinged to the top of the machine, is a four-sided revolving bar, or cylinder, each side being perforated so as to match exactly the perforations of the needle board.

If the flap, with the cylinder in it, be pressed against the board, and the block raised, nothing different will happen, because the points of the needles will have been free to enter the holes in the cylinder. If, however, a card covering all the holes be fixed to one side of the cylinder and the cylinder then be brought close up, presenting each side in regular succession, every time the card comes in contact with the needle points the needles will be pressed inward, push the hooks off the bars of the griffe, and the block will rise without them.

[295]

It follows, then, that if we interpose between the needle points and the side of the cylinder, as it presses the needle board, a card perforated according to an arranged design, wherever a hole is covered by the card a needle will be pressed in, and consequently a hook will be pushed off the griffe bar and left down as the block rises. Each card, therefore, affects, in one way or another, every hook in the machine with its necking cords and leashes; and these, of course, determine the rising or remaining down of every thread of the warp from edge to edge of the web.

At the back of the machine a shallow box is fitted, containing 400 small spiral springs, one for each needle. When, therefore, any needle is pressed inward by the card on the cylinder, its opposite end is forced into the spring box, but as soon as the pressure is relaxed the needle, driven back by the spring, regains its normal position, holding the hook upright.

The mechanical contrivances by means of which the cylinder is moved, pressed against the needle board and rotated as the block rises and descends, are most ingenious, and subject to a great deal of variation. They are, however, not essential to the principles of the machine and can be passed over. But the method by which the perforated cards are adjusted to the cylinder and interpose between it and the needle board must be explained.

Figure 56 shows a detached cylinder and four cards punched with a pattern called a four-lined twill. This pattern repeats on every four lines; accordingly only four cards are needed to weave it. At the ends of the cylinder, close to the perforations, pegs are fixed and holes matching these pegs in size and position are punched in the cards. These pegs hold the card in its proper place, so that its perforations correspond exactly with those of the cylinder.

Each side of the cylinder as it rotates, being covered

with a card held close to it by two elastic bands will press against a different set of needles at each of its four move-ments. The fifth movement, of course, brings the first set of needles again into play. When, however, as is generally the case, more than four lines of design are required, the

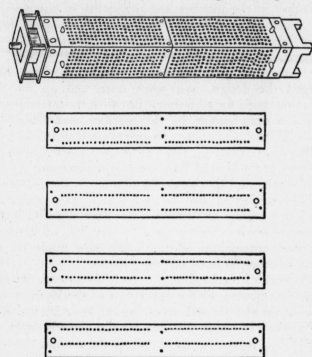

FIG. 56.   Cylinder and cards for a Jacquard machine.
Courtesy of the Royal Society of Arts

cards have to be laced together in an endless band hung upon a rack at the side of the loom, and carried around the cylinder.

The most striking advantage of the use of the Jacquard machine in the textile arts is the facility it gives for a fre-quent change of design. It is only necessary to take down one set of cards and hang up another in order to change the pattern. The result of this facility was that the early part of the nineteenth century witnessed a perfect orgy of fantastic ornamentation. The manufacturers of all sorts of ornamental silk and fine woolen textiles vied with each other in the number and originality of the designs they could produce. The profession of designer may almost be said to be an outcome of the invention of Jacquard. Previously to this time the master weaver, or some person in practical touch with the looms, had arranged the design, and when once tied up on the loom it was good for a lifetime. But with the introduction of the new draw engine, as the machine was called, all this was altered, and restless change of pattern and fashion was the result. Plate 94, right, shows a Jacquard loom on exhibition at the United States National Museum.

At first the machine was only adopted in the silk trade for the weaving of rich brocades and other elaborate materials for dress or furniture, but ever since its introduction its use has been gradually extending, all kinds of plain and ornamental textiles being now made by its means, whether on hand or power looms.

As a work of mechanism it is truly wonderful. It can be made to govern all the operations of the loom except throwing the shuttle and actuating the lever by which it itself works. It opens the shed for the pattern, however complicated, regulates the length of the design, changes the shuttle boxes in proper succession, rings a bell when certain points in a design requiring special treatment are reached, regulates the take-up of the woven cloth on the front roller, and works out many other details, all by means of a few holes punched in a set of cards. Its great defects are the dreadful noise it makes, the ease with which it gets out of order, and the difficulty of putting it right. These render it only suitable for factory use, where noise does not seem to matter, and where a machinist is constantly at hand to keep the mechanism in good order.

In order to find the earliest recorded attempt to weave by power we must carry our imagination back to the latter part of the sixteenth century and look in on the fathers of the city of Danzig in council chamber solemnly assembled. They are deciding the fate of a prisoner accused and found guilty of the crime of inventing a very ingenious machine for weaving narrow tape several breadths at a time. The council, having carefully considered the machine, and bearing in mind the state of the trade, were "afraid that by this invention a great many workmen might be reduced to beggary." They, therefore, mercifully ordered the machine to be suppressed and the inventor of it to be privately strangled or drowned!

The operations of the loom in weaving are four in number: To open the shed, to throw and catch the shuttle, to beat the weft together, and to wind up the woven cloth. All these, except the second, are comparatively easy to arrange for, even in broad weaving, by means of a power-driven turning shaft furnished with cranks and eccentrics, fitted up in some convenient position in the loom. In narrow weaving the spaces of warp are so small that the passing through of the several shuttles presents no difficulty; consequently the invention of a practical automatic machine loom for narrow weaving was an early one.

Many attempts were made in the seventeenth and early part of the eighteenth century to weave broad webs by power, but they all failed to solve the problem of the shuttle. It has been partially overcome since, but the great defect of the machine loom today is in the driving and catching of the shuttle. The invention which partially solved the difficulty and eventually rendered the machine loom practicable was the fly shuttle, intended by John Kay, its inventor, for use on the hand loom. Its purpose was to enable the weaver to weave, without the aid of an assistant, wider webs than he could manipulate with the hand shuttle.

Previously to this invention all attempts to pass the weft through the shed in machine looms failed to achieve anything like the speed of the hand-thrown shuttle; consequently they could not compete with the hand loom. Even when the fly-shuttle method was adopted the difficulty of catching the shuttle baffled the skill of inventors for many years. It was not till 1786, when Dr. Edmund Cartwright devoted himself and his fortune to mechanical invention, that a practical broad-weaving power loom was evolved. Doctor Cartwright established a weaving and spinning factory at Doncaster, but after spending £30,000 and nine years in experiments he was obliged to give it up. He had, however, succeeded in devising a power loom for plain weaving, which it was believed could compete with the hand loom.

Plate 97 is a room filled with modern power looms for worsted weaving at a modern textile factory. You will notice at once how the levers for driving the shuttle, and the shuttle boxes, have increased in size and strength. It was found that in order to catch the shuttle and prevent it rebounding, its entry into the opposite box had to be resisted. This rendered it necessary that the shuttle itself should be enormously increased in weight, and that great force should be used in driving it. Half the power expended in actuating the machine loom is required thus to drive the shuttle into the opposing box.

The addition and adaptation of the Jacquard machine to the power loom was not attempted till late in the nineteenth century, but when that was done the loom had arrived at the point of development at which we find it today.

INVENTIONS CONCERNED WITH AGRICULTURE

Of the many nineteenth century inventions that reduced farm labor, including plows, harrows, manure spreaders, corn planters, grain seeders, cultivators, mowers, horse rakes, tedders, hay loaders, fruit pickers, milkers, cream separators, and many more, none were so revolutionary in their influence on the productivity of American agriculture as the cotton gin, the harvester, and the applications of mechanical power.

At the close of the Revolutionary War cotton was sparsely raised in the South, but the labor of separating the fiber from the seeds was so great that flax, hemp, wool, silk, and fur were far more important sources of clothing and textiles. Radical was the change produced by Eli Whitney's invention of the cotton gin. It is estimated that it increased the productivity of the worker a thousandfold. In open court, Federal Judge Johnson of Georgia stated its importance thus:

Is there a man who hears us who has not experienced its utility? The whole interior of the Southern States was languishing and its inhabitants emigrating for want of some object to engage their attention and employ their industry, when the invention of this machine at once opened views to them which set the whole country in active motion . . . Our debts have been paid off, our capitals have increased, and our lands trebled themselves in value. We cannot express the weight of the obligation which the country owes to this invention.

Eli Whitney (1765–1825) was a native of Westborough, Mass. After graduating from Yale he became a private teacher in Georgia, in the family of Gen. Nathaniel Greene, of Revolutionary fame. His ingenuity attracted the attention of Mrs. Greene, and she directed his thought to the problem of separating the cotton seeds. A neighbor, Phineas Miller, also from New England and a graduate of Yale, became interested, and entered into a partnership with Whitney to promote the invention. The experiments were carried on in Miller's house. Whitney had only the most primitive implements, but in the course of the winter of 1793 he advanced so far as to be assured of success.

Generally a great invention has to create its market by laborious promotion of its advantages. In this case the result was quite the reverse. When it became known that Whitney was making a machine to gin cotton, crowds threw fairness to the winds, broke into the workroom, and carried the machine away. Before patent proceedings could be completed by the partners, dozens of pirate cotton gins had been put to use in the cotton fields.

The simplicity of Whitney's cotton gin worked against the recovery by the partners of fair compensation for their efforts. In principle it comprises merely a cylinder armed with numerous fine-toothed circular saws operating through slots leading into a box of seed cotton. The saw teeth catch and draw away the fibers, but the seeds are excluded by the sides of the narrow slots. A second, more rapidly rotating cylinder armed with brushes removes the cotton lint from the saw teeth. Figure 57 gives a cross-section of a gin showing one of the saws and accessories.

Many suits were instituted by Whitney and Miller to protect their rights under the patents, but they were often unsuccessful. It is said that juries were more alive to local interests than to doing justice to the inventor and his partner, natives of distant States. A fire destroyed Whitney's factory in New Haven, with all his gins and papers. In 1803 Phineas Miller died without ever having received adequate compensation for his share in the introduction of the invaluable cotton gin. Whitney succeeded in persuading the legislatures of South Carolina, North Carolina, and Tennessee to appropriate some money in payment for rights to use the cotton gin within those States. But he never received from his invention any adequate return. He amassed a competency later by manufacturing arms for the Government. He died at the age of 60, seven years after his very happy marriage.

Several of the features of the successful reapers of McCormick and of Hussey were included in partially successful British inventions of Joseph Mann, 1820; Henry Ogle, 1822; and Patrick Bell, 1826. Mann, like McCormick, had the main traction wheel directly behind the horse. Ogle had the vibrating cutter-bar, the reel, the platform, and the divider to separate the swath from the

PLATE 98

Eli Whitney, inventor of the cotton gin

PLATE 99

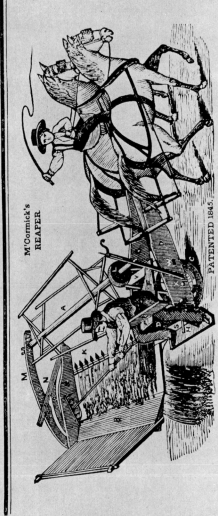

McCormick reaper of 1845.   From "The Cultivator," Albany, N. Y., May, 1846

uncut grain. Bell also had the reel and the divider, and he foreshadowed a feature of the modern harvester, for he had an endless canvas belt to remove the cut grain from the platform, depositing it in an orderly row along the ground.

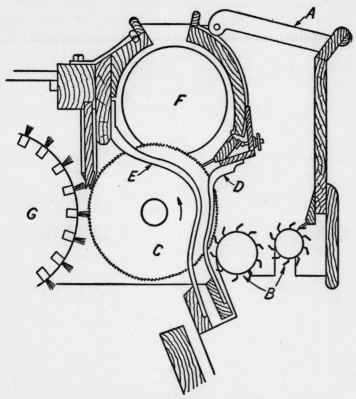

Fig. 57. Cross sectional diagram of a cotton gin. Courtesy of John Wiley & Sons, Inc., publishers

The McCormick reaper, patented by Cyrus Hall McCormick in 1834, was first used in substantially that form in the harvest of 1831 at several farms in Walnut Grove, Rockbridge County, in the Valley of Virginia.

Prior to that, Robert McCormick, father of Cyrus, had made several partially successful reapers. He had a blacksmith shop and tools for working both wood and iron. The successful reaper was made by the hands of the two McCormicks, father and son. Figure 58 shows a restoration of it, as indicated by the patent of 1834.

The traction wheel is directly behind the horse, and the grain is cut at the side, so as to avoid trampling. A

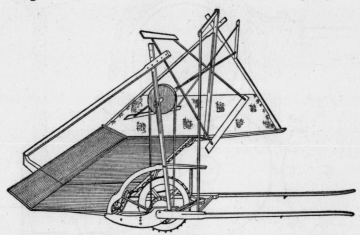

Fig. 58. Restoration of McCormick reaper, 1834. Drawing from patent specifications of C. H. McCormick, omitting the pusher device

vibrating cutter-bar with plain or serrated cutting edge lies horizontally a few inches above the ground. A series of curved fingers at intervals along the blade hold the stalks of grain for the sawing action of the vibrating knife. A reel of four slats, revolving above the cutter-bar, bends the grain toward it to promote cutting, particularly in case the grain is "lodged," or the wind blowing it forward so that it is not vertical. Behind the cutter-bar is a platform on which the cut grain falls parallel to the horse. A man, walking behind, periodically rakes the grain off the platform in bundles, called gavels, for binding. On the

PLATE 100

Modern harvester. Courtesy of the International Harvester Company

PLATE 101

McCormick-Deering harvester-thresher.   Courtesy of the International Harvester Company

outer end of the platform is a divider with pointed front to separate the grain to be cut from the grain standing beyond.

In the year 1833 Obed Hussey, in Ohio, invented and constructed a reaper which he patented in December, 1833, a little before the McCormick patent was issued. His machine was carried like a modern mowing machine on two equal traction wheels, with a vibrating cutter-bar at the side. On a platform behind the cutter-bar rode a man with a rake, whose duty it was to bend the standing grain toward the cutter, and push it off the platform to the ground when cut. The Hussey cutter-bar was his principal improvement. Like a modern mowing machine, it had a series of adjacent triangular knives, sliding between the sides of divided pointed fingers. But instead of a single bevel, his knives were beveled both from below and from above. This feature Hussey later changed to the single bevel sliding closely upon the lower finger plate. In 1847 he improved the lower finger plate by a slot to clear it of chaff and leaves, so that he then reached practically the standard cutter-bar construction of modern mowing and reaping machines.

Keen competition quickly arose between McCormick and Hussey. Both made many improvements in their machines as time passed. During the years 1839 to 1847 the Hussey machine was manufactured in Baltimore, and the McCormick at Walnut Grove, Va., by Robert McCormick. After 1845 Cyrus McCormick employed also certain other manufacturers. However, only a few hundred reapers had gone into use. In 1844 and 1845 Cyrus McCormick traveled through the Middle West to introduce his machine, and he aroused considerable interest among farmers there. Robert McCormick, the father, dying in 1846, and relations with the several manufacturers employed not being altogether satisfactory, in 1848 Cyrus McCormick established a factory in Chicago under the partnership McCormick, Ogden, and Jones. In 1849,

Ogden and Jones retired, and the firm name became McCormick & Company. Leander and William McCormick, younger brothers, joined in the enterprise. Cyrus was a very able and enterprising business man, and pushed the sales greatly. Leander was in charge of the manufacturing end of the business, and William attended to the financial end. Thousands of the improved McCormick reapers were made and sold, so that Cyrus McCormick became a millionaire, and honors were heaped upon him. In 1878 he was even elected a corresponding member of the French Academy, cited as "having done more for the cause of agriculture than any living man."

Between 1848 and 1860 he entered into a number of law suits against competitors, but not always successfully, and he failed in his attempt to have his original patent extended. Nevertheless his enterprising business methods and the excellence of the McCormick machine, led to this enormous success. The advantage of reapers was demonstrated to be so tremendous for the harvesting of wheat and other grains, that not only the McCormick but the Hussey, Mann, and other reapers were sold in thousands.

As already stated, in the early machines of McCormick and Hussey, the grain, as it was being cut, fell upon a platform a little behind the traction wheel, and a man walking behind the platform, or in later constructions riding near the platform, raked the grain intermittently in a direction parallel to the cutter-bar, so that it fell on the ground in orderly heaps called gavels, ready for binding. Plate 99, from a McCormick circular of 1845, shows the raker in his seat. From time to time there were invented various self-rakes, operated by the traction wheel, to do this work instead of the man, but even as late as 1855 the McCormick reaper held its own against the self-rake reapers.

But in 1858, C. W. and W. W. Marsh, of Illinois, patented a device wherein the platform became an endless belt. It had also a continuation in an elevating belt

PLATE 102

Gardening by power. Courtesy of the United States Department of Agriculture

PLATE 103

The farm tractor. Courtesy of the United States Department of Agriculture

like the side of a letter **A,** which carried the grain up over
the traction wheel and deposited it in a receiving box
ready for binding by two men who rode on the machine.
From the Marsh harvester has been perfected the modern
self-binding harvester.

Various automatic binding devices using wire, twine, or
straw were invented soon after, but the modern form developed from the cord binder of John P. Appleby, perfected about 1876, which combined the good points of
preceding devices, and especially the knotter of Jacob
Behel patented February, 1864.

The automatic binder merely takes the place of the two
men who rode on the side of the Marsh harvester, but it
is of such complication that one can hardly understand
a description without seeing the machine itself in operation. Plate 100 gives a view of the modern self-binding
harvester. Various slightly differing machines, all with
their good points, are manufactured by different companies. It would be difficult to exaggerate the importance
of the harvester for the food supply of the world.

In the last few decades the harvester-thresher machines
have to a considerable extent superseded the self-binding
harvester. Plate 101 shows how the grain is gathered
and threshed by such machines in those areas where the
conditions are favorable for allowing the grain heads to
dry on the stalks. In other less favorable regions the so-
called windrow harvester is used to cut off the grain tops,
leaving them in windrows to dry several days. Then the
harvester-thresher, with pick-up attachment, goes over
the field and threshes the grain without the necessity of
handling it. About midway between World Wars I and
II it was estimated that about 65,000 self-binding harvest-
ers and about 37,000 harvester-threshers were built yearly.
The former machines had a factory value of about $10,-
600,000, the latter of $50,600,000. The increase of grain
acreage in the United States in 1921–1930 over that of
1902–1905 was more than 20,000,000 acres.

The enormous increase in the population of the civilized countries of the world in the nineteenth and twentieth centuries is in great measure due to the discovery of bacteriology by Pasteur and the modern improvements in sanitation, in preventive and curative medicine, and in allied sciences. It has thrown a very great burden on agriculture, which could hardly be carried without the long list of modern labor-saving machines, some of which are enumerated above. These machines require much power, which until about the year 1890 was supplied exclusively by animals, mainly horses and mules. These animals consume much food but are not usually considered available for human food, as were the slow oxen that preceded them. Therefore it has been of marked relief to the demands upon agriculture for food production that machine traction is largely superseding animal traction in all lines, from transportation to power driving of agricultural machinery. Besides this, the greater speed resulting from mechanically powered operations has led to increased productiveness of farm labor.

Four types of power auxiliaries to farming stand out. Most important of all are automobiles and trucks, for providing rapid transportation and for marketing produce of all sorts. Second comes the multitude of individually motored tools and appliances for gardening, cultivating, dairying, water hoisting, and small power requirements of many kinds. The automobile and the small power unit are of use to every farm, large or small. Third, there are the powerful wheeled tractors, used on large farms to drag gang plows, harrows, cultivators, and harvestors where large, fairly level acreage is in cultivation. Finally, there is the caterpillar tractor which can go anywhere and pull anything. This was made familiar by its introduction during World War I as the motive power of the tanks. Plates 102 to 104 illustrate three of the applications of mechanical power to agricultural uses such as we have considered.

PLATE 104

The caterpillar tractor at work. Courtesy of the United States Department of Agriculture

CHAPTER X

OUTSTANDING MANUFACTURED PRODUCTS

In earlier chapters we have been dealing mainly with machines. Let us now consider four typical products of a manufacturing age, constantly produced in immense quantities—paper, rubber, glass, and steel.

From its slow hand-production, sheet by sheet, for writing purposes, a thousand years ago, paper has come to be manufactured by the millions of tons. Not only rags, grasses, and straw, but the forests of whole countries are used for its raw material. From its early function of providing the sheets on which the quill pen laboriously wrote, it has come to supply the material for the armies of clicking typewriters and the inconceivably intricate, rushing presses which flood the world with letters, records, advertisements, newspapers, books, and periodicals. In the form of newspapers and wrappings, paper enough to cover Ohio three times over is used every year in the United States. Boxes made of paper fill the shelves of groceries and stores of all descriptions and have displaced wooden boxes for shipping goods. Picnic parties strew their paper dishes and paper napkins from Maine to California. Exhibition buildings, statues, car wheels, dolls and playthings of many kinds have been made from paper, and even nature's flowers are imitated in paper in all but their fragrance.

More than 60 years ago James Parton [1] made out an impressive list of articles which the world then enjoyed as the fruit of the life-long inventive sacrifice of Charles Goodyear to the cause of India rubber. Mentioning things

[1] Famous Americans of recent times. Ticknor and Fields, Boston, 1867.

as various as machine belting, valve packing, and artificial teeth supports, he recalls to his readers through their recollections of the sufferings of the then recent Civil War, the following enumeration of the blessings of rubber.

Some of our readers have been out on the picket-line during the war. They know what it is to stand motionless in a wet and miry rifle-pit, in the chilling rain of a Southern winter's night. Protected by India-rubber boots, blanket, and cap, the picket-man performs in comparative comfort a duty which, without that protection, would make him a cowering and shivering wretch, and plant in his bones a latent rheumatism to be the torment of his old age. Goodyear's India-rubber enables him to come in from his pit as dry as he was when he went into it, and he comes in to lie down with an India-rubber blanket between him and the damp earth. If he is wounded, it is an India-rubber stretcher, or an ambulance provided with India-rubber springs, that gives him least pain on his way to the hospital, where, if his wound is serious, a water-bed of India-rubber gives ease to his mangled frame, and enables him to endure the wearing tedium of an unchanged posture. Bandages and supporters of India-rubber avail him much when first he begins to hobble about his ward. A piece of India-rubber at the end of his crutch lessens the jar and the noise of his motions, and a cushion of India-rubber is comfortable to his armpit. The springs which close the hospital door, the bands which exclude the drafts from doors and windows, his pocket-comb and cup and thimble, are of the same material. From jars hermetically closed with India-rubber he receives the fresh fruit that is so exquisitely delicious to a fevered mouth. The instrument-case of his surgeon and the store-room of his matron contain many articles whose utility is increased by the use of it, and some that could be made of nothing else. His shirts and sheets pass through an India-rubber clothes-wringer, which saves the strength of the washerwoman and the fibre of the fabric. When the government presents him with an artificial leg, a thick heel and elastic sole of India-rubber give him comfort every time he puts it to the ground. An India-rubber pipe with an inserted bowl of clay, a billiard-table provided with India-rubber cushions and balls, can solace his long convalescence.

To all these uses for rubber, how many more could be added today! The dental and hospital uses; the chemists' and photographers' tubes and trays; the balloons that soar for science in peace and for entangling of enemy airplanes in war; the insulation of countless miles of wire in cables and in electrical appliances; its employment to give resiliency to golf balls, tennis balls, and baseballs, and to contain air in footballs; the uses of hard rubber, called ebonite, for elegant finish or electrical insulation; the use of great quantities of rubber in floor and roof coverings; the millions of miles of rubber hose; and besides a thousand other uses too many to enumerate, the manufacture of tons and tons of rubber into the tires of the automobiles not even dreamed of by Goodyear or Parton.

Of glass there is scarcely any need to recall its value. How few of my readers past middle life could dispense with reading lenses! Yet prior to A.D. 1300 it is doubtful if the failing vision of any one in the world's history was ever aided by glasses. Very early, it is true, in China, Egypt, Rome, Greece, and the ancient world generally, glass was known and used for decorative purposes. Long before it was an aid to vision, the beautiful glasses of cathedral windows bore testimony to the skill of the craftsmen and the esthetic culture of the artist. Not until modern times, however, could the ordinary man afford to use glass for welcoming the sunlight and repulsing the wind and cold in his dwellings. Nothing of its use for optical instruments in the forms of lenses, prisms, and mirrors was known until about the year 1600. In our day glass is everywhere. Homes are lighted by its use; the factories have scarcely any other walls; the chemist has his tubes and retorts; billions of electric lights shine through it; bottles by the trillions bring pure materials, germless preparations, and preserved foods to the plainest of homes; electricity is carried safely in millions of miles of wire through the use of glass insulators, and the scientist with his optical instruments searches every problem from those of the heavens to those of the atoms by the aid of glass.

If glass requires little to recall its value, steel is universally known to be indispensable. All the machines which are described in these pages are largely built of steel, and the machines by which they are made and as-sembled are made of steel and used along with tools of steel. Weapons of war and instruments for the crafts of peace alike are fashioned of steel. Steel locomotives run on endless tracks of steel and draw their long trains loaded with structural steel, out of which are fashioned those towering buildings that make up a skyline like New York's.

PAPER

Discovered at least two centuries before Christ by the Chinese, the secret of the manufacture of paper reached western Asia about the eighth century A.D. Though paper manuscripts have been found in Egypt dating from about A.D. 1075, western Europe saw the first manufacturing of paper about the middle of the twelfth century under the auspices of the Moorish conquerors in Spain. Then, and for more than six centuries afterward, paper was made by hand, sheet by sheet. Some of the choicest paper both from Oriental and Western sources is still hand-made. The first machines for paper making were invented in 1798 by Louis Robert, an employee of the Essonne Paper Mills in France, but have been improved by many inventors in Europe and America toward their present degree of perfection.

The machine process follows closely the hand method, except that it proceeds continuously by the aid of carriers and rolls so as to manufacture paper in endless lengths of fixed width instead of single sheets. The earlier steps in paper making are intended merely to clean and bleach the materials, to remove all substances other than plant fiber, and to reduce the remaining fibers to short lengths, finely divided and held in suspension as a smooth watery pulp free from lumps. These steps are accomplished first by beating the rags employed (if a rag stock is being made), sucking away the dust, and reducing them to small-sized pieces. Then, whether rags, esparto, or straw, the stock is boiled in alkaline solution under steam

PLATE 105

Machines for paper making. Courtesy of the West Virginia Pulp and Paper Company

PLATE 106

The ending of the paper-making process.   Courtesy of the West Virginia Pulp and Paper Company

pressure for hours. After being washed, the mass is reduced to pulp by a revolving drum armed with many knives and working close to a set of parallel steel bars. When the fibers are thoroughly teased apart in this way the pulp is bleached with chlorine compound and after being washed is ready for paper making proper.

A very large quantity of paper is made partly or wholly of wood pulp. Fir, spruce, poplar, and aspen from Scandinavia and Canada are the principal staple woods for paper making. The logs are furnished in 4-foot lengths; the bark and knots are first removed, and then the logs are cut into tiny chips by a power cutter. These chips are bruised between iron rolls and screened to remove dust, after which they are boiled for hours, either in caustic soda or sulphurous acid under 6 to 10 atmospheres steam pressure. After being bleached, the wood pulp is washed and is then ready for paper making.

The pulp, whether of rags, straw, or wood, is not yet fine and smooth enough for matting on the wire cloth. It goes to a beating engine or refiner, one type of which consists of a hollow conical cylinder armed within with steel bars and containing a rotary grooved conical grinder which can be adjusted to fit closer and closer within the enclosing conical sheath. As the pulp is forced into this machine while the grinder revolves at high speed in close proximity to the steel bars, the pulp is reduced to a fine, even suspension. Paper, however, unless it be blotting paper or coarse wrapping paper, requires more or less of resin, glue, or other kind of sizing to prevent the ink from sinking in and spreading. Such materials, and sometimes china-clay, are next added as required, together with any dyes which may be desired for color.

In the old days of hand paper making a sufficient quantity of the prepared pulp would be dipped from the vat to make a sheet of paper of the thickness desired and spread evenly on a fine wire sieve. To keep the charge in place on the sieve, a frame of wood called the deckle was laid over it. To form the water mark, certain designs would be woven so as to be raised slightly above the general surface of the wire cloth. When the screen was lifted from the vat, the water would run away leaving the fibers matted down on the wire. The deckle was then removed and the screen turned over upon a flat sheet of felt, to which the paper pulp adhered so that the screen could be removed. After a number of sheets of pulp were piled up alternately with felts, the whole pile was strongly compressed to squeeze out the water. The felts could then be removed and the paper sheets could be more strongly pressed, dried, and sized.

The machine process is based on the hand method. From the vat the pulp runs through tortuous channels armed with baffles to catch the lumps, and thence onto a table to distribute it evenly. Thence it flows onto an endless wire-cloth belt carried forward by rollers and fenced on either side by rubber deckle strips. Suction is applied at the farther end of the wire cloth belt to dry the pulp, and there, too, the water mark is impressed from above by the "dandy-roll." Then come the couch rolls covered with felt, which compress the pulp enough so that it can leave the wire cloth. And now the paper goes on, being dried and compressed by felt-covered rolls heated by steam from within, the heat being applied sometimes by rollers above, sometimes from below. While still a little moist, the paper passes between polished iron rolls to smooth it and give it surface. It is thus calendered between as many sets of rolls as necessary to suit the purpose intended, and then wound upon a roll. For certain grades of paper intended for writing or illustrating, the necessary sizing to keep the ink from spreading may be applied after the paper is formed by leading it from the dryers through a vat of hot gelatin solution with a little alum, after which it is calendered between hot rolls. Plates 105 and 106 show paper making. In Plate 105 the pulp tanks and forming wire screen are shown in the foreground, and the drying rolls beyond. In Plate 106 we see the end of the process and the paper wound on the enormous roll ready for use.

Heavily glazed paper for half-tone illustrations must be made very smooth and even in surface. This is accomplished on coated paper by heavy pressure and friction between polished rolls. In the machine called the super-calender the rolls are alternately of chilled iron and compressed cotton or paper, and they drive at unequal rates so as to produce friction to smooth the surfaces.

Paper deteriorates at very different rates according to its composition, chemical treatment, and texture. Standards of quality are now set up and enforced by Government departments in order to assure sufficient permanence to important documents. Money and bonds are printed only on paper made of the most durable materials and containing certain inconspicuous identifying threads very difficult to imitate.

About one twentieth of the cut timber of the world is now used for paper, besides all the rags, straw, esparto, and other substances available. The United States manufactures and uses more than half of the world's paper production. In peace the production in the United States exceeds 10,000,000 tons.

RUBBER

India rubber, like Indian corn, potatoes, and tobacco, was a New World discovery, though it is now made also from several Old World trees and vines. Its common compound name betokens its earliest use by the South American Indians, and also its earliest use in civilized lands to erase lead pencil marks. Several families of trees and vines furnish the milky latex which yields rubber, but the best of these sources is the *Hevea brasiliensis*, a tree which grows naturally in Brazil to a height of nearly 100 feet and a diameter of 3 or 4 feet. From the latex of this tree, a fluid somewhat like that of the milkweed or the dandelion, comes Para rubber. Much first-quality Para rubber is collected by the native Indians according to their traditional methods, but plantations of *Hevea brasiliensis* have been set out in Africa, the Malay Peninsula, and other tropical regions, which now furnish almost all of the world's rubber.

The latex holds the rubber particles in suspension as the cream is held in cow's milk. By cutting in the bark a long vertical V-groove almost through to the wood of the tree and joining to it herringbone patterns of short inclined V-grooves about 12 inches apart, the latex is caused to run down into a cup at the bottom of the tree. Preferably only the lower 6 feet of the tree is thus tapped, and a herringbone pattern usually occupies only one fourth of the circumference of a young plantation tree. Nearly every day a fine shaving is cut from the lower side of the herringbone grooves to keep the flow running. After about a year of continued slicing, all the bark between the slots is removed. One-fourth of the tree being thus stripped of bark, the opposite quadrant is employed for the next year. After this another quadrant is used and finally the fourth. But in the four years that have elasped new bark has grown on the original area, and the process can then be repeated. The average yield of rubber from 10-year-old trees is about 2 pounds per tree per year. Plate 107 shows a native engaged in tapping.

Various methods are used to extract rubber from the latex. Some varieties need only centrifuging, the method by which cream is extracted from milk. Others yield to heat and time. In most plantations acetic acid is used to promote the separation. Natives in some countries use the juice of certain astringent vines to coagulate the latex. The natives of South America heat and smoke the latex on a stick, the hot astringent smoke drying out and coagulating the latex into rubber. Each day's collection is added to the stick and gets its smoking in turn, until a large lump of rubber has been made. In the plantations the rubber, after being washed, is squeezed dry between rolls, and before shipment it is further dried by hanging it in dark sheds, or by vacuum driers.

Rubber can also be made by the chemist from the products of coal tar by a combination technically called polymerization of the molecules of several terpenes, especially isoprene. This is a substance composed of eight atoms of hydrogen and five atoms of carbon per molecule. Rubber, however, is much more complex, for its molecules each contain probably eight or ten molecules of isoprene. Although the synthetic production of rubber from isoprene was accomplished more than 25 years ago, it is not profitable as compared to collecting rubber, either from the wild trees of South America and Africa, or from the rubber plantations now abundant in many parts of the tropical world. During World War II, however, the enormous demand, and the capture by Japan of the principal rubber sources, forced the development of synthetic rubbers which may be in future our main reliance, even in times of peace.

Rubber was used to some extent to shed water more than a century ago. The name Mackintosh for a rubber coat comes from the use of rubber sheets by one Mackintosh, about 1820, for producing waterproof fabrics. To prevent stickiness, he placed his rubber sheet between two thin layers of cloth. No general use of rubber in the modern way was possible until the discovery of vulcanization by Goodyear in 1839, for whatever was made of natural rubber in winter melted under the warmth of summer.

Charles Goodyear and his family were martyrs to rubber. Born in 1800, Goodyear learned about 1833 of the failure of a prosperous company which had been organized shortly before in Roxbury, Mass., to exploit a supposed valuable method of curing rubber for use in shoes and coats. Millions had been spent by that company, but the summer heat had ruined the shoes and garments sold, and the company itself, the stock of which had at first a spectacular rise, had totally failed.

From 1833 until his death in 1860 Charles Goodyear thought of nothing but rubber, experimented on rubber, borrowed and begged for rubber, wearied his friends by his talk of rubber, wore rubber, went to prison for debts many times on account of rubber, pawned his wife's clothes for rubber, sold his childrens's school books for rubber, nearly starved for rubber, allowed a child to die for rubber, crossed the ocean for rubber, engaged in lawsuits for rubber, and in a word lived for rubber. Without Charles Goodyear's sacrifice for rubber it is improbable that the world would ever have used it. The process of vulcanization by admixture with sulphur is not likely to have ever been discovered had Goodyear not stumbled upon it and spent his life in bringing it to perfection. Yet though he gave the world this great boon, he died penniless, leaving no provision for his family.

It was in 1836 that Goodyear got the first inkling of the value of sulphur in curing rubber, when he observed superficial vulcanization of rubber by the action of sulphuric acid. He at first believed then that he had the full secret, and began to do a prosperous business in shoes and coats. The process was indeed successful for very thin goods, but his success was turned into costly failure when 150 mail bags, made for a government order, melted down in the heat of autumn. His acid curing was merely superficial. From a man in his employ he next bought a patent method for combining sulphur with rubber in sunshine, which again he thought to be the secret, but which proved of little use.

It was by a lucky accident that in 1839 he laid a rubber sheet partially cured with sulphur against a red hot stove. Certain areas of the sheet were converted into hard rubber which we now call vulcanite, and certain other areas were cured into a rubber more elastic than the

PLATE 107

Native tapping a rubber tree

PLATE 108

Charles Goodyear

crude product, free from stickiness under all temperatures below boiling, and impervious to acids and oils. But many obstacles yet remained before full success came. To perfect processes for the satisfactory vulcanization of rubber surely and evenly, Goodyear reduced himself and his family to penury in the following years. Not until 1844, after the expenditure of many thousands of dollars by his brother-in-law, William De Forest, who at last came to Goodyear's assistance, was the process of vulcanization finally made uniformly successful.

So poor a business man was Goodyear that he sold the right to make rubber shoes for a royalty of only one-half cent a pair. But the licensees under his patent expended, it is said, $25,000 to retain Daniel Webster in its defense, against Rufus Choate, counsel for the infringers, in the famous suit Goodyear v. Day which was decided for the Goodyear patents in 1852. Even after this success, Goodyear was imprisoned several times for debt in America and France, and he died in 1860 a poor man.

Prior to World War II nearly 700,000 tons of crude rubber were manufactured annually, of which a little came from wild sources, the remainder being from plantations, chiefly in Malaysia. A large amount of reclaimed rubber was also used. Most of this latter material is prepared by the process of A. H. Marks, patented in 1889, whereby the scrap is ground up and heated for 12 hours or more to about 350° F., with dilute caustic soda. This, of course, takes away all cloth or vegetable fiber used in previous manufactures. Large quantities of reclaimed rubber are used with crude rubber. Various substances are compounded therewith in order to produce resistance to wear, acids, steam, or oils. In addition, the flowers of sulphur are added to produce vulcanization. Most goods require from 3 to 5 per cent of sulphur, but hard rubber contains from 10 to 50 per cent. Compounded rubber becomes soft and pliable by repeated rolling between cool rolls. Great care must be used in thoroughly mixing and blending the compositions. This is done by rolls cooled by water, lest the intense heat of friction vulcanize the mixture.

Plastic rubber can be rolled by calender rolls into smooth sheet form, and a very great deal of rubber manufacture involves this step. Rubber bands, for instance, are made by first cementing up rubber tubes from sheets and then cutting off narrow sections of the tubes. Cloth is used alternately with rubber to prevent the rubber sheets from adhering to each other. Frequently two- and three-ply goods are made in this way. Calendered products may be of uneven thickness. Tire treads and footwear, as well as ordinary rubber cloth, are calendered. Soft rubber may be squeezed into the meshes of cloth by calender rolls. Often thin sheet rubber is caused to adhere as a coating to a background of cloth into which rubber has thus been forced.

Plastic rubber may be extruded under great pressure from dies of proper forms to make seamless tubes and lengthy articles of many sorts. Inner tubes for tires, tire treads, hose pipe, strap rubber, and a great variety of other shapes may be made in this way. Molds are also much used, many of them having the makers' names, numbers, lettering, or other designations incised therein so as to print the rubber with raised symbols.

The curing of plastic rubber containing the requisite sulphur is done by heating either with steam or hot water, or dry heat, according to conditions. Molded articles are stacked in hydraulic presses and cured with hot steam from one to eight hours, according to the mass of rubber contained. Hollow articles, including bulbs, tennis balls, and many other forms, are forced into their molds by inside pressure of steam and thus vulcanized. Rubber shoes on perforated lasts are forced against their molds by steam pressure. Garden hose is cured by steam from without, which sends its heat through a temporary lead sheath, and at the same time by hot water under pressure from within.

The addition of flowers of sulphur and the application of heat are not the only means of curing rubber. Surgeons' gloves, finger cots, and many other thin articles are made on forms dipped in a cement made from crude rubber without foreign admixtures. They are vulcanized in the cold after the evaporation of the solvent, by leaving them for a sufficient time in vapor of sulphur monochloride. Plate 109 shows rubber gloves being made by dipping. This process of vulcanizing by sulphur monochloride was invented in 1846 by Alexander Parker, of Birmingham, England. Another method of vulcanization, suitable for thin goods, was devised by S. J. Peachy, of London. He employed sulphur dioxide gas, following that treatment after some time by hydrogen sulphide gas.

In recent years the advantage has been recognized of manufacturing certain goods directly from latex, instead of from rubber. But two-thirds of the latex being water, the cost of transportation of the fluid from the Tropics to the factories would be a serious drawback. Various means of concentration are employed, such as filtration, evaporation, and centrifuging.

The vulcanization of latex may be accomplished by stirring powdered sulphur into the fluid and heating the mixture to 140° C. Also the mere evaporation of latex to dryness gives a strong film of vulcanized rubber, providing a very simple method of making rubber cloth. Metal as well as cloth may thus be coated firmly with rubber, and latex may even be deposited electrically on metal somewhat as silver is plated on baser metals. Many kinds of hollow rubber goods as well as rubber-plated goods are deposited electrically, the electrical action depending on the fact that the latex particles are negatively charged and therefore migrate to the positive pole when electric tension is applied. Latex-made goods are stronger than those made from rubber.

The magnitude of present-day rubber manufacture is very great. Even prior to World War II the United States produced about 5,000,000 pairs of rubber boots and 53,000,000 pairs of rubber shoes and overshoes, besides rubber-soled tennis shoes and rubber heels well up in the millions. The demands of the war cut off most of the civilian uses, but substituted an enormous military employment.

GLASS

At least 1,400 years before Christ the Egyptians practiced decorative artistry in glass. They did not, it is true, use the blowpipe, with which such intensely interesting feats are now accomplished, but they wound their rods and threads of glass about sand molds and welded them into vessels and ornaments. Their colorless glass contained approximately, according to the analysis of Neumann, silica 64 per cent, lime 8, magnesia 4, soda 23, with traces of potash, alumina, and iron. Already they were familiar with the coloring of glass by the use of oxides of copper, iron, and manganese. Their craft was so well developed that we must suppose it had its beginnings much earlier. By 1200 B.C. the Egyptians used molds and made pressed glassware.

In the luxurious times of the Roman rule of the world, glass artistry was in great demand. Specimens of the work of about the beginning of the Christian era have come down to us which can hardly be surpassed in beauty. Among them is the celebrated Portland vase in the Gold Room of the British Museum, a blue body covered with opal glass, decorated with beautiful figures in relief.

Venetian glass of the thirteenth to the eighteenth centuries is justly famed for its wonderful embodiments of skill in form and embellishment by patterns of lace, filigree, and enamel. Saxony and Bohemia became famed centers of art glasswork about the sixteenth century, and remain so to this day. Their use of potash rather than soda helped to give luster to their work. The introduction of lead oxide in English glass in the seventeenth century

PLATE 109

Rubber gloves made by dipping

gave a highly lustrous surface that enhanced the beauty of English crystal.

The basis of glass is quartz sand, known to chemists as silica, or the oxide of silicon. In pyrex, that notably heat-resisting glass invented in America at the Corning Glass Works, it runs to nearly 81 per cent. Other common glasses have less silica, 60 per cent or less in some cases. In certain special optical glasses there is a much smaller proportion of silica, even as little as 20 per cent in very dense flint, which has 80 per cent of lead oxide. The two common alkalies soda and potassa, the oxides of sodium and potassium, make up in combination from 10 to 25 per cent of most glasses. In the ancient glasses, soda was used almost exclusively, and it still occupies the more prominent place as the alkali in glassmaking. But for certain optical glasses and for lustrous ware, potassa is preferred. Next in importance are the oxides of calcium and barium, alkaline earth metals. Calcium oxide, well known as lime, is by far the more common of the two in glass, but barium gives a higher elasticity and toughness and besides is largely used in optical glasses to give certain desired refractive values. Lead oxide increases the luster, and is much used in fine table ware and cut glass. It also is of great value for optical glasses of certain types. Alumina, and zinc and magnesium oxides are also used for imparting certain desired properties. Boric acid, from which comes sodium borate, commonly known as borax, is used for certain optical glasses and to increase the toughness of glasses subject to sudden changes of temperature, such as lamp chimneys and thermometers.

Though not particularly objectionable for bottle and window glass, the *bête noire* of fine glassmaking is iron oxide, which is invariably found in the sand and also in the clay used for the melting pots. Iron oxide imparts a green color to the glass and diminishes its transparency, as may be seen by looking edgewise through a sheet of window glass. Accordingly, the world has been searched for sands and clays as free from iron oxide as possible. The best European sand is that of Fontainebleau in France, but during World War I a search for American sand suitable for optical glass led to the discovery of a sand at Rockwood, Mich., even freer from iron than that of Fontainebleau. The effect of contamination of the melt by iron in the pots may be reduced by glazing the inside of the pots at a very high temperature before using them for the melt. It has been the practice for many centuries in fine artistic glassmaking to cover up the green color due to iron impurity by imparting certain nearly complementary colors. For this purpose small quantities of the oxides of magnesium, selenium, nickel, and cobalt are sometimes used as decolorizing agents. They can not cover the effects of large quantities of iron, and they do not, of course, prevent the loss of transparency but rather augment it.

Sulphur, which often enters with the potassa, is another troublesome impurity in fine glasses. It tends to cloud the glass and diminish transparency. On the other hand it is intentionally introduced in the amber glasses used for decorative purposes.

The various constituents required to produce a certain desired quality of glass are thoroughly mixed together in a powdered dry condition before melting. In making optical glass, during melting and until the glass nearly solidifies, the mass is stirred by infusable rods in order to keep a uniform mixture and to eliminate bubbles from the melt. Glass may be regarded as a solid solution. That is to say, there is not an inseparable chemical union of the constituents in definite proportions such, for instance, as in the union of sodium and chlorine in common salt, but rather a mere mixture of constituents as of alcohol with water. The constituents tend to separate, owing to their unequal specific gravities. Some glasses also tend to crystallize at about the solidifying temperature, which would destroy not only their transparency but the finished smoothness of their surfaces and make them more apt to dissolve into contained liquids.

Pots used for melting glass are built up by the ancient art of the potter from fire clay. It takes a great while to prepare a pot. After the bottom is made, only a part of the sides can be built up at first. Time must be allowed for partial stiffening before further building, which requires several operations with drying periods between. When finally complete, the pot must rest about two months to become thoroughly dried out and seasoned before firing. The heat must be applied gradually, so that the firing of a pot occupies some two weeks.

Glass in pots or tanks is usually melted by so-called "producer gas," prepared at the works by incomplete combustion of soft coal in a closed furnace. This gas includes some carbon dioxide and much nitrogen as neutral diluents. Its heating properties depend mainly on carbon monoxide and hydrogen, which together may make up about one third of the mixed gases given off. Sometimes this mixture is enriched by the addition of "water gas," made by blowing air and steam through hot coal or coke. Such a gas may consist of over 90 per cent hydrogen and carbon monoxide contained in about equal proportions.

In modern warfare both naval and land artillery are required to make hits on targets 10 or 15 miles away which are invisible to the gunner. Others must observe by accurate methods and apprise him of the required pointing. This involves range finders, telescopes, field glasses and many optical devices of high accuracy. Prior to World War I, the United States had imported from Europe almost all the optical glass manufactured here. When war was declared by the United States in the spring of 1917, very few pounds of optical glass were in the country, there were facilities available for production of only perhaps 2,000 pounds a month, and a demand for 2,000 pounds a day was looming up.

GREAT INVENTIONS

In these anxious circumstances the matter of producing optical glass was placed in the care of Dr. Arthur L. Day and his associates of the Geophysical Laboratory of the Carnegie Institution of Washington. All the staff and facilities of that laboratory were placed by the trustees of the Carnegie Institution at the disposal of our Government for the duration of the war. Associated with them were members of the staff of the United States Bureau of Standards.

What happened may best be described by quotations from an account by Doctor Day entitled "Optical Glass and its Future as an American Industry," presented at a joint meeting of physicists and chemists with the American Chemical Society, March 25, 1920, and printed in the Journal of the Franklin Institute for October, 1920.

. . . In 1912 the Bausch & Lomb Company, who were the largest manufacturers of instruments of precision in the United States, determined to control their own glass supply, and with the aid of a Belgian expert began making optical glass in their plant at Rochester. A factory fire soon afterward consumed the building and some delay occurred, but in 1914 very creditable samples of optical glass were produced in this plant. Because of the demands of the great war this industry flourished and the initial small pot furnace was soon replaced by other larger ones, and at the period when this record begins (March, 1917) this company was engaged upon large contracts for field glasses for the Canadian Government and for the British Field Service, in which the glass used was in part, at least, of American manufacture. The total output of this plant which might be considered available for American use at this critical moment was perhaps as much as 2000 pounds per month, a quantity sufficient in their expert hands for a considerable number of optical instruments.

. . . .

At the time when our situation was most critical (March, 1917) the experimental work of the Bureau of Standards had not proceeded far enough to be of great assistance. Their experimental work with pots was not finished and only one type of optical glass (a borosilicate crown) had been successfully made.

During this period also, and more or less in collaboration with the Bureau of Standards, Mr. Carl Keuffel, of the firm of Keuffel & Esser, had erected at the works of his company in Hoboken a small furnace

[326]

in which also a successful attempt had been made to produce this type of glass, using pots of his own design and manufacture.

In the year 1916 the Spencer Lens Company, of Buffalo, erected a small plant at Hamburg, N. Y., and also began the manufacture of optical glass with a view to replace the foreign sources of supply already closed by the war. The capacity of the plant, as operated during the late months of 1916 and early 1917, was not above 200 pounds per month, and actual production was considerably less than this, being uncertain both in quantity and quality.

The chemist of the Hazel-Atlas Company, Washington, Pa., Mr. Duval, who was also reputed to have been a successful maker of optical glass in Europe in earlier years, had already set up an extemporized furnace in this country and had melted a single pot of glass of such quality as to win favorable consideration from a firm as exacting in its requirements as the John A. Brashear Company, of Pittsburgh.

It also appeared that in 1915 the Pittsburgh Plate Glass Company, at its plant in Charleroi, Pa., had begun making considerable quantities of spectacle glass and other high grade special glasses not particularly intended for optical instruments, but nevertheless of excellent commercial quality. Incidentally, this plant proved to be the largest in the United States which might be deemed immediately available for the production of optical glass, and if it should be possible to improve the quality up to the standards of the army and navy, might contribute much to relieve the immediate need.

. . . It appeared clear that all of the sources of optical glass available in May, 1917, could together produce only about half of the quantity required, assuming that all of the glass produced was of quality suitable for war equipment. At that time the Bausch & Lomb Company [where several of the Geophysical staff were engaged] alone were producing glass of such quality. Moreover, it was estimated that they might, by extending their plant, carry approximately one-half of the war load. To maintain the other half there appeared to be but a single course open, namely, in some manner to make the Charleroi plant of the Pittsburgh Plate Glass Company available and to place someone in charge of it who should have sufficient knowledge of the requirements and technique to raise the quality of glass produced there to the standard which the Government required and which they had not hitherto attained alone.

. . . . . .

In practice there was some disappointment in carrying out this plan. At the close of the year 1917 the Bausch & Lomb Company was producing in Rochester at the rate of about 40,000 pounds per month, while the Pittsburgh Plate Glass Company had not been able in the eight months interval to provide any glass which would pass the Government inspection standards.

At that time Mr. Raymond, General Manager of the Pittsburgh Company, decided that the basis upon which they were producing was not destined to prove successful, and application was made to the Geophysical Laboratory to divide its force at Rochester and to permit a number of the chemists who had been successful there to take up the Pittsburgh problem. This was practically laying the entire load upon the Geophysical Laboratory, because only one month previous (December 4, 1917) the Laboratory had taken the responsibility for production in the third of the optical plants, that of the Spencer Lens Company, of Buffalo, and every man of its force was occupied to the limit of his capacity. . . .

. . . Sixteen furnaces were available which had already been used for glassmaking, and others which might be turned to the task should circumstances require, but all of the furnaces were of an old type without regeneration and without means for controlling the temperature in individual furnaces within 100 degrees centigrade, whereas it was already established by our experience at Rochester that a control as close as 5 degrees must be continuously maintained in each individual furnace to insure success.

The Pittsburgh Company was liberal in its plans and the Government placed a large contract, amounting to 100,000 pounds, with the company in order to afford an incentive to press forward as rapidly as possible the improvements which were needed. Certain specified improvements were even authorized to be charged against cost of the glass delivered. Nevertheless production lagged, and it was not until the following July that the output contemplated in the original plan was attained. In the intervening months the average production had been from 3000 to 6000 pounds per month, which afforded a modest contribution in addition to the production elsewhere, but it amounted to scarcely 10 per cent of the production of the Rochester plant throughout the spring months.

• • • • • •

Ordinary spectacle glass in its conventional use appears clear and white, but if it is held so as to permit looking through the glass edgewise considerable color may usually be detected, so that it might occur to one as doubtful whether it would be possible to see clearly through the same glass if the thickness were represented by the width of the glasses rather than by their shortest dimension. For optical purposes, notably in the case of prisms used in range finders and periscopes, very much greater thicknesses than this are common, and a glass for such a purpose must be optically perfect throughout its thickness, which may often reach four or five inches.

The qualities assigned for test in establishing standards of inspection for optical glass, very briefly, are these:

(1) Homogeneity, by which is meant uniformity in chemical composition, freedom from striation, bubbles, inclusions and crystallization.

(2) A constant refractive index and a constant dispersion ratio throughout.

(3) Freedom from color.

(4) High transparency.

(5) Both physical and chemical stability, by which is meant durability under exposure to the weather, chemical fumes, etc., as well as toughness and hardness for protection against misuse.

(6) Physical homogeneity, by which is meant freedom from strains or internal stresses caused by uneven cooling of the molten glass.

To produce glasses with these qualities the first obvious requirement is high chemical purity in all the ingredients of the glass itself and the second either an insoluble pot in which to melt it, or one in which the ingredients entering the glass from the pot shall not impair the development of the above qualities.

The search for such materials, which was immediately instituted by the Geophysical Laboratory when it was first authorized to take up the optical glass problem, yielded the following results:

After a search of the sand quarries from the State of Washington to Florida, including more than forty-five different localities, a sand was finally located at Rockwood, Mich., of which the analysis indicated greater purity than that from any known source of supply, even including in the comparison the wonderful sand of Fontainebleau (France) which has been used both in France and England for artistic glassware for a hundred years.

A number of sources of potash were canvassed, in the course of which much disappointment was experienced. Not only were the efforts, which were first put forth in this country to make potassium carbonate, less successful than might be wished, but the cost of manufacture was almost prohibitive. European potash was laid down in New York before the war at six cents per pound, while the major portion of the American-made potassium carbonate used in the manufacture of optical glass cost the Government in the neighborhood of $1.00 per pound. This fact is of some importance as an indication of the outlook in store for an independent optical glass industry in this country now that the war has closed.

It is to the credit of the Armour Company, of Chicago, that the first potassium carbonate of adequate purity was produced in this country. Subsequently it was found possible to substitute the nitrate for the carbonate, either in part or altogether, and so to obtain a salt which was equally good and much more generally available. But even so, the necessary provision for potash in some of the glasses remained to haunt us throughout our entire experience of glass manufacture without reaching an altogether satisfactory final solution. Sulphur and chlorine, one or both, were very often found, and a small percentage of either is usually sufficient to give a milky cast to the finished product.

In view of the long period of time needed (about four months) to manufacture, to dry, and to burn the pots which must contain the glass during melting, to which allusion has been made above, this investigation also was never quite satisfactorily concluded. In the beginning it was of course necessary to purchase in the open market such pots as were then available. These had not been made with a view to their use in the manufacture of glass of high purity, and in general were found to contain about one hundred times as much iron per cubic centimeter as could safely be permitted in the finished glass (2.0 per cent., compared with 0.02 per cent.). . . .

Nevertheless our pot makers, with a single exception, put forth a splendid effort to meet the situation by conducting experiments simultaneously in several plants, and it proved possible within four or five months to obtain containers in which the raw material was sufficiently free from contaminating elements so that glasses of a purity comparable with the best European glasses could be obtained. This conclusion was aided considerably by the discovery that if the pot was first burned in a furnace at a temperature considerably higher than any which would be required for melting the glass, burned even until the side walls showed signs of sagging and the surface became more or less glazed, then the solution of pot material in the glass was very greatly diminished. . . .

. . . It should be borne in mind that a glass solution is never in equilibrium, but is constantly changing in composition. Lead oxide and the alkalies are somewhat volatile, while the containing vessel continually contributes alumina, silica, and usually iron. It is therefore necessary for the student of glass melting who wishes above everything to attain to a prescribed chemical composition, to establish precise data upon the rate of evaporation at particular temperatures of those ingredients which pass out of the furnace and, at least approximately, the rate of solution of the pot in the glass. Knowing these quantities and the time of exposure necessary to mature a glass which is free from stones (that is, completely dissolved) and free from tiny bubbles, of which there is constant danger with every shift in the temperature, it is possible to produce successful pots of glass of accurately uniform composition and so to define and to reproduce definite optical constants.

The general relation between composition and optical constants is obviously the main issue in optical glass manufacture, and is therefore very conspicuous by its almost complete absence from the literature of the subject. Much of the optical glass technique has been enveloped in profound secrecy in all the three countries where it has been mainly produced, and although more or less freedom has been permitted in the publication of technical details of temperature, of stirring, and even of chemical composition, the manner of varying optical constants in any desired way through changes in composition has remained a trade secret up to the present time.

In this connection it is perhaps interesting to remark parenthetically that at the time when the French Liaison Commission visited this country after our entry into the war, to aid us with their experience in the production of war material, it was not permitted to divulge any details regarding the manufacture of optical glass upon the ground that the integrity of the existing glass monopoly in France had always been respected by the Government and must be so still, in spite of the war pressure. . . .

It became necessary therefore to proceed much as a scientific man is accustomed to proceed in other unknown fields, by varying quantitatively each ingredient present and plotting the results in curves through which the effect of each ingredient on the optical constants of the resulting glass might be determined. This was done systematically and very successfully, so that within a period of three months from the beginning of our efforts it became possible for Dr. Fred E. Wright, who was in charge of the work at Rochester, to write formulae for any of the typical glasses required for war service without advice from the glass expert employed there, and indeed to prepare new glasses directly from the optical specifications when needed. A special heavy flint, for example, which was desired by the Government, was made with no more than two trials. To properly appreciate just what this progress means, it may perhaps be recalled that in the days of rule-of-thumb glassmaking, as many as 150 essays were necessary before a glass of predetermined optical constants resulted. This kind of knowledge applied intelligently commanded for the Laboratory workers the immediate respect and confidence of the workmen who had hitherto believed these things to be shrouded in impenetrable mystery, and contributed in no small degree to the rapid progress and whole-hearted cooperation obtained.

. . . Most of the optical glasses in general use fall into two types, generally designated as flint and crown, both of which when melted form viscous mixtures which give little difficulty except in maintaining homogeneity. The barium crowns and flints, on the other hand, appear almost as thin as water in comparison and possess the disadvantage that they are taken up by the pots almost as rapidly as coffee is taken up by a lump of sugar. The most serious question encountered in connection with the barium glasses therefore was not to discover the composition appropriate to the prescribed optical constants, but to provide a suitable container in which the ingredients could be melted. [See in Plate 110 the improved resistance offered by Fulcher's new product against solvent action in the glass furnace.]

There is one other problem to which allusion should be made which is on the whole the most persistent and difficult problem encountered in the entire glass technique; it is the question of obtaining a homogeneous product. By this the glassmaker understands primarily freedom from striations or cords. It is fairly obvious that in a mixture, parts of which are volatile and into which other ingredients are entering through the solution of the containing vessel, inhomogeneity is constantly to be feared. Moreover, in the heavier glasses the differences of specific gravity among the ingredients amount to as much as three or four to one. These are the causes of the glassmaker's cords and striations, of which traces are found in the finest product of the glassmaker's art. It is to meet this situation that stirring is resorted to at several stages of the process.

Theoretically, if the stirring were vigorous enough, homogeneity would result except for the losses due to evaporation and the accessions (chiefly of alumina) from the pot wall; practically, this result is not so simply attained. Practically, indeed, perfect homogeneity in glass melts is unobtainable. Alumina in particular, even when present in very small quantity, yields a glass of lower refractive index than the surrounding mass and becomes immediately conspicuous. Incomplete solution of silica grains will sometimes leave a train through the mixture resembling a comet's tail. Such striations are very persistent and require stirring, either constantly or at frequent intervals, not only during melting but during the cooling, in order to diminish, so far as possible, the convection currents or other migration within the melt. Even with all the precautions taken which the experience at the several factories suggested to us, rejections by Government officials were mainly on account of striations.

Toward the close of the war a new scheme of melting was developed, partly in the hope of providing a quicker process than the normal one and partly in order to render the striations innocuous by orienting them perpendicular to the plane of light transmission. . . .

It also proved practical to carry out the entire melting process within a period of 24 hours. Where before the war two weeks was not an uncommon period through which to nurse the melting operation in order to secure the best results, a 24-hour schedule was worked out by Doctor Morey at the Spencer Lens Company's plant under which glass equal in quality to any which was supplied to the Government during the war period was produced.

. . . . . .

I venture to remark that before the beginning of this experience at the Bausch & Lomb plant no member of the group of men who undertook the war work there had ever followed a pot of glass through the process of melting. Moreover, with the long record of secrecy continuously maintained in two of the glass-producing countries, and in the third also, except for a portion of its early history, no information was available from without. Here as in many other cases, however, when the details are finally brought to light by time, the maintenance of secrecy has frequently been shown to be a cloak to cover limitations rather than profound knowledge. The processes of glassmaking are simple and the traditions of the glass-house are as often the result of cumulative superstition as experience. The heart of the whole matter lies in the relations between the ingredients at the various temperatures through which they pass and their reaction velocities. The solution of these relations is not a task for the glass-house, but rather for the most exacting application of silicate chemistry at high temperatures.

The Geophysical Laboratory has published freely the results of its experience in the glass industry, and in so far as this experience was not available before, it is now for any individual or group who may wish to make a beginning of a permanent optical glass industry in this country.

. . . . . .

It remains true to-day, as it did during the war period, that the cost of several of the necessary ingredients is necessarily greater in this country than in European countries where similar products originate. In quality our raw materials are equally good, our experience in technique is adequate if not equally extensive with some of our European contemporaries, but the cost of potash, for example, will always lay a burden upon the American product, and other ingredients might be mentioned which fall in the same category. If there were a market sufficient to stimulate production on a very large scale these difficulties could be overcome by improved technique and organization, as in the case of other conspicuous American industries, but the demand for optical glass will probably never be large, and the incentive to large-scale processes and cheaper production will therefore probably always be lacking unless the Government determines upon a definite program of preparedness. The instrument maker may find it advantageous to make his own glass for the reason that he can then arrange for the precise optical constants which he wishes to use in his instrument, and he may have them within a period of a few days instead of weeks or months, but the trade itself will perhaps never furnish sufficient incentive to build up a large industry in this country.

. . . . . .

The total quantity of glass supplied by various firms from April 6, 1917, to November 11, 1918, the war period, is approximately 650,000 pounds,[2] divided as follows:

Bausch & Lomb Optical Company....450,000 pounds, approximately
Spencer Lens Company............... 75,000 pounds, approximately
Pittsburgh Plate Glass Company......125,000 pounds, approximately

In addition to this production the Bureau of Standards supplied a little more than 19,000 pounds.

Except for occasional shipments of a few pounds from the Parra Mantois Company, in France; from the British Government plant at Derby, and that produced by the Keuffel & Esser Company, of New York for their own contracts (about 9,000 pounds for the period of the war), no other optical glass was available to the Government for war operations.

The varieties of glass are so different that the manufacture of the various types may almost be regarded as separate industries. To illustrate: there is transparent sheet glass for windows, cases, and mirrors; colored sheet glass for artistic decoration of cathedral windows and elsewhere, in which transparency is secondary to color effects; cheap hollow ware, such as bottles, used mainly for containing and keeping free from contamination fluids, medicines, and other substances; fine quality decorated hollow ware, such as goblets, pitchers, wine glasses, and shades; electric light bulbs; pressed and molded glass, including electrical insulators, trays, tumblers, decorative articles, etc.; chemical glass, including tubing, beakers, and flasks; and finally optical glass, the highest product of the glassmaker's art.

The greatest contribution of America to glassmaking has been in the invention and development of automatic machines for drawing sheet glass, plate glass grinding, tube drawing, bulb making, and other processes. Several of the foremost American glass companies have already

[2] Informal records of the Geophysical Laboratory.

PLATE 110

Differences between refractories in withstanding hot glass action. The Fulcher electrocast mullite blocks occupy the center of the furnace wall. Courtesy of the Corning Glass Works

been mentioned in Doctor Day's account. Another of the progressive glass producers in the United States is the Corning Glass Works, which owns plants at Corning, N. Y., Wellsboro, Pa., Kingsport, Tenn., and Central Falls, R. I. This company was formed in 1868 and early appreciated the advantage of scientific research. It has been a leader in introducing scientific and automatic methods of production. Among its best known products is pyrex, a high-melting-point glass of such composition as to give it a very small coefficient of temperature expansion. Accordingly it is much used, not only in the household, but also especially for laboratory purposes.

In conclusion, let us consider one of the most remarkable of automatic glass machines. Plate 111 illustrates the Corning bulb machine, designed by David E. Gray, chief engineer of the Corning Glass Works. It is the culmination of a series of more and more automatic glass-blowing machines made by this company to produce incandescent electric light bulbs. This single machine, which is fully automatic, can turn out accurate bulbs at the rate of 400,000 per day. An excellent description of it by F. W. Preston may be found in the journal, The Glass Industry, for August, 1931.

A glass fairly high in alumina is melted in a tank of special form with a capacity of 40 to 50 tons per day. The bulb machine, which is provided with a wheel base, is run up under the forehearth of the tank, where it remains from two to three days before being withdrawn for reconditioning. When the machine is in place, a steady stream of molten glass falls between a pair of rollers which make of it a ribbon loaded at intervals of 3.9 inches with glowing red buttons of glass, each of which is just large enough to become a lamp bulb.

A conveyor of steel plates corresponding in position to the glass buttons, each plate perforated in its center, carries the glass ribbon with its load of buttons along. Every button falls centrally over the hole in its steel plate, and begins to sag through it. But within one or two seconds a second conveyor drops onto each glass button, as it comes opposite, a blow head for forming the bulb. The blow heads are all under air pressure of about two thirds of an atmosphere, and they quickly blow the buttons into elongated test-tube-like sacks, still red hot.

Next there shuts upon each glass sack a mold form made in two halves exactly the shape of the bulb to be. These molds are carried by a conveyor, more complicated than those above mentioned, with devices which not only shut and open the molds but also rotate them while in place so that no mark such as may often be seen on a molded bottle will be left on the bulbs. When in place, a second part of each blow head delivers within each bulb a pressure of one tenth of an atmosphere, which forces the bulbs to shape.

Now the shaped bulbs are in free air, still hot, but connected to the glass ribbon which has been drawing them along. But as the bulbs arrive at a certain place, a flap of metal, which oscillates synchronously with their arrival, gives just the proper knock to separate each bulb from its place on the ribbon, and the bulbs drop onto a belt which lands them successively in an annealing machine whereby any strains in their texture are to be relieved. Each bulb drops, neck first, between two narrow steel ribbons on edge, of which one goes faster than the other, thus causing the bulb to rotate as it moves forward. Flames play upon the neck of the bulb to soften it enough to remove the strains, and finally the bulbs drop on a belt which carries them by easy stages to room temperature.

STEEL

There is so little difference between some forms of commercial iron and steel that iron and steel men have found it hard to define. Doctor Sauveur, professor of metallurgy at Harvard University, points out that ingot iron should not contain more than 0.03 per cent carbon, nor more than 0.05 per cent manganese, while the mildest steel contains not less than 0.05 per cent carbon and usually not less than 0.15 per cent manganese, so that chemically and physically, as well as historically by method of production, steel can readily be differentiated from iron. From the mildest steel of 0.05 per cent carbon the steels advance in hardness to some very high carbon steels of 1.7 per cent carbon. Above this limit we find cast iron, and iron pigs cast directly from the blast furnace, with carbon contents rising from 1.7 to 5.0 per cent.

The iron ore from which steel is made may have various chemical compositions, but by far the richest American ore is red hematite from the Lake Superior region, whence comes over 80 per cent of the iron ore mined in the United States, and 40 per cent of that produced in the whole world.

The National Geographic Society has informed us how near the United States came to losing the Lake Superior iron ore. At the time the treaty of Paris was drawn, closing the Revolutionary War, Dr. Benjamin Franklin was particularly interested in copper because of his electrical experiments. He had heard that copper had been found on Isle Royal on the northwest shore of Lake Superior; hence he insisted on including that island within our boundary. Thus it came about that not only Isle Royal but also the Mesabi iron field became a part of the United States.

Mesabi ore is largely red hematite, the oxide of iron whose chemical symbol is Fe_2O_3. The molecules of hematite each have two atoms of iron and three of oxygen. If pure, this ore would contain 70 per cent of metallic iron. Alabama ore is also red hematite but has a larger admixture of lime. Although on this account it is a lower grade ore than Mesabi, its contained lime is useful for flux in the reduction processes and takes the place of lime which otherwise would have to be added, so that Alabama ore is also of high value.

In ancient days rich iron ore mixed with charcoal was heated in holes in the ground on the sides of hills where the prevailing winds produced a blast of air. In this way small pasty masses of iron mixed with slag resulted, which were worked with the hammer into wrought iron. The reaction consisted merely in the removal of the oxygen from the iron oxide by the hot carbon of the charcoal to produce either carbonic acid gas (CO_2) or the poisonous gas, carbon monoxide (CO), or a mixture of both. Most of the slag was left in the resulting wrought iron. The wrought iron of the present day also contains much slag.

Modern methods are much the same in principle, but aim to purify the iron more completely, and to give definite proportions of alloying elements such as carbon and manganese in order to fit the product for its intended uses. Charcoal has ceased to be a very important reducing agent, its place having been taken by coke which is made by the distillation of coal. Formerly beehive coke ovens were exclusively used, and no care was taken to save any of the volatile products of coal distillation, but since 1920 most of the coke has been made in by-product ovens, from which the volatile products are saved. From Pennsylvania coal, a by-product oven yields about 75 per cent coke. A considerable proportion of the disengaged gas is used as fuel to furnish the heat required for the distillation. The residue of the volatile products saved are found to contain the following substances in approximately this proportion: (1) coal tar, 10 gallons; (2) sulphate of ammonia, 25 pounds; (3) surplus combustible gas, 6,500 cubic feet; (4) refined benzol products, 2¾ gallons. In recent years about 50,000,000 tons of coke have been produced annually for iron and steel production in the United States.

Both iron ore and coke contain impurities, including

PLATE 111

Incandescent light bulb machine. Blows 400,000 bulbs per day. Courtesy of the Corning Glass Works

PLATE 112

View of a blast furnace plant.   Courtesy of the United States Steel Corporation

silica, phosphorus, sulphur, and others, which must be separated. It is found that most of them, if combined with lime, become readily fusible and will float as a layer of liquid slag on the surface of the melted iron. To accomplish this result, a certain weight of lime as great as, or greater than, the weight of coke is added to the charge of ore. A fourth reagent is air, which must be supplied in greater weight than all the rest of the charge combined. The production of a ton of iron in the blast furnace requires fully 4 tons of heated air. The main function of the

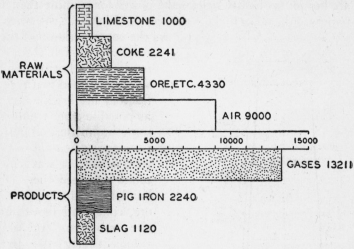

FIG. 59. Raw materials and products of the blast furnace. From Prof. H. M. Boylston's "Metallurgy of Iron and Steel." By permission of the author and John Wiley & Sons, Inc., publishers

air is to support the partial combustion of the coke to carbon monoxide and thereby to sustain the high temperature required. The diagram, Figure 59, gives a fair idea of what goes into the blast furnace and what comes out to produce a ton of pig iron.

The reduction of the iron ore is effected in part directly by hot coke itself, which takes oxygen from the iron oxide and thereby burns to carbonic acid gas or to carbon monoxide. A considerable part of the work is done, however, by carbon monoxide produced by partial combustion of the coke in the air blast, which, taking oxygen from the iron oxide, burns to carbonic acid gas. Some of the carbon monoxide escapes conversion to carbonic acid gas in these furnace reactions and formerly was lost into the atmosphere. In modern blast furnaces, however, the hot gases from the furnace top are saved and pumped back to the ground level, helping to warm the entering air as they pass. After being cleaned of dust and washed, they are burned as fuel to help make power for running the air pumps and also as fuel for the stoves which heat the entering air stream. Figure 60 shows the construction and the reactions of a blast furnace. The bottom and sides are lined with refractory fire brick as free as possible from troublesome impurities. A century ago, when furnaces were small, it was customary to feed them by hand from the top with ore, coke, and lime, but the modern furnace stands nearly 100 feet high, and in making 500 to 700 tons of pig iron daily, nearly 2,500 tons of solid matter must be fed in each day. Hence, mechanical conveyors have been devised which take the place of handwork for this purpose. Furnace lids of dome shape have also been

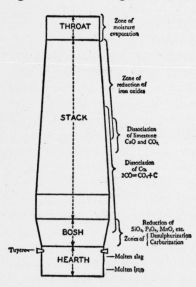

FIG. 60. Diagram of shape and chemistry of the blast furnace. From Prof. H. M. Boylston's "Metallurgy of Iron and Steel." By permission of the author and John Wiley & Sons, Inc., publishers

introduced to prevent the loss of the hot gases. These lids have to be lifted to allow the solid charge to be admitted, and are made in pairs on the vestibule principle in order to reduce the loss of gas during the feeding operation. It was found that a uniform distribution of the different-sized lumps making up the charge was necessary to avoid unequal heating around the stack. Hence the feeding mechanism has been so devised as to distribute the charge evenly. Plate 112 gives a view of a portion of a blast furnace plant. The nearer furnace, although half obscured by conveyors, feed mechanism, etc., shows some of the features described above.

When the liquid slag floating on the molten iron has risen to a certain level above the hearth, it is drawn through the vent prepared for that purpose. About once in five hours the molten iron is tapped off by drilling out its vent hole and allowed to stream out into the pig molds. These may be made in the sand floor or they may be iron molds carried on an endless conveyor belt and presented one after another under the flowing stream of iron. The molds pass through water to solidify the pigs, which fall from the molds at the proper place into the cars provided to take them away. In many cases the molten iron is run into a large vat or mixer, from which it goes directly into the steel-making operations. Almost 60 per cent of the blast-furnace iron made in the United States is used directly to make steel in this way, and is never cast as pig iron at all.

The chemical composition of pig iron varies greatly, but on the average it may be considered as containing about 92 to 95 per cent iron, 3 to 5 per cent carbon, and other constituents which may vary as indicated below:

Designation	Silicon, per cent	Sulphur, per cent	Phosphorus, per cent	Manganese, per cent
No. 1 Foundry	2.5 to 3.0	under 0.035	0.5 to 1.0	under 1.0
Bessemer	1.0 to 2.0	under 0.050	under 0.1	under 1.0
Basic Bessemer	under 1.0	under 0.050	2.0 to 3.0	1.0 to 2.0

The total United States output of pig iron, either as cast pig or used directly for steel production, has in recent years been of the order of 50,000,000 tons a year.

Excessive percentage of carbon in pig iron is the principal thing to be corrected in converting it to steel. From 0.05 to 0.10 per cent carbon in wire and wire nails, steel ranges to from 1.5 to 1.7 per cent carbon in such very hard tools as files and metal-saw blades. Silicon up to 1 or 2 per cent is not prejudicial in steels, and manganese up to 1 or 2 per cent is advantageous, because it tends to prevent the formation of iron oxide, and also because it keeps the sulphur in a harmless state as manganese sulphide. Phosphorus and sulphur are the injurious impurities, and in good steel neither is allowed to exceed 0.1 per cent. Excessive sulphur makes steel brittle at high temperatures, and excessive phosphorus makes it brittle at low temperatures.

The two principal steel-making processes are that of Sir Henry Bessemer and the open-hearth process of Sir William Siemens. The Bessemer process prevailed in the United States from about 1865 until about 1910, when the open-hearth process took the lead; the latter now exceeds its rival in productivity more than five to one.

The Bessemer process, in an imperfect state, was first developed by William Kelly, an American, who secured patents in 1857. Sir Henry Bessemer independently developed the method a little later than Kelly and carried it to much greater success. Their conflicting legal interests were eventually compromised, and Kelly dropped out of the development. The process consists primarily in forcing cold air through melted pig iron. The consequence is that the carbon is almost completely burned to carbonic acid gas and escapes with the blast. The reader may think that the process might be stopped at such a stage as to leave the desired proportion of carbon, but it proceeds very fast and is usually carried beyond this point to its finish, when the melt is recarburized to the desired

A Bessemer converter in action.   Courtesy of the United States Steel Corporation

PLATE 114

Vertical section of Wellman producer gas plant. Courtesy of the
Wellman Engineering Company

percentage. Two principal difficulties were encountered by Sir Henry Bessemer. At high temperatures the steel was apt to be found brittle. This defect was cured by adding manganese, which through its superior attraction for oxygen overcame the tendency to produce iron oxide in the melt and also, by producing manganese sulphide, rendered the sulphur innocuous. He also found it impossible to produce good steel from pig iron high in phosphorus, limiting the pig iron suitable for the Bessemer process to that containing not more than 0.1 per cent phosphorus.

Figure 61 is a diagram of a Bessemer converter. It is a

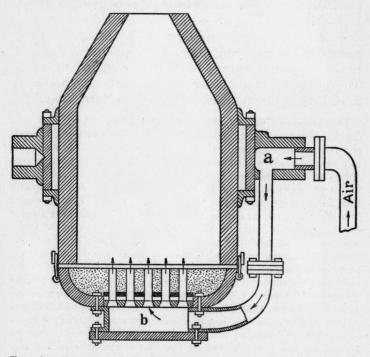

FIG. 61. Diagram of the Bessemer converter. From Prof. H. M. Boylston's "Metallurgy of Iron and Steel." By permission of the author and John Wiley & Sons, Inc., publishers

pear-shaped vessel lined with blocks of ganister, a highly refractory quartzite rock, and supported on two trunnions so that it may be rotated to pour at the proper time. Air is forced through one trunnion and enters the melted pig iron through numerous apertures at the bottom. Immediately it begins to oxidize the silica and manganese, producing a dull-red smoky flame, which lasts about 4 minutes. The silica acts, indeed, as the fuel for raising the temperature of the melt to the point where the carbon begins to burn. As the carbon starts to oxidize, the flame turns yellow and lengthens, with tongues reaching up 30 feet or more. The melt boils, and the slag containing the oxidized silica is thrown off in showers of glowing sparks. When the carbon is almost all consumed the flame suddenly drops. The operator then cuts off the air blast and turns the converter on its side. Long experience is needed to decide just the proper moment for ending the blow. The following graphic description is by the late Secretary S. P. Langley, from his book, "The New Astronomy."

The "converter" is an enormous iron pot, lined with firebrick, and capable of holding thirty or forty thousand pounds of melted metal; and it is swung on trunnions, so that it can be raised by an engine to a vertical position, or lowered by machinery so as to pour its contents out into a caldron. First the empty converter is inclined, and fifteen thousand pounds of fluid iron streams down into the mouth from an adjacent furnace where it has been melted. Then the engine lifts the converter into an erect position, while an air-blast from a blowing-engine is forced in at the bottom and through the liquid iron, which has combined with it nearly half a ton of silicon and carbon,—materials which, with the oxygen of the blast, create a heat which leaves that of the already molten iron far behind. After some time the converter is tipped forward, and fifteen hundred pounds more of melted iron is added to that already in it. What the temperature of this last is, may be judged from the fact that though ordinary melted iron is dazzlingly bright, the melted metal in the converter is so much brighter still, that the entering stream is dark brown by comparison, presenting a contrast like that of chocolate poured into a white cup. The contents are now no longer iron, but liquid steel, ready for pouring into the caldron; and, looking from the front down into the inclined vessel, we see the almost blindingly bright interior dripping with the drainage of the metal running down its side, so that the circular mouth, which is twenty-four inches in diameter, presents the effect of a disk of molten metal. . . .

The "pour" is preceded by a shower of sparks, consisting of little particles of molten steel which are projected fully a hundred feet in the direction of the open mouth of the converter.

Plate 113 shows a Bessemer converter in action. Not only have the silicon, carbon, and manganese been oxidized in the first part of the process, but considerable oxidation of the iron itself has taken place. This must be reduced to prevent blowholes and imperfections in the steel castings and forgings. The carbon also is to be restored to the desired proportion to suit the uses for which the steel is being prepared. These two objects are accomplished in one operation by adding manganese and carbon in the form of spiegeleisen or of ferro-manganese, which substances contain manganese and carbon in the proportions $3\frac{1}{2}$ to 1 and 12 to 1, respectively. This process is called recarburization, and is effected by adding the correcting substance to the melt within the converter just before pouring, as described above by Langley, or else in the ladle after pouring.

The Bessemer process just described is incompetent to convert pig iron high in phosphorus or sulphur into good steel. Messrs. Thomas and Gilchrist in England about 1880 worked out a modification adapted to handle ore richer in phosphorus and sulphur. Instead of the acid converter lining of ganister they substituted dolomite, a magnesian limestone, and also added some lime to the charge. With these modifications, the blow goes on much the same as in the usual Bessemer process, but at a higher temperature, and is continued six or seven minutes longer, during which time the phosphorus is changed to calcium phosphate and goes into the slag. Recarburization is done in the ladle. As we have noted, both Bessemer processes have yielded for the most part in the United States to open-hearth steel making.

In the open-hearth process the carbon of the pig iron is oxidized by oxygen supplied by fresh pure iron ore added to the melt. In order to get a temperature high enough for this reaction the charge is boiled in a regenerative furnace fed by gaseous fuel. The reaction proceeds much less rapidly than in the Bessemer process, requiring several hours for completion. This permits the condition of the carbon to be tested from time to time by taking samples, cooling them, breaking them to study their fracture, and even by chemically analyzing them. When the percentage of carbon has been diminished and adjusted to that desired, the process is stopped.

Sir William Siemens invented the regenerative or reverberatory furnace but did not immediately adapt it to the steel industry. It consists of a rectangular, boxlike hearth, with a roof of silica brick at the proper height to condense the heat. Fuel gas and air enter the box in combustion at one end, and the hot gases of combustion leave at the other end, passing through a checker work of fire brick before reaching the stack. About once every half hour the direction of the gases is reversed. In this way they come to combustion at a hotter temperature with each reversal, so that the temperature within the hearth rises higher and higher until the proper heat is attained.

The gaseous fuel used in the reverberatory furnace is usually the so-called producer gas, made from soft coal. It consists of about 25 per cent carbon monoxide, 12 to 15 per cent hydrogen, a little marsh gas and other hydrocarbons, and some 55 per cent of noncombustible gases, mostly nitrogen. Producer gas is made in special retorts with fire-brick linings, wherein the soft coal is fed mechanically from the top through an air-tight trap and kept in partial combustion by a blast of air and steam forced up from the bottom. The ash is removed by automatic machinery through an air-tight trap at the bottom. The hot producer gas is drawn off at the top

PLATE 115

Charging side of an open-hearth furnace steel plant.   Courtesy of the United States Steel Corporation

PLATE 116

White-hot steel ingot being drawn from the soaking pit.   Courtesy of the United States Steel Corporation

through a pipe leading to the open-hearth furnace. Plate 114 illustrates a vertical section of a producer gas plant.

Open hearths are built both with acid linings of silica brick and with basic linings of magnesite or dolomite brick. In the former case, as there is no removal of phosphorus or sulphur, these objectionable elements must be kept well below 0.1 per cent in the charge. From 1 to 2 per cent of manganese and about 0.5 per cent of silicon are included in the charge. These metals, by their strong affinity for oxygen, prevent much oxidation of the iron, which, if allowed to take place, would tend to make defective spots in the steel. Of course, the oxidation of the manganese and silica add to the heat available to make the melt. When so large a proportion of scrap steel is used in the charge that the available carbon is insufficient, coal or charcoal may be mixed into the charge to supply the deficiency. As the furnace is kept hot continuously, the charge is inserted by mechanical means, comprising steel charging boxes carried on long rams into the furnace and dumped there. When hot metal direct from the blast furnace is to be charged, it is poured from the ladle into the furnace door through a trough. Toward the end of the melt, special substances such as carbon, manganese, aluminum, and silicon are added in such proportions as tests and experience dictate to improve the composition and casting quality of the steel. Plate 115 shows the charging side of an open-hearth steel plant.

In the basic open-hearth furnace, lime is added to the charge. The charge must be low in silicon and in sulphur, because the former would neutralize the basic action of the lime, and the prejudicial influence of the latter can be corrected only partially by the use of manganese toward the end of the melt. But ores high in phosphorus can be used with the basic open hearth, because phosphorus unites with the lime and goes into the slag. Care must be taken only to keep the slag strongly basic by addition of more lime from time to time if necessary. Tilting furnaces, though more costly, are preferable for open hearths, especially of the basic sort, because the slag can be run off at any time to avoid recontamination of the steel by its injurious constituents.

In recent times a considerable proportion of the steel manufactured in the United States has been melted in electric furnaces. In foreign countries ore is also smelted electrically, but that process is too expensive in this country. Both basic and acid steel-making processes are conducted electrically.

Melted steel, however produced, is poured into open-ended ingot molds about 6 feet high, resting on heavy iron plates at their bottoms. They are nearly 2 feet square at the bottom, and tapered to a smaller section at the top, so that the molds may readily be lifted off the ingots when the outer shells of steel have solidified in the molds. The ingots are then placed in the so-called "soaking pits," which are closed, heat-insulated chambers, where the cooling of the steel becomes more uniform until the solidification is complete. In Plate 116, we see an ingot, still white-hot, being drawn from the soaking pit. From the soaking pits they go to the rolling mills and forges, where the ingots are formed into "blooms" and "billets" and, by further working, into rails, bars, and commercial shapes. These processes are conducted on both hot and cold steel, the temperature selected for working depending on the carbon content and on the shape desired. In rolling and drawing processes the cross-section of the steel is gradually reduced by successive steps until the final shape is attained. This can often be accomplished in the cold. Plate 117 shows a white-hot ingot being rolled out in the slabbing mill.

The picturesque figure in the history of steel making in the United States is Andrew Carnegie (1835–1919), the son of a hand weaver in Dunfermline, Scotland. The introduction of machinery deprived his father of an occupation and drove the family to emigrate to the United States in 1848, aided by a small loan from a friend for passage money. The boy Andrew was then in his 13th year and attended school no longer, except for night school during one winter in Pittsburgh, where the family settled. There the father began weaving tablecloths and selling them from door to door. The mother took in shoes to bind, and Andrew got a job at a dollar and twenty cents a week as bobbin boy in a cotton factory. The hours of labor lasted in winter from before dawn till after dark. From this small beginning he was soon advanced to a position paying two dollars a week with a Scotsman, for whom he did all sorts of jobs, from running a small steam engine and firing the boiler to bathing wooden bobbins in oil. As he was good at figures, he sometimes helped to make out bills.

The turn in Andrew Carnegie's fortune came in 1850, when he was engaged to deliver messages from the telegraph office. Here he wore his Sunday suit to make a good appearance, and every Saturday night, no matter how late he might return from delivering messages, his mother washed these clothes and ironed them, so that he could put them on fresh for Sabbath morning.

He felt that the telegraph office job was his opportunity, and concentrated his attention on learning streets and business addresses throughout Pittsburgh. He also took pains to learn the faces of the business men themselves, so that he would be able to deliver a telegram on the street if he happened to meet the recipient. In these ways Andrew Carnegie became more and more efficient and better and better known. Such men as Edwin M. Stanton, afterward Lincoln's famous Secretary of War, William Thaw, the business man and philanthropist, and many others of Pittsburgh's most substantial men came to know the little Scotch boy. He also took every opportunity to learn and practice telegraphy.

Col. Thomas Anderson had opened his private library to working boys, but at first boys employed as messengers and in clerical jobs were not admitted. Andrew Carnegie wrote a letter to the Pittsburgh Dispatch urging that this distinction be removed. It was removed. Every week he drew out a book and thus read history and literature. Later in life he presented to the city of Allegheny a monument to Colonel Anderson, and the generosity of this man was instrumental in influencing Carnegie later on to give millions of dollars to establish libraries all over the world. Occasionally the Scotch messenger had a telegram to deliver to the theater, and in return he was given a seat in the second balcony. In this way he came to know and appreciate the plays of Shakespeare and others.

Continually improving himself and his efficiency, in about a year he was promoted above all the other messenger boys and received $13.50 a month. One morning, before the regular operators came, he took a message from Philadelphia, and little by little was called on afterward to watch the instrument when someone was called away. Some operators were learning to read Morse by sound, and Andrew Carnegie was one of the earliest to master it. Soon an operator 30 miles from Pittsburgh was called away for two weeks, and Carnegie, though but a boy, supplied his place. From that beginning he was soon promoted, while yet in his 17th year, to be an assistant operator.

Then came the great opportunity that started his career. In February, 1853, he was selected by Thomas A. Scott, superintendent of the Pittsburgh division of the Pennsylvania Railroad to be clerk and operator, at an initial salary of $35 a month. As Scott advanced, Carnegie advanced, succeeding to the superintendency of the Pittsburgh division when Scott became Vice President of the Pennsylvania in 1859.

Soon after came the Civil War, and Scott and Carnegie

PLATE 117

White-hot steel ingot being rolled in the slabbing mill. Courtesy of the
United States Steel Corporation

PLATE 118

Andrew Carnegie.   Photograph by Davis and Sanford

went to Washington to organize the immense railway and telegraph expansion of the War Department. Through this experience Carnegie came to know well Stanton, Grant, Cameron, and other powerful leaders. Carnegie's health was injured by strenuous work in the great heat of southern summer, so that in 1862, after being recalled to the Pennsylvania Railroad, he revisited his native Scotland with his mother. The tremendous impression this made upon him he describes most vividly in his autobiography. Indeed, his love for Scotland and his home town of Dunfermline was always a master passion. After his retirement from active business, he purchased property in Scotland and spent a part of each year there. Many gifts he gave to Scotland, and he nourished her old customs. Always in his Highland mansion the piper led the way for the family and guests to dine.

Carnegie was one of the first to see the need of the sleeping car on American railroads. He joined with the inventor, T. T. Woodruff, in forming a company to construct sleeping cars for the Pennsylvania Railroad. Later on he combined with George M. Pullman in forming the Pullman Palace Car Company. These were very profitable investments.

Another profitable venture was the organization with Thomas N. Miller in 1866 of the Pittsburgh Locomotive Works. In 1906 its $100 shares sold at $3,000, an appreciation of thirtyfold. Carnegie was quick to see also that the day of wooden bridges was passing, and with four associates he organized the Keystone Bridge Company in 1863. They built many cast iron bridges in the early days, but Carnegie soon realized the advantage of Bessemer steel for bridges and rails. His long service with the Pennsylvania Railroad had shown him the weakness of iron rails. In 1873 Carnegie and others organized the Edgar Thomson Steel Company at Braddock, Pa. The business of the Pennsylvania and Baltimore & Ohio railroads as well as other lines flowed in. Mills were added to mills, and the great firm of Carnegie, Phipps and Company was created. Mines and transportation were taken into their enormous steel industry which at last merged in the United States Steel Corporation.

Carnegie also had a profitable part in the development of oil in Pennsylvania. About 1870 he removed to New York with his mother and took part in great financial operations, involving such powerful organizations as the firms of Pierpont Morgan and Company, the Barings in London, and others. In short, Andrew Carnegie was not only the great steel magnate, but the great man of affairs, exercising a powerful national and international influence for many years.

In April 1887, at the age of 52 years, he married Louise Whitfield, with whom he lived a most ideally happy life.

In 1901, having built up an immense fortune, Andrew Carnegie retired at 66 years of age, and devoted himself to giving this fortune away. To his friends, the workmen in the steel mills; to Carnegie Libraries; the Carnegie Hero Fund Trusts; Carnegie organs; the Carnegie Institute at Pittsburgh; the Carnegie Institution of Washington; the Pan American Union Building at Washington; the Peace Palace at the Hague; the Carnegie Corporation of New York; the Carnegie Trust for the Universities of Scotland; the Carnegie Dunfermline Trust; the Carnegie United Kingdom Trust; the Carnegie Foundation for the Advancement of Teaching; the Carnegie Endowment for International Peace—gifts to all these philanthropies organized during his lifetime involved the expenditure of $350,000,000.

CHAPTER XI

THE GRAPHIC ARTS

PICTURES have always been considered valuable as an aid to the printed word but never to the extent that they are at present. In olden times their rarity must have made them doubly precious. The beauty of the ancient hand work lends great charm to early manuscript books.

WOOD AND METAL ENGRAVING

At the time of the invention of printing from movable type, ascribed to Johan Gutenberg of Mainz (1398–1468) about the year 1450, the art of the woodcut engraving was already available for crude illustrations. Indeed from the time wood carving was begun, prints of a sort must have been made. In its simplest form, the removal of the wood from around a letter or image drawn upon its surface leaves in relief a structure which, if inked, will print itself reversed, left for right. But such a print is only a black mark on a white ground. The next step is to make shading. This is done by cutting lines, parallel or crisscrossed in parallels, across the raised structure. If the incised lines are thin, the black print is but little lightened, but if the lines are wide, so as to cut away a large proportion of the raised structure, a light shade results in the print. Thus all varieties of shade can be made in a woodcut by altering the proportion of printing structure cut away by incising lines across it.

The work of illustrating by woodcuts naturally divided itself between two artists, the draughtsman who composed the picture, and the engraver who reduced it to a printing form. It was easy for the engraver, if he had little artistic imagination, or but little skill, to spoil the choicest composition of an artist. Some men combined the two professions in their own persons. Thus Albrecht Dürer (1471–1528), who has been called "the typical artist of the German nation" was at the same time a great painter, a great wood engraver, and a master of copper engraving. Plate 119 is an example of his work.

Boxwood cut across the grain and smoothed to a fine flat surface was the usual medium of wood engraving. The drawing could be made directly on such a surface, but it was an improvement to coat it first with Chinese white. Then the drawing stood out as if on white paper. The artist might indeed indicate the degree of shading by drawing every line the engraver was to incise, but this was too laborious in general, and the shading was merely indicated by broad sweeps, leaving its execution to the skill of the engraver. A very long time was required to illustrate a book by these methods, a single large engraving sometimes occupying the craftsman for a month. Accordingly, it was customary to divide the block containing the picture into sections, each to be engraved by a different workman, and all finally joined together for printing.

Metal plates were used for printing pictures about as early as wood. But here we find the opposite application of the ink. For it remained in the incised lines and was wiped from the smooth surface. By heavy pressure the paper was forced into the incised lines and carried away the ink therein. The deeper the lines, the more ink they carried and the darker the shade produced on the print. Copper was easier to engrave, but steel was more durable and hence more suitable when numerous copies were to be struck off. Not only Dürer, but other great painters, as Rubens and Raphael, favored the metal engraving, and some of them became adepts in the art. Steel engraving has become nearly obsolete for works of pure artistry, being used principally for the engraving of business and calling cards, bank notes, and certificates of various kinds.

We have mentioned two contrasting classes of engraving. Wood engraving is an example of printing surfaces produced in relief, steel engraving an example of the intaglio, wherein incised lines hold the ink. There are, besides, methods of lithography in which the printing surface is neither raised nor lowered, but selected by chemical preferences. Lithography, as its name indicates, arose from the use of hard, flat, polished limestone as the printing surface. This stone was selected by Alois Senefelder (1771–1834), the inventor of lithography, at Solenhofen in Bavaria. No better stone for lithography has ever been found elsewhere, but, in recent years, aluminum or zinc is substituted for stone. A drawing may be made in a special kind of ink resistant to the action of acids. The remainder of the surface not inked, may then be etched away to a certain depth with acid leaving the inked parts as a printing structure in relief. This was the original method of Senefelder, though he devised and practiced nearly all of the varieties of lithography known even at the present day. If the stone is fine-ground, but not quite polished, drawings may be made upon it with greasy crayon. If the whole stone is dampened, the ink from an inking roller will adhere to the greasy portions but not to the others. Thus there is produced a printing surface neither raised nor lowered.

In the several methods of reproduction thus far mentioned, left and right become reversed in printing, so that if the drawings are made directly on the printing surfaces to be engraved, they must be drawn with this in mind. It is possible, however, to make a drawing on paper in natural form with such inks or crayons that when the drawing is inverted and pressed down upon the lithographic stone it will be printed in greasy lines in the inverted form required. Then the engraving process may be carried out on the duplicated drawing as thus reversed, left for right.

Compared with wood or steel engraving, lithography is much less expensive and, at the same time, more rapid. It lends itself well to color work. For this purpose, a number of stones are prepared, each containing only those parts of the picture to be printed in the same color. An outline of the picture is prepared on a stone called the key, and the patches to be printed in different colors are carefully outlined thereon. Each color-stone is then prepared in exact duplication of only those parts of the key which are to be in the particular color selected. All the contributing color-stones are then printed one after another with exact superposition or, as it is called, register.

A great advantage of lithography, and that which particularly appealed to Senefelder, is the facility and cheapness with which drawings may be multiplied by it. Any line drawing or sketch if made in an ink rubbed up in linseed oil, giving it a greasy quality, may be transferred to stone by mere impression, leaving the drawing itself unimpaired. The stone, first dampened, may be "rolled up" in any color of printing ink. The ink will adhere only in the greasy lines, and impression after impression may be taken from it by merely repeating the dampening and "rolling up." As the stone carries a reverse image in greasy lines, all the impressions from it are exact duplicates of the original drawing or sketch.

PHOTOGRAPHY

The art of illustrating has been entirely revolutionized in the last half century by the introduction of photographic methods. It will be convenient to defer further description of the illustrative processes of the present day until we have mentioned the discovery and development of photography.

It is said that the gradual blackening of silver and its compounds was known to the ancient Egyptians. It was

PLATE 119

The Knight and the Lansquenet. Woodcut by Albrecht Dürer, 1497.
Courtesy of R. P. Tolman

Heinrich Schulze, however, who published in 1727 the proof that it was not air or heat, but light, that had the power to blacken the salts of silver. He exposed to sunlight paper moistened with silver solutions under stencils cut with words and sentences, and found that the parts on which the stencils permitted light to fall were blackened. In 1777 the great Swedish chemist, Carl Wilhelm Scheele, exposed silver chloride to light for a long time, until it became thoroughly blackened. Then he removed what was left of the unchanged silver chloride by dissolving it in caustic spirit of sal ammoniac. A black powder remained. This, he was able to prove, was metallic silver. Thus the action of light was proved by Scheele to consist in the reduction of silver salts by the separation of metallic silver.

Although the sensitiveness of the salts of silver to the action of light is by far the most important fact in photography, it was not the basis of the first practical photographic process—that invented by Joseph Nicéphore Niepce (1765–1833). For his light-sensitive coating he used the bitumen of Judea, a kind of asphaltum, dissolved in the essential oil of lavender. This he spread thinly as a varnish on a glass or silver plate and warmed it upon a heated iron till the varnish ceased to simmer. After a sufficient exposure in the camera, often six or eight hours, a very faint outline became visible. The image was developed in a solution of one part by volume of essential oil of lavender in ten parts of the oil of white petroleum. When the image had sufficiently developed, the plate was washed in running water and dried. But the picture had to be protected from the action of light and humidity. Copies of engravings could be made with long exposure to light by pressing them upon the varnished glass plates already described or on varnish laid on polished silver. The silver could afterward be etched with acid to prepare it for printing if desired. After some years Niepce adopted the improvement of darkening the silver plate with iodine, and this led the way to the true beginnings of modern photography in the beautiful work of Louis Jacques Mandé Daguerre (1789–1851).

In January, 1839, six months before Daguerre published his process, William Henry Fox Talbot (1800–1877) communicated to the Royal Society of Great Britain his method of preparing sensitive photographic paper by alternately dipping it in a weak solution of common salt and applying to one side only a weak wash of nitrate of silver. The chloride of silver thus formed upon the surface of the paper proved very sensitive to light, so that Talbot was able to get good images of objects with exposures in the camera of a half second. He found that the sensitiveness could sometimes be enhanced by setting the paper aside for several weeks, and then again washing it with silver nitrate.

Niepce, having learned of the experimental work of Daguerre, made a partnership with him in 1829, continued after Niepce's death in 1833 by his son, Isidore Niepce. Daguerre's invention was not reported until 1839, when he and Niepce were pensioned for life by the French Government. Daguerreotypes were made on polished silver-plated copper. The polishing must be done immediately before the next operation of sensitizing the surface with the vapor of iodine. The action of the iodine vapor was continued in a closed box until the silver had taken on a golden-yellow color, which, depending on the prevailing temperature, occurred in from 5 to 30 minutes. Only weak light could be admitted for viewing the condition of the plate. Exposure was then made in the camera and continued from 3 to 30 minutes, according to the light. The plate was then inclined face downward in a tight box, and exposed to the vapor of mercury. In a few minutes the picture was developed, but still had to be withheld from the light. After being washed in water, the image was finally fixed by rocking the plate face downward in a bath of a weak solution of sodium hypo-sulphite. When all the yellow color disappeared, the plate was carefully washed and all drops of water blown from its surface. The shadows in the daguerreotype are given by the polished silver, the lights by the adhering mercury. As discovered by the Swedish chemist, Scheele, metallic silver was thrown down in the silver iodide coating under the influence of light. The metallic silver grains alloyed with mercury produced the high lights. Glass covers were placed over daguerreotypes to protect their surfaces. Their beauty is proverbial.

Fox Talbot improved his paper-coating process by substituting the iodide for the chloride of silver, and patented it in 1841. It was called the calotype process, and was repeatedly improved by him to secure great sensitiveness. He accomplished instantaneous photography in 1851. By that time he was using as the surface to be sensitized a glass plate coated with albumen, which, when dry, he dipped in an alcoholic aqueous solution of silver nitrate and again dried it. The nitrate seemed to unite with the albumen in a chemical union, resulting in a hard insoluble surface. The plate was next washed to remove the excess of silver nitrate. To an aqueous solution of the protoiodide of iron was added an equal volume of acetic acid and 10 volumes of alcohol, and after standing several days the preparation was ready for use. The plate was dipped therein for a few seconds only. All the preceding operations could be done in weak light, but when the plate was then dipped in a weak solution of silver nitrate to which acetic acid had been added, it became highly sensitive and was placed in the camera without delay. To develop the image, it was dipped in a solution of the protosulphate of iron, whereupon the image quickly appeared. After being washed, the plate was dipped for a minute in a solution of hyposulphite of soda and then again washed.

Here we find for the first time Fox Talbot using a glass plate coated with an organic substance as the carrier for the sensitive silver salt, but he was not its earliest user. Its invention is ascribed to Niepce de Saint-Victor, a nephew of the elder Niepce, in 1848. Collodion, and later gelatin, were substituted for albumen, but the practice of using a wet plate in photography was continued, as in Fox Talbot's experiments, for many years. It was inconvenient and entirely unsuitable for the use of the traveler. Fox Talbot had by this time invented the process of silver printing, so that pictures could be indefinitely multiplied.

In 1864 W. B. Bolton and B. J. Sayce introduced dry plates, the improvement which revolutionized photography. Prior to this time the collodion films in use were first impregnated with the bromide or iodide of potassium or sodium. Corresponding silver salts were thrown down in the film by immersion of the plate in silver nitrate. Silver iodide was still preferred, but Bolton and Sayce turned to silver bromide as the sensitive salt and found it possible to prepare it in a state of fine suspension with collodion. When the glass plate was coated with this preparation it could be used wet, as usual, but it was also effective when dry. Carey Lea, of Philadelphia, greatly improved this emulsion process and increased its sensitiveness. By this time the discovery had been made of the action of alkaline developers to bring out the image.

During the decade of 1870–1880 many investigators improved the dry plate, substituting gelatin for collodion in the emulsion, and increasing the rapidity of the film till it became about 100,000 times as fast as the original daguerreotype. The next decade saw another revolution in photography, brought about by the devotion of a bank clerk amateur.

What Thomas A. Edison was to incandescent electric lighting, and Henry Ford to automobiling, George

PLATE 120

George Eastman.   Courtesy of the Eastman Kodak Company

PLATE 121

Modern method of manufacturing kodak films.   Courtesy of the Eastman Kodak Company

THE GRAPHIC ARTS

Eastman (1854–1932) was to photography. He made it universal. Even more, not content with making every traveler and vacationist his own photographer, he created the largest and most all-embracing photographic business in the world. There is no ramification of the art, from astronomical photography to moving pictures, that has not received scientific advancement, leading to important commercial values, from the Eastman Kodak Company of Rochester, N. Y. In that gigantic business enterprise George Eastman made a huge fortune, but, like Andrew Carnegie, he gave it nearly all away before he died. His known benefactions to educational and humanitarian projects, as listed by the Associated Press and quoted in the Literary Digest for March 26, 1932, exceeded $75,000,000.

George Eastman, son of George W. Eastman, who conducted a business training school called Eastman's Commercial College, was born at Waterville, N. Y. His father's income, though sufficient, was small, and when he died in 1862, Mrs. Eastman was forced to resort to taking in boarders. Thus, like Carnegie, George Eastman knew poverty as a boy. In 1868 he left school to go to work with an insurance firm, and began at once to keep a cash book. At the end of the year he made this entry: [1]

```
      Recapitulation                    1868
1868  Rec'd during Year          ($) 131.00
  "   Paid
          Clothes           39.00
          Board             22.22
          Sundries          16.35
          Shoes              8.05
          Underclothes, etc. 3.03
          Hats               3.35          92.00
                                           39.00
                                         Assets
                              1868—Mar. 2d  ($)  5.
                              1869—Jan. 1        39.
                              Increase     ($)  34.
```

[1] George Eastman, by Carl W. Ackerman. Houghton, Mifflin Company, Boston, 1930.

Early in 1869 he began to make entries recording the purchase of photographic materials. In April, 1874, he received the post of junior bookkeeper in the Rochester Savings Bank, and in 1876, then receiving a salary of $1,400, he relieved his mother of all financial responsibilities. By January 1, 1877, he had saved $3,600. Toward the end of that year, he became so much interested in photography that he purchased the then cumbersome outfit required for picture making and took lessons of a local photographer. It was the wet collodion plate process. Eastman records that his outfit, which included only essentials, comprised a good-sized camera, a heavy tripod, a large plate holder, a dark tent, a nitrate bath, and a jug of water. He says: "Since I took my views mostly outdoors—I had no studio—the bulk of the paraphernalia worried me. It seemed that one ought to be able to carry less than a pack-horse load."

Then he learned that dry plates could be made, and he attempted to make them, at first with little success. But working long hours at night he found a coating of gelatin and silver bromide that worked successfully. Then he thought, "I will sometime give up the bank and go altogether into the photographic business, making and selling dry plates." He asked his uncle Horace Eastman to help him start in this venture as a partner, but his uncle declined. But George Eastman was not discouraged. He took his own savings and began working outside bank hours. In 1879 he invented an improved process for coating dry plates, and registered the patent in England and France as well as in the United States. He went to England to push the introduction of his process, and in December, 1879, sold the English rights for about £500. In 1880 he invented a second radical improvement in dry-plate making, and by the end of that year he had a well-established, widely known business, with foreign connections in several principal countries.

Just at the end of 1880, Col. Henry A. Strong joined

him as a partner, and in September, 1881, George Eastman gave up his position with the bank to devote himself entirely to photography. Eastman first conceived the idea of the transparent photographic film, independent of a glass backing, early in 1884. A modern method of manufacturing kodak film is shown in Plate 121. He made many experiments in that year by coating glass and also paper with solutions of nitrocellulose, stripping the film from the glass or paper when solidified. But at first his nitrocellulose films were too thin for camera exposures if used alone. Therefore he decided to leave the film on the paper until after exposure. A patent on the new product was applied for in March, 1884, and shortly afterward its adjunct, the roll-holder, was worked out by Eastman and W. H. Walker in a form adapted to be used in any camera instead of glass plates. The film was wound on spools and moved by a clock key from outside. Rolls containing 24 exposures were supplied.

On October 1, 1884, the Eastman Dry Plate and Film Company of Rochester was incorporated with a paid up capital of $200,000. There were 14 stockholders. The officers were Henry A. Strong, president; J. H. Kent, vice president; George Eastman, treasurer; and W. H. Walker, secretary.

The paper-backed film, though successful, was not what Eastman wanted, and in November, 1886, he engaged a young chemist, Henry M. Reichenbach, to try to develop the film that could be exposed alone. About this time he bought a patent of a young Dakota farmer, David H. Houston, which was a visible indicator and film-puncturing device, suitable to point out when a length of film had reached the required position for exposure.

Reichenbach solved the film problem in 1889. By dissolving nitrocellulose in wood alcohol and adding camphor, fusel oil, and amyl acetate to the solution, the film when dry came out firm, transparent, and flexible.

Eastman invented the roll devices for exposing these films, and patents were applied for March 3, 1889. The patents covered the chemical formula, the mechanical processes for making and coating films, and the apparatus for holding and exposing them in the camera.

Even before this, in September, 1888, the kodak had been born. The word and the camera it signifies were both of Eastman's invention. The word was his coinage of a name that was short, incapable of being misspelled to destroy its identity, vigorous in sound, and able to meet foreign trademark requirements. Kodak Camera No. 1 was a box 6¾ by 3¾ by 3¾ inches, producing a circular picture 2½ inches in diameter and loaded with a stripping film roll for 100 exposures. The camera had to be sent back to Rochester by the user, where the film was unloaded, developed and a new film inserted. In his advertisements Eastman coined the slogan "You press the button—We do the rest." It took like wildfire, even penetrating into the Gilbert and Sullivan opera, "Utopia." Two modest maidens carrying kodaks amid a chorus of kodakers sing:

> Then all the crowd take down our looks
> In pocket memorandum books.
> To diagnose
> Our modest pose
> The kodaks do their best:
> If evidence you would possess
> Of what is maiden bashfulness,
> You only need a button press—
> And we will do the rest.

Amateur photographers multiplied all over the world so fast that the company could not increase facilities fast enough to meet their demands.

Soon after Reichenbach's film came out, Edison, who was working on his moving picture inventions, began to order films. Later on, when the Edison invention came into popular vogue, after 1900, the moving picture film business became a principal line of the Kodak Company.

PLATE 122

Assembling kodak shutters.   Courtesy of the Eastman Kodak Company

PLATE 123

Beater preparing pulp to be made into photographic paper. Courtesy of the Eastman Kodak Company

A far-reaching commercial arrangement was entered into by many of the movie producers with Edison and Eastman.

As business in all photographic products and associated lines was added to the kodak industry, the great establishment in Kodak Park at Rochester was built up. Plates 122 and 123 show the assembling of kodak shutters and a beater preparing pulp to be made into photographic paper. A great factory was also established at Harrow, England. So extensive became the ramifications of the Kodak Company that the Government, during Woodrow Wilson's administration, attacked it in suits under the Sherman Act. These suits were pending over a long term of years but were held in abeyance during World War I, while the exertions of Eastman and the company were a powerful support to the Government and the Allies. Eventually the antitrust suit of the Government prevailed, and some of the subsidiaries of the company were excised.

Eastman was a pioneer in building up his production and executive staffs with men of technical school or college training. He had obtained several first-rate men from the Massachusetts Institute of Technology, one of whom, Frank W. Lovejoy, served as the general manager and later president of the Kodak Company. Dr. Richard MacLaurin, the revered president of the Institute, whose untimely death was so greatly deplored, explained to Eastman his visions of what the future growth of Technology demanded. Greatly to MacLaurin's surprise and delight Eastman entered enthusiastically into these large enterprises, and only stipulating that his name should be concealed, in a period of several years he gave toward the establishment and development of the great institution now on the bank of the Charles River no less than $19,500,000. Many other educational enterprises enlisted Eastman's attention during the latter years of his life, to which he gave not only much thought and time, but, as has been said, very large sums of money.

The introduction of photography had an enormous effect on the arts of illustration. The camera could reproduce any view almost instantly, with far greater fidelity of detail than the most skillful artist. To be sure the photograph might fall short of the drawing or painting in artistic feeling, but when an automatic process was found for transferring the photograph to the printed page, the final result might be more artistic than a copy of the artist's sketch if unskillfully reproduced by hand engraving.

PHOTOENGRAVING

Photographic engraving came in about 1860. It is based on a curious property of albumen, gelatin, and other colloidal substances. When a suitable film of gelatin (or gelatin and albumen), impregnated with potassium bichromate, is exposed to light, the film tends to become insoluble in water. The degree of indifference to water, roughly speaking, is proportional to the intensity and duration of the exposure to light.

In applying this discovery, which was made by one Mungo Ponton, to the reproduction of line drawings, India-ink cartoons, and similar figures, which have only narrow blacks and whites but no half tones, a contrasty negative photograph of the desired size is first made. As it is convenient to strip off the negative film from the glass plate, the photoengraver uses special plates of strong contrast adapted to the film stripping required. Usually the object gained by removing the film is merely to have left and right interchanged. Otherwise the reproduction would be a mirror image of the original. If left and right were to be exchanged in the next step of the process without stripping the film, it would be necessary to print with the glass side next to the bichromated film, which would give blurred indistinct lines.

A prepared zinc or copper plate having been coated with the gelatin-albumen-bichromate film, the stripped negative is closely pressed thereon under glass and printed by suitable light exposure. Hardly any visible effect is produced, but the clear spaces, which in the negative represent the lines going to make up the drawing or cartoon, give hardened insoluble reproductions in the bichromatized film. The dark parts of the negative, on the contrary, are unaffected, and remain soluble in water.

The metal plate is next "rolled up" with an ink roller carrying acid-resisting ink, and then soaked in cold water, which softens the parts not exposed to light till they can be washed away. After the plate is scrubbed it is next etched with nitric acid in order to leave the parts covered by the insoluble film in relief. After the etching has gone deep enough to clearly mark the drawing, the plate is dusted with asphaltum or with dragon's blood, a product of a West Indian plant, and warmed so that the sort of varnish thus produced may more effectively protect the lines which now represent the drawing or cartoon from undercutting by further etching. After several such treatments all large etched areas are "routed out" deeper with a mechanical cutter. The plate is then mounted on a wooden block, type-high, and is ready to be inserted in its place in the page for printing.

When large editions are to be printed, printers do not rely on the original blocks and type, but use them only for making wax impressions, which are placed in an electroplating bath, and upon which is deposited a copper replica of the original printing surface, exact in every detail. This surface, suitably backed, is used for printing. It is possible by this method to make duplicate sets of electrotype plates for use in case the first set becomes worn.

Such a process of line engraving by photography came into use more than a half century ago and speedily displaced wood engraving, except for especially artistic work. But it was not immediately applicable for views containing large areas of continuous shade and grays, rather than blacks. Some means of breaking up such half tones and shades into narrow blacks and whites was required. This was furnished by the invention perfected by Frederic E. Ives, of Philadelphia. Imagine a flat glass plate, coated with an acid-resisting film, to be scratched with parallel lines, about 150 to the inch, so that it becomes alternately transparent and opaque. This glass plate is etched with hydrofluoric acid to deepen the transparent lines, and then the film is removed and the incised lines are filled with opaque. Ives combined two such screeens at right angles, by pressing the two screens together face to face and cementing them together. The device then becomes a uniform black ground pierced with a great number of regularly spaced pinholes.

When such a screen is placed within the copying camera, close to the plate on which a negative of a picture is to be made, the result is to break up all the half tones and extended whites of the negative by inserting thereon a multitude of black dots. Such a negative may be used as already described for photoengraving, and the shades will appear to the unaided eye as if continuously printed. Under a microscope every half-tone engraving shows the multitude of dots by means of which it was produced.

It is a matter of great nicety to adjust the distance of the half-tone screen from the negative, the size and shape of the aperture of the camera lens, and the length of the exposure so as to produce a negative capable of giving the most satisfactory reproduction of a picture. Owing in part to the irradiation and diffraction of light, the cone of rays which diverges from one of the pinhole apertures of the screen toward the negative is enlarged. It is the more enlarged the larger the lens aperture, the longer the exposure, the greater the separation of the screen from the negative, and the brighter the light. The high lights from the picture produce on the negative dots of the shape of the diaphragm of the lens, which are so large as almost to coalesce and blacken the negative. Medium shades produce smaller dots, and the dark shades produce very small ones, leaving most of the negative in their region clear. When the negative is printed on bichromatized gelatin, the parts corresponding to high lights on the original picture receive little light, and nearly wash away. Those corresponding to deep shades are strongly illuminated. In these regions, the gelatin is hardened and washing does not remove it. Therefore, when the plate is etched and printed, we find the same sort of shading as in the original picture, but the accuracy of the reproduction depends on the skill of the engraver in his adjustment of the items mentioned above. Where several printings are made for color work, the dot-lines of the screen are inclined at different angles to the vertical in each, so as to avoid interference of the dots.

A great deal of modern illustration involves color. Prof. James Clerk Maxwell showed in 1861 that any desired color may be reproduced by a proper mixture of three well-chosen primary colors. The colors required may be chosen in several ways, but are often taken as red, yellow, and blue. In 1881, Frederic E. Ives, of Philadelphia, perfected a modification of the half-tone photoengraving process adapted for color printing. He was able to produce three filters, which, when interposed before the negative, cut off, respectively, all the light from the object not red, all not yellow, and all not blue. Such filters may be made of transparent colored glass, coated glass, or colored water cells.

Taking then, through appropriate color screens, three equal-sized negatives, printing plates could be made from them by the ordinary process. Then, choosing inks of correct colors, by three superposed printings the approximate coloration of the original object or painting could be reproduced on the printed page. In many of the colored illustrations of the Smithsonian Scientific Series the colors of the originals have been imitated by the use of not three, but many more than three printings. With this meticulous care, and skillful choice of filters and inks, almost exact color reproduction is possible, but, of course, very costly.

PHOTOLITHOGRAPHY

J. W. Osborne of Melbourne, Australia, patented in 1859 his process of photolithography. It is not directly applicable to shaded pictures, and is based, like almost all photoengraving processes, on the peculiar action of light on bichromatized colloids. First, a negative is made of the picture to be reproduced. A film of bichromated albumenized gelatin is prepared and printed from the negative. As usual, the bichromated film is hardened in proportion to its exposure to light and is also rendered insoluble in water in a proportional degree. A flat zinc plate is "rolled up" with transfer ink, and the print is then pressed face down upon it, thus becoming inked all over. Next the film is floated, back downward, in water a little below the boiling temperature. The heat coagulates and hardens the albumen as it does the white of egg, and makes it tenacious enough to withstand the rubbing process to follow. The hot water penetrates the film and dissolves out the bichromate in the regions little affected by exposure to light. Next the print is scrubbed with water, which leaves the transfer ink adhering in the parts where there has been exposure to light. Transfers are then made to lithographic stones or metal plates, in the manner already described, and from these stones impressions may be struck off indefinitely as desired. A very large collection of photolithography and specimens of other photoengraving processes, the gift of J. W. Osborne, is on exhibition in the division of graphic arts, United States National Museum.

Photolithography may be extended to shaded and colored subjects by first photographing the originals through appropriate line screens and color screens as if for process engraving. Seven or eight color stones are often printed to represent a single original subject by the lithographic method.

PHOTOGRAVURE

This development of intaglio engraving is much used. The so-called rotogravure section of the Sunday newspaper is one application of it. Let us first consider the carbon tissue process. Thin tissue-backed films of gelatin, impregnated with lampblack or color to different degrees of shade, are prepared and sold to the trade. When bathed in bichromate solution they become light-sensitive. Such a film, when mounted on glass and exposed under a reversed stripped positive photographic film, becomes hardened and insoluble in water in its high lights, but not in its shadows.

A copper plate is given a reticulated ground by dusting it with bitumen or resin and warming it so that the dust adheres. The gelatin film is mounted thereon, and its tissue and soluble parts are scrubbed away with warm water. Then the copper plate is etched with acid. The acid percolates but slightly through the hardest parts of the gelatin, but more freely through the half-tone spaces, and most freely through the clear parts. In this way the shades of the original are reproduced as incised corrosions varying in depth and size according to the degree of shade. Several successive etchings may be needed, stopping out parts too much affected if necessary. Impressions are made on damp paper with soft backing, which sucks away the ink that fills the incised pockets and pits in the metal.

This process was developed by Karl Klietsch of Vienna, who removed to London and there adapted it to cylinder printing, as used in the rotogravure newspaper section of today. Its application to rotogravure is nearly identical with the process just described. Instead, however, of depending on aquatint ground for the reticulation, a crossed screen of 150 to 175 lines is printed on the carbon tissue film, in addition to the reversed positive. After being soaked in cold water, the film is squeegeed onto a chemically cleaned copper cylinder. Then water at 104° F. is applied until the carbon tissue, bichromate, and unaffected gelatin are removed. After this the cylinder is etched with acid. When printed, the cylinder revolves through a trough of ink. The excess of ink is scraped off cleanly by a razorlike blade called "the doctor," and the cylinder prints as from an etching as the soft paper absorbs the ink from the incised lines. Color engraving may be done by these photogravure processes. Separate plates or cylinders are then prepared, corresponding to each color printed. The colors are selected by photographing the subject through color screens, and the inks for printing are chosen by persons skilled in the art so as to give, when all are superposed, the most satisfactory color reproductions.

OTHER PROCESSES

A very ingenious and curious method of engraving was perfected by Walter Woodbury about 1864. He printed his negative on bichromated gelatin, and washed away the parts unhardened by light. Thus a structure was formed in which parts corresponding to the high lights of the original subject were washed away, and those parts corresponding to deep shadows were in relief. By hydraulic pressure he forced this structure into suitable soft metal, as lead or type metal. Thus he made a shallow mold into which was pressed warm gelatin impregnated with lampblack, or other more or less opaque powder. The warm gelatin was backed by white paper, which adhered to the gelatin and removed it from the mold when set. It will be seen that the white paper would shine through and make high lights where the mold was shallow, and would be obscured by the opaque gelatin where the mold was deep. These areas would correspond to the original high lights and dark shadows of the subject. Good reproductions were made in this way, but it was a costly process and never came into general use.

We have spoken of the relief process depending on etching away the ground; of the planographic process depending on chemical affinity and rejection of the ink; and of the intaglio processes where the ink is contained in incised lines or pits of greater or less depth below the printing surface, and is sucked out under high pressure by the soft, moist paper on which the impression is made. One other important type of engraving remains to be mentioned. It is the collotype or photogelatin method, which exists in numerous variations called albertype, autotype, artotype, heliotype, etc. A film of bichromated gelatin mounted on glass or metal is exposed under a photographic negative, and then washed until it slightly swells. As in the Woodburytype, the film takes on a relief structure of different degrees of relief and hardness depending on the exposure to light. Moreover, as the film dries, it cracks in innumerable directions, so as to produce a reticulation akin in its printing possibilities to that produced by a half-tone screen. The quality of these reticulations also varies with the exposure to light. The parts most exposed and hardened are insoluble, and therefore in lowest relief. They are most receptive of ink, while the parts most swelled by water are least receptive of ink. Accordingly when "rolled up" with ink, the gelatin film prints a reproduction of the lights and shades of the original subject.

These gelatin collotype processes give the most exact reproductions of fine detail of any of the methods of engraving, and their prints are very pleasing in appearance. Furthermore they, like the others, are susceptible to color methods, and in much the same way. Very beautiful color reproductions are thus produced. The collotype processes began with Poetevin in 1855, were improved by Motay and Marechal about 1865, by A. Albert of Munich a little later, and by Ernest Edwards about 1872.

Like other processes, they awaited the introduction of color screens (about 1880), and many variants of them have been devised in more recent years.

In conclusion, we must recall the useful expedient for laying on tints in drawings and engravings devised by Benjamin Day in 1879. It consists of a flexible, transparent film, as of celluloid or other similar substance, on the lower side of which is contained a reticulated surface of some sort. Many varieties of such patterns are available commercially, from cross-hatching and double cross-hatching of few or many lines per inch, to curved and waved lines and irregular reticulations. In short, the available screens cover everything in degree of shade and character of pattern that the artist might desire to place upon his drawing.

The Ben Day screen, chosen as required, may be inserted in a hinged frame which can be adjusted to lie upon a drawing or engraving plate in the making. If shading is desired in a drawing, a diaphragm of thin paper is fastened temporarily upon it, out of which are cut the shapes within which the shading is to be included. The Ben Day screen is "rolled up" with ink of the proper kind, and then let down into contact with the drawing. By means of rubber rollers of different sizes, burnishers and other special appliances, the screen is pressed down onto the paper, and prints the desired shading on the drawing everywhere it is needed and nowhere else.

Still other uses are found for the Ben Day screens. From a drawing a photographic negative of the desired size for printing is made. From this negative a faint image is printed on sensitized zinc. Those parts not requiring to be shaded are stopped out by painting with gamboge. On the remainder the Ben Day screen, after being "rolled up" with acid-resisting ink, may be impressed. Then, after washing off the gamboge, the plate is etched with acid according to usual methods of zinc etching, and used for printing as desired.

The Ben Day shading methods are much used for color work in children's books and for funny pages of the Sunday papers. They may even be used for fairly good four-color engraving, although by no means as precise in their outlines, or as delicate in gradations of shading, as other methods already mentioned.

Examples of most of the modern processes of reproducing illustrations will be found in the volumes of this Series. All of the plates in this volume except the frontispiece are reproduced by the half-tone process, and the text figures are line engravings. The frontispiece illustrates the various stages and the final product of the four-color process. In volume 9, plates 28, 41, 70, 83, 94, and 104 are examples of color lithography, and reproductions by the photogravure process appear in volume 2 as plates 6, 10, 19, 25, 35, 37, 53, and 72. The entire text matter and text illustrations of volumes 5, 7, and 8 have been reproduced by the lithographic offset process.

In every kind of engraving, great skill and long experience are indispensable for choice results. Very many fine points well known to the experts have necessarily been neglected in this brief account, but it is the hope of the author that enough has been indicated to stimulate interest in methods of illustrating in readers who have known little of engraving processes.

Indeed, the same reflection is in the author's mind regarding all the subjects treated in this volume. He begs the indulgence of expert critics, and asks them to consider that it is not for them, but for the general reader unfamiliar with electricity or machines that the book was written. The author's object will be attained if the book leads young people to a greater interest and better understanding of many of the ingenious inventions which have multiplied by a thousandfold the opportunities and comforts of modern life.

INDEX

INDEX

Coolidge, W. D., 145
 X-ray tube, 68
Cooper Hewitt, mercury arc, 70
 mercury-arc rectifier, 70
Corliss, George H., 163–165
 valve mechanism, 164
Corning Glass Works, 335
Cotton gin, 301–302
Couplings, train, 198–200
Crompton, mule spinner, 275
Crystal oscillators, 127
Curie, Professor and Madame, 54
Current, alternating, 23, 32, 35
 direct, 23–24
 polyphase, 32
 thermionic, 60, 61–63
 three-phase, 26, 41
Curtiss, Glenn, 227, 232
Cycle, Carnot's, 157
 Otto four-stroke, 172

D

Daguerre, Jacques Mandé, 358
Daguerrotypes, 358–359
Daimler, Gottleib, 215
Davy, Sir Humphrey, 1, 3–4
Day, Arthur L., 326
De Forest, Lee, audion, 60, 64, 133
De Laval, Gustav, 168
 turbine, 168
Diesel, Rudolph, engine and cycle, 175
Discharge, oscillatory, of Leyden jar, 78
Drawboy, 285, 287–288
 mechanical, 287, 288–290
Dürer, Albrecht, 354
Duryea, Charles E., 216–219
Dynamo, 18–42
 alternating, 37–42
 direct-current, 24
 early development of, 18–24
 Faraday's, 14
 theory of, 21–24

E

Eastman, George, 361–365
Edison, Thomas A., 109, 136–144
 and electron tube, 58
 early life, 136–138
 first central power station, 144
 incandescent electric light, 138–144
 bamboo filament, 141–142
 paper filament, 139–140
Efficiency, of heat engines, 180
 maximum of, 157–159
Egypt, cloth of, 271
Eiffel, Gustave, 232
Electricity, early discoveries in, 1–16
 from magnetism, 1–2, 10–16
 Faraday's dynamo, 14–15
 Faraday's iron ring experiment, 10–13
 Oersted's discovery, 1, 2
 measurement of, 7–10
 Faraday's galvanometer, 9
 Zweigger's galvanometer, 8
Electrolux Company, refrigerators, 244
Electromagnets, 72–73
Electron, 51–56
 charge, 54, 59
 tube, as wave source, 123
 Edison's, 58
Electrotype plates, 367
Emmet, W. L., 158
Engines, internal combustion, 171–180
 automobile, 176–178, 179
 Diesel, 175
 airplane, 177–178, 179, 236
 Manly's airplane, 179, 226
 Otto cycle, 172
 pioneer, 171–172
 radial, 179
 single-cylinder, 172–174

[378]

INDEX

INDEX

INDEX

INDEX

Rectifier, vacuum-tube, 68–69
  mercury-arc, 69–70
Refrigeration, 239–247
  commercial, 242–244
  principles of, 239–241
Refrigerators, absorption type,
    244–245
  compression type, 245–247
  domestic mechanical, 244–247
Regeneration, principle of, 123–
    124
Relay, telegraphic, 82
Resonance, electric, 119
Röntgen, W. C., 65
  X rays, 65–68
Roosevelt, Theodore, 207, 212,
    214
Rosse, Lord, telescope, 169
Rotogravure, 371–372
Rubber, 315–322
  manufacture, 316–317, 319–
    321
    magnitude of, 319, 321–322
  sources, 315–316, 319
  uses of, 310–311, 317
  vulcanization, 318–319, 321
Rutherford, Lord, 49

S

Salton sink, 209
San Francisco earthquake and fire,
    208
Selden, George B., 216
Senefelder, Alois, inventor of lith-
    ography, 355
Separator, cream, 31
Sewing machine, 247–265
  essentials of, 264–265
  trust, 263
Ships, clipper, 188
  iron, 189
Siemens, Sir William, 342, 346

Silk thread, 267, 276
  weaving, 278, 279, 280–281,
    282
Silver salts, light action on, 357
Singer, Isaac M., 256
  sewing machine, 256–257, 258
Sleeping-car, 351
Smith, Donald (Lord Strathcona),
    202
Smithsonian Institution, aeronau-
    tics advisory committee, 233
Space charge, 59, 63
Spindle, 268–269, 272, 273, 274,
    275
Spinning, 265, 268–269, 272–275
Stanley, William, 34, 35
Steamboat, 181–192
Steam boilers, 157
  engines, 159–171
  properties of, 155
Steel, 336–352
  composition, 337, 342
  manufacture, 342–348
    Bessemer process, 342–345
    open-hearth process, 346–348
  uses of, 311–312
Stephen, George (Lord Mount
    Stephen), 202
Stevens, John, steamboats, 183–
    185
Swan, Sir Joseph, 135–136

T

Talbot, William Henry Fox, 358,
    359
Telegraph, 73–74
  first commercial, 78–89
    Morse's, 80–85
    Wheatstone's, 78–80
  printing, 88–90
  wireless, 120–121
Telegraphy, duplex and multiplex,
    87–88, 138

INDEX